Yoga Darshan

With kind regards, ॐ and prem

Swami Niranjan

Yoga Darshan

Vision of the Yoga Upanishads

Swami Niranjanananda Saraswati

*Compiled from lectures on the Yoga Upanishads
given during the Sannyasa Training Course, conducted at
Ganga Darshan from October 1992 to March 1993*

Yoga Publications Trust, Munger, Bihar, India

Published by Sri Panchdashnam Paramahamsa Alakh Bara
    First edition 1993

Published by Yoga Publications Trust
    Second edition 2002
    Reprinted 2005
    Third edition 2009

ISBN: 978-81-86336-26-7

Publisher and distributor: Yoga Publications Trust, Ganga Darshan,
Munger, Bihar, India.

Website: www.biharyoga.net
        www.rikhiapeeth.net

Printed at Thomson Press (India) Limited, New Delhi, 110001

Dedication

*In humility we offer this dedication to
Swami Sivananda Saraswati, who initiated
Swami Satyananda Saraswati into the secrets of yoga.*

Contents

Theoretical Aspect
1. Vedic Tradition of Yoga   3
2. Sanatan Culture   12
3. Evolving Awareness   22
4. Yogic Keywords   32
5. Aspects of Yogic Discipline   45
6. Karma Yoga   59
7. Jnana Yoga   79
8. Hatha Yoga   87
9. Raja Yoga: The Role of the Vrittis   107
10. Raja Yoga: Bahiranga – External Stages   131
11. Raja Yoga: Antaranga – Internal stages   162
12. Mantra Yoga   226
13. Laya Yoga   245
14. Esoteric Yoga   254

Practical Aspect
Introduction   293
15. Asana   294
16. Pranayama   322
17. Bandhas and Granthis   382
18. Mudras   402
19. Holistic Physiology   441
20. Causes of Imbalance and Disease
    According to Yoga   447
21. Yoga of Common Sense   460

Glossary   471
Index of Practices   493
General Index   496

Theoretical Aspect

1

Vedic Tradition of Yoga

There are two main traditions of yoga: the tantric tradition and the vedic tradition. Although the tantric tradition of yoga is more in accordance with the lifestyle we lead today, the vedic and upanishadic concept of yoga is no less relevant. The Vedas are a collection of the original, spiritual, practical, moral, social and metaphysical thoughts of seers who perceived every aspect of creation as a form or manifestation of the divine nature. They are a collection of thoughts accumulated over many generations by different saints and sages.

If these enlightened people had wanted to, they could have easily evolved their philosophy into a form of organized religion. Tantra could have become a religion, Samkhya could have become a religion, the Nyayas and Vaisheshikas could have become different religions. However, the seers said, "No, we do not wish to convert our thoughts, ideas and experiences into an organized religion, because they are not the ultimate answers that we aspire for. They are an individual's understanding of reality. Therefore, let our ideas become part of a collection of ideas that deals with the same subject."

These systems of thought are known as the philosophical treatises of Sanatan culture. The collection of these ideas is called *Sanatan*, which means 'eternal'. The term Sanatan encompasses these different philosophical ideas, practical instructions and guidance, the practice of yama and niyama, lifestyle and meditation, the ultimate aim being to attain the final union or merger with God.

The Vedas fall into this category. Although there have been many writers who say that the Vedas are books of Hinduism, they are under the wrong impression. This is one point that should be clarified. Indians do not have an organized structure of religion. There have been sects or traditions which evolved their own ways of worship and interpretation of the divine. These ways of worship and interpretation have become known as different 'isms', such as Vaishnavism, Shaktism, Shaivism and so on. They have become minor religions within the whole structure of the Sanatan culture, but the six main systems of thought which make up the Sanatan structure are not part of any religion.

Schools of thought

The six main systems of thought are: Vedanta, Samkhya, Nyaya, Vaisheshika, Uttara and Poorva Mimamsa. Then comes Tantra in all its various forms and other sub-philosophical systems. These various systems or schools of thought deal exclusively with spiritual understanding and are known as darshans, which means philosophy. At the same time, however, darshan does not just mean philosophy or school of thought, rather it means something which has been personally seen, experienced and understood. *Darshan* means 'to see', 'to have a vision', 'to have a glimpse'. In the context of a school of thought, darshan means 'something which one has experienced'. It represents an aspect of reality as perceived by oneself. Darshan is, therefore, a collection of thoughts which have actually been experienced, which are true, which are real and which are not speculation or abstract ideas. Although there are many darshans in the vedic tradition, the major ones are described here.

The first major darshan is Vedanta. *Vedanta* translates literally as 'the end of perceivable knowledge'. It is comprised of the two root words, 'veda' and 'anta'. *Veda* means 'knowledge' and *anta* means 'the end'. This is the experience of the mind which is exploring its own limits and gaining a realization and an understanding of that exploration.

The second major darshan is Samkhya. *Samkhya* literally means 'numbers', but it is not a science that deals with numerology. It is a science of spirit which deals with the twenty-four attributes of our nature. These twenty-four attributes of human nature, the pure and the impure, the causal, the subtle and the gross, have been described in Samkhya.

The third major darshan is Nyaya. *Nyaya* literally means 'logic'. This logic is actual recognition of spiritual experience, which is recognized by the omniscient mind, that is all encompassing and all pervading. That recognition and acceptance of an experience is taught in Nyaya. How does one understand a spiritual experience in its proper light? How does one know when an experience is just a fantasy, when it is an expression of our external nature, or when it is a real spiritual experience?

The fourth major darshan is Vaisheshika, which is a treatise on the subtle, causal and atomic principles in relation to matter and the four other elements with spirit.

The fifth and sixth darshans are Uttara and Poorva Mimamsa, which is theology divided into two parts, one in the form of questions and the other in the form of answers.

The seventh darshan is Tantra, which deals with the transcendence of human nature from the present level of evolution and understanding to transcendental knowledge, experience and awareness.

The eighth darshan is Charvak, which is the philosophy or concept that we are living at present. It is a materialistic philosophy. The basic theme of Charvak is to accept what you perceive to be true and visible and not to accept what is beyond the scope of your receptivity. So, in one sense, it is a very practical science. You can accept the existence of something which is in front of you, but if it happens to disappear then you can no longer accept it. That is Charvak.

5

Then come the Upanishads in which certain truths from the mouths of experienced, realized teachers are conveyed. These deal mainly with an integrated lifestyle, a balanced and harmonious frame of mind and spiritual concepts. It is not possible to describe all the Upanishads in detail because there are so many; for example, there are one hundred and eight major Upanishads and over ten thousand minor Upanishads. All deal with a particular aspect of human behaviour, knowledge, expression and realization. The Upanishads dealing with yoga are twenty-two in number.

Five basic questions

All these schools of thought evolved from the following five basic questions:

1. What is the composition of this body? How does it function?
2. What is prana? What is the relationship of prana with the physical, material dimension of the body? How does prana interact with the material body?
3. What is the reason behind the manifestation of prana in different forms and what is the reason behind the creation of matter and other elements?
4. What is the soul or atma? How can one experience it?
5. How does one attain transcendence, liberation or freedom?

These five questions become the basis for further creation, development and search for ideas in order to realize our inner nature. The whole concept of spirituality in Yoga, Tantra, Vedanta and Samkhya revolves around these five basic questions. Each one has tried to give definite and concrete answers to these questions. The answers are very lengthy. Yoga is one such answer.

In the vastness of yoga we find the answer to a simple question such as, "What is the body?" In order to understand the answer to this question, one must know about annamaya kosha, the chakras, kundalini, the manifestation of energy, etc., and then how to actually go to the source or the centre

6

point from which everything started. In order to answer the question: "What is prana?" there must be an understanding of pranamaya kosha. There must be perfection of the techniques of pranayama, pratyahara and prana vidya, and the awakening of kundalini, the chakras and the subtle energies, in order to understand the performance and the function of prana on the gross level, on the subtle level and on the causal level.

Experiential theory
Although there are only five questions, the answers run into volumes, which are collections of both theory and practice. The theory is not speculative, it is an experiential theory, something which has been experienced and then described to other people. The basic theories which relate to each and everyone are the same. Theories which deal with the body, mind and emotions, expression and behaviour are practically the same, but theories which go beyond the reach and realm of the body and mind become speculative for those who have not yet attained that level of experience.

I do not know whether you have heard about the story of my great-great-grandfather. He was a very great scientist and scientists are always a little eccentric. Once it came to his mind that he should find out what the taste of cyanide was in order to tell future generations. He studied all the books related to cyanide poison. For the sake of science he decided to sacrifice his life and write down on a piece of paper what the taste of cyanide was like. So he sat down with a glass of cyanide in one hand and a pen and paper in the other. He drank the poison, quickly wrote something on the paper and – kaput! That was the last time I saw my great-great-grandfather.

Doctors and scientists came to interpret what he had written. One looked at the piece of paper and said the taste of cyanide was salty. Another said no, the taste of cyanide was sweet. Do you know what was written on the piece of paper? The letter 'S', that was all. People gave their different

7

interpretations of what the 'S' stood for. Some said sweet, some said sour, some said salty. Nobody could really know unless they had tried it themselves. That same thing also happens to us in relation to our journey inside, in the realm of the spirit.

The experience we gain is our own personal experience and it cannot be described. It is not the same for each person because of the different levels of evolution, mental perception or mental sensitivity. When we come to the spiritual aspects of yoga, things do sound a bit far-fetched and we think, "How can that be possible? It can't be true." However, once we reach that same state, that same level of experience and understanding, then we experience the same thing.

Spiritual psychotherapy

The answers to these five questions about body, prana, cause, soul and liberation revolve around the mind. It has been understood by those who have reached that dimension that the mind is a very powerful energy which is manifesting on the external level and is subject to the influence of events, circumstances and people. At the same time, there is another aspect of mind beyond our conscious awareness. In order to find the answers to these questions we have first to tune the mind and increase its sensitivity and receptivity. In order to deal with the mind we have to face many different problems. Thoughts from different traditions related to mind control and transcendence actually become thoughts of and about spiritual psychotherapy.

Spirituality became converted into psychotherapy. How does one manage an emotion? How does one manage the dissipated energy? How does one manage anger, frustration, depression, and at the same time, how does one develop the positive qualities that are dormant within? This form of psychotherapy is time tested. It is our firm belief that spiritual psychotherapy is much more effective than the Freudian, Jungian or modern psychotherapies. Sometimes questions arise as to how a spiritual tradition can accept different levels of mind such as conscious, subconscious and unconscious. We try to understand the conscious, subconscious and unconscious because the idea of having very subtle components within our mind is fascinating.

Psychology and psychotherapy have made small inroads into the subconscious and the unconscious mind, mainly for therapeutic purposes, whereas the spiritual traditions have gone far beyond the stage of psychotherapy or psychoanalysis. In actually discovering the experience and functioning of the different levels of consciousness, they lead to the highest level or the experience of the total mind. This is unknown as far as medical science is concerned, but is termed enlightenment, mukti, nirvana, etc. according to the different spiritual traditions.

The seed of desire

Although we can relate many of the spiritual principles to modern psychological ideas and concepts, for example, when we talk about the conscious mind in terms of modern understanding, yoga talks about the same thing, but yoga is not limited to these three aspects only. It deals with the self and the different influences that are constantly being put in the various dimensions of the mind, whether conscious, subconscious or unconscious. Yoga has described the mind as being both pure and impure.

There is a difference between a pure mind and an impure mind. The impure mind is bound by, or subject to, desire and the need for security in life. It is propelled by ambitions; it is motivated by ahamkara, ego, and it is through this impure mind that we experience pain and pleasure. The impure mind is considered to be an extroverted mind. It is comprised of desire, ambition, ego and ignorance. These experiences within the mind give knowledge of pain and pleasure in life. Pain and pleasure are symptoms or experiences of the impure mind. When the mind is subjected to the experiences of pain and pleasure, four different kinds of

9

knowledge dawn within. These are the knowledge of: (i) birth or the beginning, (ii) death or the end, (iii) old age or decay and (iv) illness, disease and imbalance. So, birth and death, infirmity and old age capture the whole attention of the mind and give rise to the experiences of pain and pleasure. All of this combined is known as *maya*, or illusion, in the sense that it is a partial experience or understanding of a bigger reality. Maya, illusion, does not mean false or unreal; it means partial understanding, partial knowledge.

The vedic tradition further says that the mind is moved by the force of desire, by the vayu energy. Desire represents the manifestation of Shiva and Shakti, Purusha and Prakriti. This desire is inherent in the self. Even when God had the desire to become many from one, to create, he or she or it, as an omnipotent, omniscient, omnipresent entity, had the seed of desire. That desire is considered to be the source of manifestation of consciousness at different levels. Energy is an aid to move the mental awareness from one desire to the next. So, desire represents an externalized experience of consciousness, and vayu, or the movement of mind from one object of perception and cognition to another, represents the gross manifestation of Shakti.

From the impure to the pure

This is how vedantic yoga views the impure mind. It says that the impure mind is an ignorant mind because it is not fully awakened. It is not conscious of what is real and unreal, true and false, at the same time. It cannot differentiate between right and wrong and simply moves by desire in order to satisfy itself. Right now we all have an impure mind, because there is always some desire predominant within us. Even when coming to the spiritual master you come with a desire, so that is an impurity of mind. But that same mind can lead us to transcendence, provided we use the force of the impure mind to divert our attention towards the pure mind. That becomes vidya or true knowledge. The pure mind is free from the bondage of every kind of desire

10

and ambition. This pure mind is aware of the totality of experience and not just one aspect of it.

The aim of yoga is to take one from the impure aspect of mind towards the pure aspect, from a state of scattered desire to a state of balanced desire, where the desire becomes positive, constructive and self-elevating, where the desire does not limit us to the external environment only, but also encompasses the inner dimension. By transcending the impure mind and obtaining purity of mind and by awakening the faculties of the pure mind, one attains transcendence, or *mukti*. One must go from the impure to the pure and awaken the faculties of the pure mind in order to attain transcendence.

2

Sanatan Culture

Vedic culture is known as the Sanatan or eternal culture. Yoga has been transmitted through the Sanatan culture from early times. Sanatan is not a religion in the sense that it does not have one religious doctrine. Most of the religions that exist in the world today are based on the doctrine of one preceptor, one master, whose teachings are transmitted along with the concepts of devotion, surrender, faith and prayer. In itself the Sanatan culture is not a religion because it includes the thoughts, experiences, teachings and revelations of not one, but thousands of preceptors down through the ages, which have all been compiled and transmitted in an unbiased form.

One aspect of religion or dharma is cosmic in nature and concerns the individual in relation to the cosmos, creation, divinity and the higher self or nature. This is known as the eternal, cosmic wisdom, law and action. The other aspect consists of the local religions which emerge in a certain age, disappear after one or two thousand years and are then replaced or taken over by another belief or group of practices according to the prevailing mentality and social culture of the time. When we talk about the rise and decline of religion, we talk about these time-bound religions which come up and then decline because they are subject to change. However, one concept is not subject to any kind of change, because it encompasses all the dimensions of human experience. This is called Sanatan because it is external, social, individual and also cosmic in nature. It comprises the eternal values upon which human evolution is based.

The concept of Sanatan culture is divided into three areas:

1. *Jnana kanda*, the branch of wisdom, is based on experiential knowledge which a person gains in the course of life.
2. *Karma kanda*, the branch of action or ritual, indicates the way of living in the world, while utilizing all the faculties and qualities of the body, mind, emotions and spirit. It is the implementation of bhakti and jnana in everyday work and activity.
3. *Upasana kanda*, the branch of worship, contains the ideas of surrender, trust and faith in the higher self.

Four aims in life

Sanatan culture is a culture of humanity which deals with the individual's performance, action, lifestyle and thought, as well as his spiritual search in relation to society, the universe and the concept of God. It accepts all aspects of life as being relevant to growth and evolution. Sanatan culture advocates that human beings have come into this dimension or this world with four main aims to pursue. These four aims of human life are known as the *purusharthas*, which include: artha (material need), kama (emotional need), dharma (ethical law) and moksha (spiritual aim). These four aspects of life are regarded as being necessary in order to experience fulfilment.

1. *Artha*, or material wealth, is the aim related to our external social life. This material wealth could take the form of a house, clothes, food, money, status, name and fame, etc. Once a person has attained satisfaction from acquiring material wealth, the mind is free from anxiety. There is no need to think, "How am I going to survive tomorrow?" I know that I have a good bank balance, that my stores are full of provisions and that my closets are full of clothes. So there

13

is no need to worry, there is no tension, rather there is relaxation and satisfaction.

Artha is one of the aims to be fulfilled in life. The Sanatan tradition, yoga, tantra or Vedanta are not against the principle of material gain, provided there is no selfish attitude attached to the gain. Material wealth or gain should not bloat one's ego to such an extent that it explodes. Artha or material gain has been emphasized as a necessity in life. One must have it, one must strive for it in order to find perfection in material as well as spiritual life.

2. *Kama* is emotional fulfilment. We all have desires and emotions that need to be fulfilled in order for us to have emotional or mental satisfaction. The Sanatan concept does not say this emotional need is bad, but that it is a requirement of life. So fulfil it and then there will be no craving to pull you down when you begin your spiritual journey.

3. *Dharma*, or duty, has a very broad vision. It is not the dharma known as religion. It is the duty, the obligation to the body, the mind and the self. We have certain obligations to our body, such as the maintenance of good health. Are you happy when you are ill? No. It is not the dharma of the body to be ill. Are you happy when you are hungry and there are rats running around your intestines and stomach? No.

There are family dharmas or obligations, social dharmas, moral dharmas and spiritual dharmas. We have to realize and fulfil all these obligations. This is not done by adopting an indifferent or adverse attitude towards life and its situations, but by having a clear concept of what our obligations are, of what our duties are, and fulfilling them. The Sanatan tradition does not say that one should neglect the work related to the body, family or society. One should not neglect the obligations, duties and commitments which benefit oneself as well as others.

4. *Moksha*, or liberation, is the desire to attain transcendence, the desire for freedom. Sanatan dharma says that the desire for spiritual freedom is imbibed when we are still in the womb. During the time that the little baby is inside, it

does not have to do anything. It lives in perfect quietude, harmony and peace, in other words, heaven. The mother is breathing, eating and doing everything for the child in the womb. This is the feeling of total harmony, peace and desirelessness which is remembered during rebirthing when one regresses to the time spent inside the mother's womb. The idea of moksha, or freedom, is actually implanted then. That feeling of total, self-contained harmony becomes a samskara, a desire and the motivating force in our later stages of life for the attainment of satisfaction, happiness, contentment, peace and bliss.

These are the four aspects of life within the Sanatan culture which provide material and emotional satisfaction. They give us the motivation to fulfil our natural obligations and to pursue our innermost desire to find a state of harmony, contentment and peace. This is the spiritual tradition from which the yoga and sannyasa traditions have evolved. Therefore, they follow this kind of approach to self-realization.

Four principles of life

In order to evolve progressively, Sanatan culture advocates four principles which, when combined, become the tools for attaining artha, kama, dharma and moksha. These four principles are:
1. *Vairagya* – non-attachment,
2. *Viveka* – right understanding,
3. *Shuddhata* – virtue,
4. *Mumukshutva* – desire for perfection.

The first principle that the Sanatan culture advocates is *vairagya*, which means non-attachment to the objects, situations or experiences that give us pleasure and satisfaction. Non-attachment is a quality that has to be cultivated slowly and gradually. It is considered as the first limb of spiritual life, because until we are able to stabilize ourselves in vairagya it is difficult to observe and transcend the vrittis or archetypes of our personality.

15

The second principle that the Sanatan culture advocates is *viveka*, which is translated as discrimination, although right understanding, right knowledge and wisdom are more appropriate. There is a distinction between discrimination and right perception. The idea of discrimination is subject to our experience of just and unjust, to our belief in what is right and what is wrong. What we consider as right and wrong becomes part of our discrimination or judgement. This aspect of discrimination is related to our ego, or ahamkara. Discrimination is practised in order to gain further satisfaction and enjoyment in life.

If we discriminate between right and wrong, then it is natural for us to accept the right and leave the wrong. That is what discrimination means. However, often the ability to discriminate is clouded by the weaknesses of our personality, by the ambitions of our life, and by the nature or the guna of our personality. If a tamasic person begins to discriminate against somebody, something, or some event or situation, the form and the quality of that discrimination will be tamasic. It will not be sattwic because they are expressing their nature, belief and understanding of just and unjust according to their tamasic nature. So discrimination is not the word that should be used here.

The correct definition is right understanding, which arises out of the experience of the state of wisdom. Wisdom is not knowledge, because knowledge can be acquired, but the outcome of experience. Knowledge is limited to intellectual understanding, perception and receptivity of the mind, whereas wisdom is a spontaneous expression of our understanding. The spontaneous expression of our wisdom is viveka.

The third principle advocated in Sanatan culture is *shuddhata*, or virtue, which encompasses the field of action and interaction. In the *Bhagavad Gita*, it is said by Lord Krishna that *manas*, (mind), *vacha* (speech) and *buddhi* (intellect) should function in harmony with each other, in order to have virtue. Therefore, virtue is not a quality that we superimpose upon ourselves; that is the concept of puritanism. First of all, we must be aware of the actions that we perform through the mind, speech and intellect, and make sure that they contribute positively in order to develop a harmonious interaction between ourselves and other beings, society and the cosmos. We must then make sure that there is no negativity in our thinking, actions or behaviour, no desire to pull another down from a pedestal and put ourselves on an even higher one.

There must be acceptance of life in all its aspects. The general trend is for the person at the top to be attacked from all sides. There are people who dislike that person, who wish to see that person fall from the top. Non-acceptance of life's situations and comparing one's life with the life of another is human nature. However, comparison and non-acceptance of life are not virtuous. A constructive and creative approach to life which is in harmony with oneself and with others is known as right virtue, in which acceptance of oneself and of one's situation in life manifests naturally and spontaneously.

The fourth principle advocated by Sanatan culture is *mumukshutva*, the desire for perfection. This desire is a very peculiar thing because here we are dealing with an experience of mind and a state beyond mind. Desire is an experience of mind and perfection is a state beyond mind. So, desire for perfection encompasses the gross, the subtle and the causal levels of human experience.

Four stages of life
Sanatan culture also divided the human lifespan into four parts. These were known as the four *ashramas*, or stages of life through which one progressively strives from birth till death to attain perfection. These four ashramas are brahmacharya, grihastha, vanaprastha and sannyasa.

1. *Brahmacharya ashrama* is the first stage of life, up to twenty-five years of age, where the young person aspires for knowledge and a career in order to fulfil the artha aspect, material need.

17

2. *Grihastha ashrama* is the householder stage, from twenty-five to fifty years. Here one marries, has a family and works to maintain the family and society in order to fulfil emotional needs, the kama aspect. By working to maintain the family and social structure, one fulfils the ambition, desire and need for property, name, wealth, pleasure and progeny.

3. *Vanaprastha ashrama* is the stage of retirement, from fifty to seventy-five years. It is not retirement in the sense that we understand today, where one retires from a job and is free to do as one pleases. This retirement comes after having fulfilled all the dharmas or obligations of family and social life. At this time, one must realize that all beings, including one's own family members, have their own destiny to fulfil. Therefore, it is futile to interfere with the destiny of one's children or grandchildren. We cannot change the destiny of others, but we can provide positive and qualitative samskaras through which they can work out their own life and destiny.

The role of a human being in the vanaprastha stage is to fulfil the aspect of dharma, by providing proper samskaras for the people with whom we are in contact, by encouraging them to grow and progress in life and by being a source of strength for others. In this stage of life the quest for moksha also begins, and culminates in the fourth ashrama.

4. *Sannyasa ashrama* is the stage of renunciation from seventy-five to one hundred years. It is not 'monkhood'; it is not becoming part of a glorified society. Many people who go to live in an ashram for a short time suddenly want to take sannyasa because they think they will become a part of a glorified society of sannyasins. However, that is not the concept of sannyasa ashrama.

The concept of sannyasa ashrama is to maintain a balanced view of life, in pain and in pleasure, in justice and injustice. One must maintain internal harmony and equilibrium, trust and faith in the self and in the guru at all times and in all situations. Many times our trust and faith are only

18

skin deep; we do not cultivate them deep down at the level of spirit. There is a story which illustrates this point.

One day a guru was walking along with a motley bunch of disciples. The guru suddenly entered a bar and ordered a bottle of champagne. The disciples looked at each other in amazement. "Oh well," they thought, "if our guru is having a drink, let us also have one." So each of them had a bottle of champagne. Then the guru entered a nightclub and sat down to watch a striptease show. The disciples looked at each other and said, "Oh well, our guru is an enlightened being. If he can do this, why can't we?" So, off they marched to see the striptease show.

After having a good time there, they came out and continued their walk around town. They came to a glass factory where molten glass was being poured. The guru went in, asked for a glass of molten glass and drank it down. The disciples looked at each other and said, "No thank you, we can drink champagne but not molten glass. Only our guru can do that."

Similar things happen in spiritual life also. When it is pleasant and it suits us, we follow the guru's example. However, when the guru does something that somehow creates an imbalance in our own thinking, then we say, "Oh no, only an enlightened person can do that. I am not capable of doing it." This is a way of thinking which has to be avoided in the sannyasa ashrama.

In this stage, it is necessary to perfect one's body, mind, personality and awareness to such an extent that there is total control over the forces of nature and the elements. This is important because then sannyasa becomes the pathway to moksha. One has to be open from inside. Openness is necessary, for it is possible to attain great heights with an open attitude. This is the concept of Sanatan culture.

Head, heart and hands
In Sanatan culture, bhakti or devotion, contemplation, prayer and meditation have not been given a separate identity.

19

Sanatan culture believes that bhakti is an inherent part of every individual. *Bhakti*, devotion, faith or the ability to surrender, is the result of being open in mind and spirit. If the mind is closed and one does not have a spiritual aim, then there is no bhakti, there is no faith, there is no surrender. This tradition believes that bhakti is an integral part of the human personality. The ability to let go and to open oneself up is inherent in each one of us. It is only through developing wisdom and virtue and .dissociating the mind from the objects of attachment that one can experience bhakti in its full glory.

The Sanatan tradition represents the culmination of all human belief. It is not a one-sided approach to life but an integral approach. It is acceptance of each and every state and situation in life. It is the development of human potential in every condition. Therefore, we have a saying that each human being is a combination of the qualities of head, heart and hands. You are incomplete if you neglect any one of these three – head, representing intellect, heart, representing simplicity, and hands, representing performance. These three qualities combined become the Sanatan experience.

The concept of unity

The idea of union is a very common theme, not confined to any particular belief, group or tradition. It is an idea that comes as a result of the normal evolution of consciousness. There are times when consciousness evolves in one direction and times when it evolves in another direction. There is a distinct difference between our present lifestyle, knowledge and understanding, and that of prehistoric man. Primitive people lived in caves and hunted. They did not have the concepts of civilized living we have today. This change took place with the evolution of antah karana, the aspect of mind that includes: buddhi (intellect), manas (analytical mind), chitta (subconscious mind) and ahamkara (egocentric mind).

Just as there is evolution of the antah karana, in the same way there is evolution of the spirit. This evolution of spirit makes us aware of a reality that already exists but of which we are not aware at present. Becoming aware of that reality and experiencing that to be real and not just speculative is known as spiritual evolution, becoming aware of the interaction of spirit in our life. This evolution is continuous, it never stops. It is the concept of coming closer to the source, the concept of unity. In this sense everyone is a walking religion, because everyone is trying to find that source of life and consciousness, the source of the 'big bang'.

3

Evolving Awareness

Awareness is related to practically every experience in life. The most common questions seekers ask are related to this subject. What is the yogic view of awareness? How can the awareness be broadened through yoga? Awareness is different to consciousness. According to yogic principles, there is just one continuous state of being, of perception, of knowledge, which is called chetana. *Chetana* is known as 'consciousness'. This consciousness never changes; it is changeless.

In diagram 1 on the following page, the horizontal line represents the continuity of consciousness, which is known as *anadi*, or endless, having no beginning or end. This total field of consciousness is divided into three states of experience. The first state is known as *jagriti*, or wakefulness. The second state is *swapna*, or dream. The third state is *nidra*, or deep sleep. In modern psychology these three areas of consciousness have been related to the terms conscious mind, subconscious mind and unconscious mind. The conscious state relates to gross experience, the subconscious state to subtle experience and the unconscious state to causal experience.

Now, where is awareness in this diagram? It does not exist. For most people there is no awareness as such of these states. Awareness only happens when buddhi, often translated as 'intellect', begins to function. Awareness is an

22

attribute or an expression of buddhi. In this diagram, the circle with I in the middle represents that intellect. Generally speaking, intellect is the energy which perceives, receives, analyzes, compares, stores and later on brings the information to the surface, but buddhi is not bound by our concepts or by external concepts of right and wrong which give birth to the baby known as awareness.

Diagram 1: Anadi Chetana (endless consciousness)

JAGRITI (wakefulness)	SWAPNA (dream)	NIDRA (deep sleep)
Conscious mind	Subconscious mind	Unconscious mind
Gross (Sthoola)	Subtle (Sukshma)	Causal (Karana)

A B C D E F G H I J K L M N O P Q R S T U V W X Y Z

I ←—Intellect (Buddhi)

What is awareness?

Are you aware of the jagriti dimension right now? Think carefully, what are you aware of right now? Are you aware of the totality of the waking state or just a part of it? Think about your answer. Now consider my answer and then compare the two. The body is here. The mind and senses are active in the body. The faculties, perceptions and expressions of the body and mind are active at present. But are we aware of each and every experience and activity of the body and mind? No! So, we can safely say that awareness is different from the state of jagriti or the conscious mind. Jagriti is an expression, a state or a range of conscious experiences when we are awake, in the gross dimension, shown as the range from A to H in the diagram. Swapna is

23

from H to Q, representing the range of subconscious experiences while we are dreaming in the subtle dimension. Nidra is from Q to Z, representing the range of unconscious experiences while we are in the state of deep sleep in the causal dimension.

Now, from A to Z there are twenty-six points and normally we are aware of only one point at a time. For example, if we are reading we are aware of what we are reading, but we are not aware of the physical body and the experiences it is having until and unless those experiences create some form of imbalance, disturbance or alteration in the perception of buddhi. Another example is heat. We know that it is hot, but this is an intellectual concept. It is not until we suddenly realize that we are sweating, that our clothes are wet and we need to cool down, that we become aware of the heat. We become uncomfortable because our awareness has been diverted. In this way our awareness is continually being diverted from one area to another, from one point of concentration to another, from one state of experience to another.

Developing awareness
Broadening the awareness means expanding the receptivity and the analytical structure of buddhi. Although buddhi is translated as intellect, it is not intellect as we normally understand it, but intellect in its broad sense. The awareness changes according to the situations and conditions in which we find ourselves. Take vision for example. Outdoors we can see forms, colours and shapes clearly in three dimensions. However, the same eyes see everything differently when we are under water. When we dive into the ocean or a river and open our eyes, the eyes are the same, but the vision changes. Everything is seen in a hazy way. Neither the instrument, in this case the eyes, nor the intellect has changed, but the environment, the situation and the conditions create different states of experience. These changing states of experience alter the perception of awareness.

Broadening of awareness at the level of jagriti, or the conscious level, means broadening the scope of our perception and analysis from a limited range, such as D to F, to a more comprehensive vision, such as from C to G. Fully achieving that potential means becoming aware from the beginning (A) to the end of that state (H), seeing the total dimension in one glimpse. This is not only a theory, it is proof of how limited our vision, our perception or our awareness is. We have our eyes open, we are aware of someone's movements and we are observing them. At the same time, the eyes are also receiving inputs from the surrounding area, but these inputs are not registered until there is a shift in the mental concentration. When this occurs due to some distraction or disturbance, then, for example, we become aware of the person who is sitting beside us. Perhaps he is scratching himself and we ask ourselves, "Why is he scratching himself?" Suddenly our whole awareness is diverted there and we lose sight of the person we were aware of previously!

We should always strive to develop awareness. Never think that to be aware of everything is simple. That is a very deluding and false concept. After we have developed the ability to observe all the points of the jagriti level from A to H, we must shift the focus to the swapna level, the subtle plane. Later, we will have to shift the whole focus to the nidra level, the causal plane. Once the nidra level has been perceived and there is an extension of the field of awareness, encompassing all three states of jagriti, swapna and nidra, that broad awareness is known as turiya. Some people describe turiya as super mind, but it does not mean this. *Turiya* means 'simultaneous awareness of all three states' which takes us closer to the state of enlightenment.

Deepening awareness

Think about your awareness and how broad it is. The aim of yoga practice is to become fully aware. That awareness is not superficial. While practising an asana, how deep is your awareness of your body? Even at that time the awareness is external. Your body may be twisted in such a way that you can feel the stretch of the muscles in the back, the movement of the joints and contraction in of the ligaments, but that is not total awareness. It is just partial recognition of a physical condition; it is limited awareness. In class, you are often told to put yourself inside the body, to feel the stretch of every muscle, every nerve, to feel the flexing of every joint and to feel everything from inside as if it is the first time. You are asked to make yourself tiny, to go inside your own body and see how things work. Even the simple concept of developing physical awareness is very difficult in practice. Full awareness of every moment is becoming one with the whole experience of the movement.

Superficial knowledge will not take us beyond the state of jagriti. It will give us a few experiences, perhaps from A to D or E or F, but if we continue in the way we are going at present, we will achieve only limited experience of jagriti in one lifetime. Maybe we can experience the areas between I to K or L or M or P of the subtle state, swapna. However, at the level of nidra we can forget it, because the moment we become established at R, we are asleep. Developing the awareness of nidra, the unconscious mind, is very difficult. It can only be done by following a meditative process which involves the projection of the total areas the broad field of buddhi, like a beam of light. Buddhi is like a big searchlight that lights up an area. You just have to expand the area of light. The more you expand the area of light, the clearer things become. Clarity of vision, knowledge and experience, and clarity in the situation and environment are some of the benefits of evolving awareness.

The word buddhi is translated as intellect, but actually buddhi is derived from the root *bodh*, which means 'to be aware of', 'to know', 'to have the experience of'. Therefore, buddhi means recognized experience, and it is this aspect of recognition that takes place through the intellect. Intellect is a broad description of buddhi. *Buddhi* is the faculty of awareness. The intellectual aspect of awareness analyzes the present situations and circumstances, compares them with past memories and decides whether the experience is acceptable or unacceptable, right or wrong. So the intellect can be understood as the analytical and comparative aspect of mind. You are using your intellect while you are reading, analyzing and comparing what has been said here. Simultaneously you are having an experience of buddhi, being aware of the present circumstances, the present situation that you are in. So, bodh, awareness, and buddhi, the faculty of being aware, are different from intellect. Intellect is a faculty of the manifest mind, whereas buddhi is a quality of consciousness. The word bodhi is derived from the root bodh. Even the words Buddha, the enlightened one, the one who is aware, and Buddhism, the path of enlightenment, of awareness, are derived from the root bodh.

Dissociation from the senses

Consciousness is a continuous stream of the state of being. In this continuous stream of being there are three divisions, or states of decreasing sensory awareness: conscious, subconscious and unconscious. In the state of jagriti, there is full activity of the senses which is recognized and understood by buddhi. As we move from jagriti to swapna, the light of sensory perception diminishes and therefore the field of our external perception becomes narrower. As we move further, from swapna to the state of nidra, the field of perception diminishes even further. It becomes very narrow so there is practically no awareness at all of the phenomenal world, as we perceive it in the normal, waking state. It is similar to diving into the ocean. Near the surface there is enough light to perceive things around you. However, as you continue diving deeper and deeper, the light becomes less and less, and the darkness increases until eventually you can see nothing. The rays of the sun being filtered through the water eventually diminish and in the end there is total darkness. This is similar to the concept of buddhi.

27

Look at diagram 1 (page 23) to clarify the concept of buddhi, which is aware of the jagriti, swapna and nidra states. You will see that the first section of the horizontal line represents the jagriti state or dimension. Many small vertical lines intercept it (from A to H), each representing one point of experience or perception in that dimension. It is like our vision. When we look at somebody, our vision is directed towards that person but, at the same time, there is also feedback from the periphery of our vision.

In the diagram, the direct vision is the apex of the V and the peripheral vision is the shaded area of the V. It is that direct vision which is known as bodh, being aware of. I am aware of something that I see, but while I am aware of that, I do not recognize the peripheral inputs which I am receiving. The moment I begin to recognize the peripheral inputs then the field of buddhi expands. This broadening of vision or broadening of perception is the expansion of awareness.

Underneath the V there are some lightning streaks which represent the sensory input into buddhi. For example, we experience heat through our skin, the smell of incense or cigarettes through our nostrils, the sound of the fan or the whistle of the train through our ears, the taste of salt through our tongue. These sensory experiences are happening constantly through all the senses. The moment the search-light of buddhi focuses on one of them, we become aware of that also.

Relationship between senses and awareness

It is possible to cut off the sensory input into buddhi through certain means, such as external shock, sleep and the practices of pratyahara, dharana and dhyana. However, there is a difference between these experiences. The first aspect of buddhi is experienced in external shock. External shock causes a total cut off of the senses and blanks out the buddhi aspect of consciousness, as if buddhi even dies at one stage. Because of the total dissociation of buddhi from the senses, there is the experience of blackout.

28

The second aspect of buddhi is experienced in sleep. In sleep also the sensory perceptions are cut off, but one faculty of buddhi remains active. That faculty of buddhi is aware of the condition we are in at the time of deep sleep and it stops us from rolling off the bed. If that faculty were inactive, we would roll off the bed and hurt ourselves. You could call that faculty self-preservation, or the instinctive faculty of buddhi, which is responsible for our well-being. This instinctive awareness within buddhi is a very subtle faculty. Generally it is called instinct, but it is controlled by that knowing aspect of the self. If a fire is burning and you come too close, you will automatically draw back. People call this instinct, but yoga calls it an attribute of buddhi, because instinct would not even function if buddhi was inactive.

The third aspect of buddhi is experienced in pratyahara, where there is wilful dissociation from the senses. The mind is withdrawn from the senses and centred in its own experience and being. In this state there is no loss of awareness, there is a state of total awareness, yet dissociation of the mind from the senses takes place. It is very similar to the experience we have in yoga nidra when we are not sleeping but still we miss the instructions. We remember the teacher saying, 'right hand thumb' and the next thing we remember she is saying, 'the whole body, the whole body, the whole body'. We were not asleep at that time, so where did we go? So this kind of dissociation from the senses is also an experience of buddhi, the faculty of awareness, in the absence of sensory experience.

Awareness, the absence of awareness and the broadening of awareness are states which can be experienced through self-stimulation or shock, through sensory deprivation in sleep, or in pratyahara, dharana, dhyana or samadhi. This shows that the experience of consciousness is different from the experience of the senses and their link with the mind. The difference between mind, consciousness and awareness is difficult to explain in any language because these terms intermingle. One cannot really define these states unless

29

one has reflected upon the experience of them. We all sleep at night and we practise yoga nidra and meditation, but there is a difference between these experiences. What is that difference? During yoga nidra awareness takes one form, during sleep it takes another form and during meditation it takes a different form again.

There is a controversy here. One-pointedness of mind or one-pointed awareness, according to this description, would mean being aware of one thing at a time, and this is the initial state of becoming aware. Out of the many distractions happening around us, we become aware of one thing and we broaden our awareness by gradually including previously discarded information brought by our senses. Later on, when progressing through pratyahara into dharana and dhyana, this also changes. Although there is dissociation from the senses, the awareness or the inner vision expands, and in that expanded field there is one-pointed concentration. Initially there should be awareness of one item at a time and later on, with the growth of the human faculties, it is possible to be aware of different items simultaneously.

Expanded awareness

In diagram 1 the vertical lines each represent one area of experience and these remain the same, but the V vision encompasses a larger field. There is a word in Hindi, *savadhan*, which means 'attention', 'alert'. This word is a distorted form of the word *saptavatan*, being aware of seven things simultaneously, sapta meaning seven. We should all try to develop the faculty of saptavatan.

There are moments when the mind is transported into another frame of experience, another dimension, where instead of remaining as one piece on the chessboard, we become the player. We begin to see the whole chessboard in front of us and we see how all the pieces are being moved. It may be a momentary experience, but if someone asks a question at that time, we are lost and it takes some time to come out of that state. It is very similar to the state of

30

spacing out, but it is not the same. It is broadening of the vision. That state cannot be described. It can happen at anytime, at any moment. If it were to happen to you right now, you would not be able to communicate with anyone; you would just space out. At that moment it is difficult to find a link between the external and the internal states. Maybe in another twenty or thirty year's time we will find the link. Even in this kind of broad awareness which you may experience sometimes, there is one-pointed concentration. It is similar to the state of jagriti meditation. This is not an introverted meditation; it is a meditation which happens in the state of jagriti, external consciousness. Suddenly there is awareness from point A to G or H or I. Of course, the condition of the mind is different at this time also, so it is difficult to come back to the normal state.

The experience described in yoga is that the state of superconscious mind, of samadhi, or of turiya, is actually when these three areas of conscious, subconscious and unconscious are experienced together with equal intensity of awareness. Rather than separate experiences of jagriti, swapna and nidra, there is only one homogeneous experience, only one state of perception. So, superconscious mind, or the state of samadhi, is in no way influenced by the intellect or the analytical and comparative mind. This final state is experienced with the awakening of the bodhi aspect of the self. In yoga this bodhi aspect of the self is known as the *drashta*, 'the seer'. It is the witness, the seer behind the action, behind the scenes of life and living.

4

Yogic Keywords

Before beginning the study of yoga, it is necessary to have some idea of the keywords that will be used. It is important to know the meaning and usage of these yogic keywords because they do not really have equivalents in English. The word viveka, for example, does not mean right understanding or discrimination exactly, this is only an approximate definition. Therefore, it is better to know the approximate meaning and then later on it can be converted according to the context that we have experienced and understood.

UNMANIFEST DIMENSION

We will begin with a general understanding of the environment in which we live. This understanding is classified into two categories, one is maya and the other is mind.

Maya

Maya is a combination or symptom of the two experiences of pain and pleasure which we encounter in our external life and in our mental and emotional life. The whole life experience is also considered to be false and unreal, because the spiritual traditions believe the soul to be beyond the experiences of pain and pleasure. They have described the soul as the real nature, the real identity of the individual,

32

which is not subject to birth or death, decay or disease. Everything in creation, whether animate or inanimate, comes within the scope of evolution and is subject to transformation and change within the laws of birth and death, decay and disease. Disease is an unbalanced state of being. Decay is a process of ongoing evolution, or maturity, and we have no control over it. If we want to be five-year-old children again today, we cannot. This is the realm of maya, which is known as illusion.

Total mind
The second aspect is mind. The concept of mind described in the yogic traditions is not the conscious mind that we know. It is not the subconscious mind that we experience sometimes in dreams. Nor is it the unconscious mind about which we speculate. In the yogic tradition the two external principles of consciousness and energy are known as the total mind.

The mind is also divided into pure or higher and impure or lower. The impure mind is subject to desires, ambition and ego, and follows the sense objects. It is subject to different cravings, it seeks fulfilment in the world around it, whereas the pure mind is just luminous, it does not seek any external stimulation or experience. The saying, "There is nothing new under the sun," actually relates to the pure mind. The experiences of past, present and future are all contained within the pure mind. When we go somewhere new, however, that becomes something new under the sun for us. That is our impure mind, which is seeking, craving and aspiring for new input, for new stimulation. The still mind, the self-effulgent, luminous mind is pure, whereas the dissipated, ambitious, seeking mind is impure. In order to attain transcendence one must move from the impure mind to the pure mind and awaken or realize the faculties of the pure mind. Upon realization of the faculties of the pure mind, there is mukti and transcendence.

33

Unmanifest elements

What is the cause or process of creation? How did we happen to come here in the form of a human body, and how did we subject ourselves to all these different levels of experience – pain, pleasure and maya? The vedic and tantric traditions have given a clue. They say that initially everything was in an unmanifest state. In this state there is only one experience, and that is the experience of Om. Do you know why we chant Om three times? The first is for Omniscience, the second for Omnipotence and the third for Omnipresence. When we chant Om three times, we are acknowledging the transcendental aspects of the self.

The spiritual traditions do not speak of God, they speak about the self. This transcendental, higher self contains the three faculties of omniscience, omnipotence and omnipresence, and is known as *Brahman*, which means 'the ever-expanding consciousness'. The word Brahman comes from the root word *brinh*, which means 'to expand continuously'. Brahman is the consciousness which keeps on expanding and expanding. So the higher self is known as Brahman and that is an invisible, unmanifest dimension, known as avyakta.

Vyakta means 'seen' or 'manifest', and by adding the prefix 'a' to vyakta the meaning becomes 'unmanifest'. *Avyakta* is the unmanifest dimension where everything is in seed form. This seed form contains the total knowledge of how to become, for example, a sapling, a tree; how to bear fruit and flowers; how to die and again become a seed. Just as a seed which is given the proper combination of compost, water, air and sun will grow into a small sapling and then into a large and strong tree, in the same way, Brahman, or the ever-expanding consciousness, is the seed of human existence, and from this unmanifest state, the different aspects of consciousness evolved.

The first state to manifest from Brahman was *mahat*, meaning 'supreme intelligence'. This supreme intelligence is the all-knowing aspect of omniscience. In the beginning there were three qualities, omniscience, omnipotence and omnipresence. From the original combination of these three qualities in Brahman, the first state to manifest was mahat, the supreme intelligence.

From mahat manifests ahamkara or ego, the identity of individuality. This individuality actually begins to manifest in the state of supreme intelligence, when the single unit of knowledge comes forward from the group of three. The moment this single unit emerges, it is recognized by the ego, the ahamkara – 'that I am', 'I am what I am'. This ego manifests differently in different levels of evolution. It is subtle, causal and gross. When it is gross, we know what the ego is like. When it is subtle, we can experience the same ego in the form of craving, desire and achievement: 'I have done it, I have achieved it'. When it is causal, it is the single idea of 'I am what I am'.

Now, out of that ego, the tanmatras or the essence of creation manifest. The word *tanmatra* means 'the nature or quality of the elements'. The nature of fire is to burn, to radiate heat, to provide warmth and light. That is the tanmatra of the fire element. After defining the nature of the elements, the elements in their gross form follow. The gross form of the elements is what we perceive today in the form of matter or earth, water, fire, air and ether.

This same principle has also been beautifully described and defined by yoga in the form of the chakras. Sahasrara is unmanifest consciousness. Ajna is mahat, the command centre. Vishuddhi is the ether element, the sky. Anahata is the air element. Manipura is the fire element. Swadhisthana is the water element. Mooladhara is the earth element. Yoga says that the kundalini energy came down from sahasrara to mooladhara where it is lying dormant. That has been the evolution of energy from the unmanifest to the manifest, from the transcendental to the externalized visible form, from the sublime to the ridiculous.

Each element has a particular density. Ether is the least dense of the elements and earth is the most dense. Thus the

35

evolution of energy and consciousness has come down from sahasrara, the unmanifest consciousness, to mooladhara, the earth element. In kundalini yoga, when we try to reverse the flow of energy and raise the kundalini from mooladhara to sahasrara, we are actually reversing the whole process of manifestation and coming back from the manifest to the unmanifest source of creation. The concept of kundalini yoga describes this process and the experience of evolving from the manifest to the unmanifest dimension in the form of the chakras.

MANIFEST DIMENSION

In the unmanifest aspect, the ever-expanding consciousness manifests in the form of the supreme intelligence, then in the form of the ego and the tanmatras. Our discussion of the manifest aspect of the self begins with the bhootas. The five *bhootas* can be understood as the unmanifest elements with defined qualities and natures. They are (i) *akasha*, ether, (ii) *vayu*, air, (iii) *agni*, fire, (iv) *apas*, water and (v) *prithvi*, matter. These are the manifestations of the bhootas, the elements, in a concrete and definite form or shape having a particular quality, nature and attribute. It is this progression of elements, from the state of ether to the state of matter, which has been described in kundalini yoga, in the form of the chakras.

Manifest elements

Vishuddhi chakra represents akasha or the sky, the least dense of the elements. The vastness and purity of this element is experienced in vishuddhi. Even the name vishuddhi means the energy centre which is pure in nature, *shuddha*, and not subject to any kind of decay, movement or sensation as experienced in the other chakras. Vishuddhi chakra or the akasha element is just a state in which one experiences time, space and object. All three experiences of time, space and object happen at the akasha or vishuddhi level.

36

The elements progressively increase in density. After akasha comes vayu, the air element. Although air does not have a definite shape, it is experienced in the form of motion or current. It does not have a visible shape which can be perceived by the eyes, but the movement can be felt. Air is the denser form of the akasha element. After air comes agni, fire, which has a recognizable form, shape and attribute. We can see the shape of a flame; we can recognize the colours of a flame. That recognition is an actual manifestation on the level of the senses, the vision, sight. Water, apas, is the next densest element and, finally, prithvi, matter or earth, is the most dense. This progression represents an accumulation and concentration of energy at different levels of creation, manifestation and experience. These elements further control certain other aspects of our expression and tools of experience.

Akasha is the controller of the *antah karana*, which is known as 'the experienced or manifest mind'. The four principles of the antah karana are manas (mind), buddhi (intellect), chitta (memory) and ahamkara (ego). Manas is the rational mind which sees, perceives and analyzes in relation to the interaction between the subtle awareness and the external, manifest, gross awareness. Buddhi is intellect. This intellect is analytical, critical and comparative in nature. The role of buddhi is to acquire understanding and knowledge.

The word chitta cannot really be translated into English. It means 'to see'. Chitta is the seer aspect of consciousness. It is from here that the discussion on yoga begins in the *Yoga Sutras* of Patanjali. When Patanjali uses the term 'chitta vritti', he points to the experience of the mind which is seeing, not the experience of the mind which is experiencing. The seer principle that is talked about in yoga is known as chitta, observation of the gross, subtle and causal manifestations, and experiences of consciousness and energy.

The ahamkara which forms part of the antah karana is distinct and different from the ahamkara discussed

37

previously. Here ahamkara is in relation to the body which is subject to sensory, sensual and intellectual experiences. It is the seed of manifest ego which we experience in our day to day life. If somebody harms or praises us, it is this ego principle which is affected. In times of joy, fear, insecurity or love, it is this ego principle which manifests and is affected. It gives a definite identity to my feeling, my understanding, my experience, my nature. This feeling of 'my' or 'mineness' in relation to physical, emotional, intellectual and psychic experience is controlled, motivated, directed and guided by the ego. These four aspects of mind are called the antah karana, the cause and identity of the inner personality. *Antah* means 'inner' and *karana* means 'cause'.

Vayu, the air element, the principle of activity, motion and movement, is responsible for the movement of the pranas. The pranas are the energies that vitalize the five sheaths, or *koshas*. Annamaya kosha is the body of matter, the physical body. Pranamaya kosha is the body of vital energies, linking the gross and the subtle. Manomaya kosha is the body of mind, antah karana. Vijnanamaya kosha is the body of higher realization and understanding, and anandamaya kosha is the body of beatitude or bliss.

Pranamaya kosha links all these bodies together and vitalizes them. It manifests in the form of physical strength, vitality and heat, in the form of mental motivation and determination, sankalpa, willpower, electrical currents within the body and brain waves. Alpha, beta, theta and delta waves are electrical currents in the brain which are the physio-electrical aspect of prana. These are the many manifestations of prana. Prana is just energy in different forms that flows through the pranic channels, known as *nadis*, the nerve meridians in the gross and subtle bodies. Prana is experienced as a current of light moving within the body.

Agni, the fire element, controls all the *indriyas*, or sense organs. Even the antah karana is considered to be a sense organ. Fire, which is responsible for vitality and stimulation, covers all the sense organs. There are five karmendriyas,

38

five jnanendriyas, four antah karanas, five major pranas and five sub-pranas, making twenty-four in all. Agni represents dynamism, vitality and activity. The sense organs represent constant and ceaseless activity of the elements in the body. The activity of the sense organs is not restricted or limited to the state of wakefulness. They are active at the time of dormancy, and even when the body is dead they remain active for some time. Although the awareness may leave the body, the function of prana continues within the body for some time even after death.

One example of this is that even when the head of a chicken is chopped off, the headless body continues to run around in circles. That is due to the indriyas which are constantly active and which remain active until the pranic battery charge is finished. The battery slows down but does not end abruptly. There is a gradual reduction in the charge of the pranas which is infusing the sense organs with vitality. This is also visible in the human body in the form of body heat. Even after death, it takes time for rigor mortis, stiffening of the limbs, to set in. Once the heat or the vitality of the body is finished, the body becomes stiff and hard. So the fire element is responsible for the ceaseless activity of the different sense organs, or indriyas, and the mind.

Apas, the water element, controls the jnanendriyas. *Jnana* means 'wisdom' and *indriya* means 'organ'. The *jnanendriyas* are five in number – eyes, ears, nose, mouth and skin, which are responsible for sight, hearing, smell, taste and touch. These are the five senses through which knowledge of the outside world is received. For example, sight is a very powerful tool for receiving information from the outside world. Vision extends to regions well beyond the body. If you look out of the window, you can see for miles around you. Vision has very broad limits, but there are some jnanendriyas which are confined to experiences within the frame of the body itself, like taste. You can only taste something when you put it in your mouth. You cannot taste something which is seen by the eye ten miles away. So the jnanendriyas are limited in their function and performance. These five senses – sight, hearing, smell, taste and touch, are controlled by the water element in the body.

Prithvi, the earth element, controls the organs of action, the *karmendriyas*. *Karma* means 'action'. There are five karmendriyas through which the body moves and action takes place – speech, legs, hands, excretory and reproductive organs. These are physical organs performing the physical jobs of communicating, walking, carrying, excreting and reproducing. Of these five organs of action, speech is the most active. It is like the jnanendriya of sight. The organ of speech is constantly being utilized to communicate with other people and the environment.

The five elements – akasha (ether), vayu (air), agni (fire), apas (water) and prithvi (matter) – are known as the manifest or vyakta tattwas, meaning that they perform a specific job. Manifestation in the yogic tradition means something which has a definite identity and purpose and which performs a specific job. This is the answer to the question, "What is the composition of the body?" The body is composed of the unmanifest tattwas, which are Brahman, mahat, buddhi, chitta, manas and ahamkara, and the manifest tattwas, which include akasha, vayu, agni, apas and prithvi, all the way through to the five jnanendriyas and the five karmendriyas. This is how the yogic tradition views the human body.

Experience of the five koshas

Annamaya kosha, the body of matter, is the first level of our experience. The human body is not just a composition of bones, blood, muscles and skin. The entire human structure has both a manifest and an unmanifest dimension. The ranges of the body extend beyond the physical structure. They interact in the dimension of matter through annamaya kosha; the movement of the body from one place to another, feelings of hunger and thirst, the needs of the physical body, all belong to the experience of annamaya kosha.

40

At our present stage of evolution, we have not gone beyond annamaya kosha. Our whole awareness and observation of ourselves is based on the experiences of the physical body. If I feel pain in any part of the body, my concentration and awareness are diverted. If my body is feeling pleasure, a sense of well-being and balance, then my mind is free to pursue other directions and goals in life. The body becomes the focal point of both our attention and our attraction. Just imagine what it takes to raise the level of awareness beyond the experience of the body, beyond the physical dimension. Annamaya awareness occupies about seventy-five percent of our consciousness in daily life in relation to the other koshas and experiences. Manomaya experience occupies about twenty percent of our consciousness.

In *manomaya kosha*, the mental body, we are generally aware of our needs, weaknesses, desires, ambitions – what I like, what I dislike, what I wish, what I do not wish. This dissipation of mental energies makes us aware of the superficiality of manomaya kosha. I am using the word 'superficiality' because there is no real analytical process guiding the activities of manomaya kosha. Therefore, one important point has been emphasized in yoga – be aware. Be aware, observe, understand everything in the right frame of mind. Have a broad, positive outlook on life. This emphasis on being aware, on observing ourselves, is to expand the range of manomaya experience so that we are able to perceive and stabilize the mental experiences. Then we will be able to understand the needs, the weaknesses, the ambitions and the desires in the right perspective.

Pranamaya kosha, the dimension of energy, is also limited within us. How do we become aware of energy? Through what faculty do we become aware of the energy that pervades everything around us, that exists inside us? Generally through feeling. If I come in front of somebody who has a good nature, I say, "He has good energy." I am receiving something from him, but to actually experience that energy, which he is expressing in the form of prana, is practically

41

impossible for us. So, of the remaining five percent of our conscious awareness, only about two percent is aware of pranamaya kosha, because even the awareness of energy is linked with the experience of the mind, and through the mind it is not really possible to have an in-depth experience of energy.

Energy is composed of different substances from that of the mind. Mind is awareness, mind is consciousness. The structure of the mind is different from the structure of prana. The external manifestation of energy in the body can be experienced in the form of heat. The internal manifestation of that bioenergy, prana, can be experienced in the form of electrical impulses, linking different centres of the brain together. The psychic manifestation of energy is experienced in the form of a current, a movement, flowing in the different nadis.

With the knowledge and awakening of pranamaya kosha, sometimes one part of the body becomes very hot while the other remains cold. Sometimes there is a trembling sensation throughout the body, which is coming from inside and has nothing to do with the external environment. The purpose of many yogic practices, such as pranayama, prana vidya or other techniques, is to gradually build up a subtle awareness of prana and its function in annamaya kosha and manomaya kosha, before becoming aware of it in pranamaya kosha.

Vijnanamaya kosha, the higher mental body, comes next. *Vijnana* can be explained as 'intuitive ability of mind'. It refers to the level of mind which is conscious on the internal as well as the external level. Vijnanamaya kosha is actually this spontaneous and intuitive awareness of the self, which manifests in about two percent of our consciousness. Even here, we often doubt whether the intuition we have received is true or false because the input of vijnanamaya is filtered and recognized through manomaya kosha. So we wonder whether the instruction we have received is from God or from the devil, and what we should do about it. Should we do as our mind tells us, or should we think twice about it and see what happens? Should we go ahead or should we hold back? This flash of intuition is very rare. One experiences it in states of deep meditation, when the rational boundary and the intellectual concepts of mind are transcended, and when there is intense self-awareness generated inside. That intuition has to be awakened because it represents the other half of our personality, the unmanifest side of consciousness, wisdom, understanding and knowledge. So eventually the purpose of meditation is to go into the unmanifest, the subtle dimension of mind.

Anandamaya kosha is the experience of bliss. This experience of bliss is not the same one we experience in meditation. When it is experienced, it is indescribable, because here fusion of the individual mind with the cosmic mind has taken place. The feeling is so intense and so powerful that the whole body, the whole being, is changed by that experience. The whole body undergoes a transformation. Every atomic particle of the body becomes full of vitality, joy, pleasure and happiness, and you can experience it physically too. If you happen to touch the body of someone who has attained the anandamaya experience, you will feel a current of energy and your own consciousness will change.

You may have heard many stories of saints or evolved beings who carry this charge with them and who radiate this feeling to everybody. A person may be feeling totally down in the dumps, but after being with such an evolved person for even one minute, he will come out smiling and seeing the world in a new light, with all his problems gone and finished. This is the state of a siddha. *Siddha* means 'a perfect being'. A being who has become perfect cannot become imperfect again, because change has taken place in all these other dimensions of experience – vijnanamaya, pranamaya, manomaya and annamaya koshas.

Perfection of body and mind
The yogic tradition views a human being as a composition of these five kinds of experiences. Since body and mind play

43

a vital role in the awakening of consciousness, initially we have to deal with the practices that are physical or mental in nature. Therefore, many techniques of asana, pranayama, pratyahara and dharana are given. As we begin to experience the subtle aspects of ourselves, there is no necessity to keep on doing the same thing with the body and mind.

In primary school one really has to work hard, but the education one receives in primary school becomes very useful in higher classes. The same principle is applied to the techniques which help the consciousness evolve beyond the body and mind. Initially one has to undergo a lot of hardship because in order to understand the harmonious state of the body we have to experiment with our body to find that state of harmony. There is a lot of trial and error involved. We try something and it works; we try something else and it does not work, then we have to try something else again. We have to find the right combination in order to create that harmony and balance within ourselves.

Therefore, a lot of emphasis has been put on the practices of asana, pranayama, mudra, bandha, shatkarma and so forth, in order to purify the body and mind, to focus the mind, to improve the performance of the body and mind. There are rules that one has to follow in regard to the health of the body and mind, but once the limits of physical and mental experience are transcended, everything becomes natural and spontaneous. When we were children, it was very hard to understand the arithmetic tables and we had to learn them off by heart. Nowadays people have calculators and they do not even know the two times tables! But initially we had to memorize the arithmetic tables and now if we are asked to calculate a problem we can do so in a moment without having to learn the tables again. So, memorizing is initially an effort and later on that ability becomes a spontaneous expression. In the same way perfection of body and mind is initially an effort in yoga and later on it becomes a spontaneous expression.

5

Aspects of Yogic Discipline

1. Yama	9. Karma	15. Tarka
2. Niyama	10. Jnana	16. Tyaga
3. Asana	11. Hatha	17. Mouna
4. Pranayama	12. Raja	18. Desha
5. Pratyahara	13. Mantra	19. Kaala
6. Dharana	14. Laya	20. Bandha
7. Dhyana		21. Dehasamya
8. Samadhi		22. Drishtisamya

| Ashtanga yoga (eightfold path) | Yoga systems | Other yogic disciplines |

There are many aspects of yoga which are not commonly known, many of which are understood and experienced as we progress on our yogic path. Some of the systems and principles of yoga have been outlined in the different vedic and upanishadic scriptures, as well as in the tantric traditions. There are eight points common to all the different vedic thoughts, upanishadic literature and tantric traditions. These eight points are known as *ashtanga yoga*, or the eightfold path of yoga: yama, niyama, asana, pranayama, pratyahara, dharana, dhyana and samadhi (numbers 1–8).

This eightfold path of yoga does not necessarily belong to any one branch of yoga, such as raja yoga or hatha yoga. It is common knowledge that the techniques we learn have to be used in relation to the systems of yoga. Pratyahara can be practised in raja yoga, in kriya yoga or in kundalini yoga, just as it can be practised in mantra, laya, nada or any other yoga. Dharana can be practised in any yoga. The yamas and niyamas can be practised in conjunction with any yoga. Asana and pranayama can also be used in combination with other yogas.

The common belief is that the eightfold path of yoga comprises the aspects of raja yoga only, because most modern commentators have described the process of yama, niyama, asana, pranayama, pratyahara, dharana, dhyana and samadhi as being aspects of raja yoga. According to the tradition, however, the eightfold path of yoga is an integral part of all the yogas and does not belong to any one specific system.

The eightfold path is commonly known because it has been mentioned over and over again. However, the traditions mention a twenty-two fold path of yoga. The first eight comprise the eightfold path. The next six (numbers 9–14) are the different yogic paths, such as karma yoga, jnana yoga, hatha yoga, raja yoga, mantra yoga and laya yoga. The last eight (numbers 15–22) are the other aspects of yogic discipline common to all the yogic paths.

In this chapter, we are going to discuss points 15–22, because although they are almost unknown they are very valid aspects of our yogic practice. In the following chapters we will discuss the six yogas which have been mentioned in the different Upanishads as being necessary to awaken spiritual awareness. Afterwards, we will deal with the well-known eightfold path of yoga from yama and niyama to samadhi. All these points (1–22) are known as the *yoga angas*, meaning parts or aspects of yoga.

LESSER KNOWN ASPECTS

Tarka: to know

Tarka means 'discussion', 'analysis', a process of understanding the techniques and principles that we are following. Tarka is considered to be an important aspect of yogic discipline because it enables our mind to realize the process that will be adopted in the course of our practice. Another name for tarka can be satsang, clarification of the techniques and principles that we are practising.

Tarka, discussion, clarification or analysis, is used in order to develop an awareness of the relationship between the body, mind, emotions, intellect, behaviour, actions and the techniques that we are using. How does an asana influence and awaken the pranic system of our body? The explanation of that theory and principle is tarka. When we have understood it in the right perspective, when we have analyzed it properly, then that is the fulfilment of tarka.

Tyaga: renunciation

The second aspect is *tyaga*, which literally means 'renunciation', or dissociation of the mind from the objects that provide sensory and sensual satisfaction. It is not the concept of renunciation that we carry within us, of leaving something behind. Tyaga is actually a concept of gradual dissociation of the mind from the objects of the sensory and sensual world of experience, so that there is no craving left to pull us back again to the dimension of matter.

Many people believe that renunciation is an important aspect of spiritual life, and such a concept of renunciation is generally related to home, family, name, wealth, position, status and so forth. In a way that concept is correct, but you have to remove the seed of desire from your mind before such renunciation can fructify. Leaving behind or dissociating oneself from the seed of desire is actual tyaga, actual renunciation. Renouncing home, family or friends is not considered to be renunciation, rather it is a show of tyaga ambition.

Initially, in order to obtain a state of mental harmony and equilibrium, one should observe the reactions and transformation created within the personality when we begin to dissociate ourselves from objects of pain and pleasure. If we dissociate ourselves from an object of pain, from an

47

experience of pain, there is happiness and contentment. That contentment or satisfaction is the result or symptom of having left something, but still it is a reaction within the mind. If we leave something positive which gives us pleasure, we experience the reaction of attachment. We feel that something has been taken away from us.

Generally we observe the external action and not the internal experience or the internal reactions. If we have to give away something that we like and hold dear, the attachment causes us to feel different kinds of experiences of loss, depression, anxiety or frustration for some time, until we eventually come out of that situation. If we give away something that we do not want, need or desire, then the feeling of happiness remains with us for some time, until we outgrow that stage.

Renunciation is not considered initially to be an external act, rather it is considered to be a process of self-observation. Yoga states very clearly that because we are very weak internally, we cannot renounce anything with a clear mind and a balanced attitude. There are very few people who have the determination and ability to renounce something and not look back at all. They are known as the brave ones, who are able to tread the path which the angels fear to tread. There are very few such people.

We may leave our home for some time, go up into the mountains and follow vigorous spiritual training and discipline, but even while our body is confined to the mountain area, every day our mind goes to our home and thinks about what is happening there. So which renunciation is complete? Is the external renunciation complete or is the internal renunciation complete? Knowing this human weakness and knowing that we do not have the knowledge or awareness of our inner desires, the tradition says begin to dissociate yourself gradually and develop the concept of renunciation in your mind internally. When the cravings for comfort, luxury, pleasure and contentment are exhausted, then that concept of renunciation will manifest in the external world. So, tyaga is the second important principle which deals not only with dissociation of the mind from the ideas of the material world, but also purifies one in the dimension of samskara and karma.

Mouna: silence

Mouna, or silence, is the next aspect. Through mouna it is possible to attain and experience the nature of spirit. Silence represents the state of harmony and oneness within. Speech or vocalization is a physical activity which externalizes our awareness and senses. By stopping that activity, we gradually internalize the main sensory field which is utilized in order to express ourselves in the material world, and which distracts the mind from being aware of the self. This is the first aspect of mouna.

The second aspect of mouna is to make us realize that if we cannot control the wagging tongue in our external life, then how can we control the wagging mind? It is something external that we should be able to control and forget about. If we cannot, and there is a great urge to speak, then in order to fulfil that urge we create necessities and say, "Oh, this was important and I had to speak." The mind can also create many such excuses and continue to chatter. The chattering mind never knows peace.

The purpose of mouna, which can be translated as harmonious silence within, is twofold. Firstly, it controls the indriya or organ of speech and the externalization of the mind. Secondly, it helps to quieten the mental and emotional agitations and to stop the dissipation of energy. By balancing the pranic, emotional and intellectual fields, mouna provides a balanced personality.

Desha: place

The next principle is *desha*, place or location. Place has been mentioned because the external environment should be conducive to one's spiritual search. This applies to aspirants or sadhakas who are dedicated to realizing their spirituality.

49

If the external environment is disturbed and the energies are dissipated, then our minds and actions will be affected by that dissipation and distraction. So, finding a suitable place where the external environment is conducive to spiritual growth is advised.

The yogic texts such as *Hatha Yoga Pradipika* and *Gherand Samhita* also state that the place of sadhana should not be located deep in the forest or jungle, but in the locality of a town or village, so that there is easy access and one does not have to think too much about food, shelter and security. The place should have a conducive, auspicious climate, neither too hot nor too cold, where you do not have to worry about climatic changes or extremes, and where you can be at ease, physically and mentally.

This concept of the proper place for sadhana arose five thousand years ago when the planet was less populated and there was no industrialization. Keeping the social conditions of those times in view, a suitable place was described. However, this idea of an ideal place will create a lot of problems in the future when the world becomes one big city. Where will one go? Maybe to another planet! Therefore, the concept of a suitable place changes according to the time and the era. In your own life, if you decide strictly to follow one path until you become adept, perfect and realized in it, then you should be the best judge of the kind of place it should be.

The right place for sadhana is one where nature provides plenty of shade, natural foods, fruits and water. The local spirits and the vibrations of that place should assist you and not be detrimental or harmful to your sadhana. We know two such examples of favourable places for sadhana: one is the location of Ganga Darshan in Munger and the other is the location at Rikhia, Deoghar, where Paramahamsa Satyananda performed his sadhana.

In 1989, when Paramahamsa Satyananda had completed his tour of the *teerthasthanas*, or holy places, of India, he went to Trayambakeshwar in order to spend the period of chaturmas, the rainy season, in the proximity of his ishta, Lord Mrityunjaya. During this period he pondered the future possibilities of where he might find a suitable place to continue his sadhana. Many places had been offered to him but he reserved his decision until the direction was made clear to him. On the 8th September, he woke up at midnight and found himself enveloped by a strange light. He clearly heard the command: "Go to my cremation ground, the *smashan bhoomi*."

That same morning a swami arrived at Paramahamsaji's kutir. The first instruction he gave the swami was to find the place for him. He gave a glimpse of what he had seen in the vision and described its setting and topography. Barely three hours after arriving, the swami left in search of the place Paramahamsaji had described, and went to Deoghar, the city of the gods, which from ancient times has been known as Lord Shiva's smashan bhoomi. The following morning, the swami first went to Baidyanath Dham, an ancient temple of Lord Shiva which houses one of the twelve jyotir lingams. When the swami was leaving the temple a pandit standing there asked, "Why have you come here?" The swami answered, "I have come to look for some land for the sadhana of my guru." The pandit said, "I know of such a place. Come and see it for yourself."

After reaching that place, the swami got a surprise. It was the exact place that Paramahamsaji had described from two thousand kilometres away, and he had never been in that locality in his life. The swami then went to meet the owner of the land, who said, "Why have you come here? How did you know about this piece of land? It was only this morning that I decided to sell it." So the land which the owner decided to sell that morning had been seen two days before in Paramahamsaji's vision. The owner said, "I do not wish to bargain with you. Take it, please, for a very small price." So we purchased the land, and on the 12th of September, which was his sannyasa initiation day, Paramahamsaji arrived at that place.

Right from the start we have had absolutely no problems whatsoever with that piece of land. Anything that is planted there just shoots up. Paramahamsaji says that in each and every tree of the place, there resides a particular deity, devata, or tree spirit, and they are also helping him to perform his sadhana. There is a well on the property in which the water is pure, crystal clear, and only about fifteen feet below ground level. Such things happen and it is really incredible how and why they do. When the right time comes, the right location calls the person, and the person is attuned to the vibration of that particular land.

The same thing happened with Ganga Darshan. Paramahamsaji had many visions in the location of our Jyoti Mandir. There was an ancient platform there and when he meditated on that platform he used to see different visions. While meditating on this platform he learnt of the departure of Swami Sivananda from his body. He had a vision of this seven-storey building and how the ashram was going to develop while meditating here many years ago, and eventually things happened in such a way that the Ganga Darshan ashram was built here. I am sure that many others have had similar experiences in their own lives, with their own homes and properties. In some places you really have to struggle hard and in other places things just happen as if divine providence is guiding you.

That is the concept of desha, finding a suitable place which is conducive to spiritual upliftment and sadhana. Of course, you may have to search for the right location. Initially, therefore, until such a place is found and you are established in your own spiritual discipline, it is always advisable to live in an ashram environment so that you are able to perfect your own sadhana. Whether that takes one month, one year or one lifetime makes no difference. Only after you have reached a certain point in your evolution will the right place be shown or known to you, and not before.

Kaala: time

Next comes *kaala*, 'time'. The tradition says that one has to look at time from different angles. Have time set aside for yourself. During that time there should be no encroachment by other people. In a span of twenty-four hours, you should have one or two hours that are devoted purely to your personal sadhana and growth. Until you find this time for yourself, you will not be able to concentrate fully.

A very common question that people ask is: "What should I do if I don't have time to practise?" The answer that I generally give is, "Don't worry. If you don't have time to practise, why even bother asking?" One makes time for resting, one makes time for meals, one makes time for talking. So why does it suddenly become difficult to make time for sadhana? This time has to be adjusted according to situations and circumstances.

Often when I am out travelling, people ask me, "What should I do? I really don't have time." I tell them, "Set the alarm for twelve o'clock midnight. As soon as the alarm goes off, sit up in bed, do your sadhana for fifteen minutes, then lie back down again and go to sleep." Many people did this, and even today when I get their letters they say that is the best period of their twenty-four hours.

There was a person who said, "I want to practise but my wife won't let me." So I said, "Put ear plugs in her ears." He somehow convinced his wife to do this. Some time later we received a letter from him describing the experiences of his sadhana. At the end he had written a sentence saying, "My wife still uses the ear plugs." So, time has to be made and it should be your time. If you wish to progress, you must make a specific time for yourself to practise yoga.

Bandha: psychic lock

The next principle is *bandha*, or lock. Very few scriptures have mentioned the practice of bandha as being separate from the main body of asana, pranayama and pratyahara. Even in ashtanga yoga, the eightfold path of yoga, asanas

53

and pranayama are mentioned but bandhas are not. Bandhas have a different and definite function. Bandhas lock the flow of energy and concentrate it at one point, at one psychic centre. The literature dealing with kundalini yoga, or with the pranic awakening in the body, also incorporates this aspect of bandha as a separate and distinct practice from asana and pranayama.

It is said that with the use of bandhas, apart from awakening and channelling the pranic energy, it is also possible to block the flow of the chitta vrittis. Here practices are used which alter the flow of prana in order to affect, influence and alter the experiences of the mind. It makes a lot of sense because the mind is a composition of consciousness and energy. In the practices of pratyahara and dharana we are trying to expand the horizons of our consciousness, to become aware of the different activities that take place in our consciousness. This energy is not actually experienced in the same way as thoughts are experienced. Even though thoughts are also energy, the main body and structure of thought is controlled by consciousness. Desire, love and compassion, hatred and anger, are all forms of energy, but consciousness controls them.

The other aspect of mind, the energy aspect, is controlled by prana. So when the pranas are balanced and channelled, the mind also becomes still and balanced. Therefore, the practice of bandhas has been prescribed separately. Bandhas are equally as important as the practice of asana and pranayama, because while pranayama awakens the prana, bandhas concentrate it. Bandhas stop the dissipation of prana and channel the pranic forces for the awakening of kundalini.

Dehasamya: body stillness
Then comes *dehasamya*, which is known as stillness of the body. The stillness of the body described in dehasamya is different from the stillness which one experiences at the time of asana practice. In the *Yoga Sutras*, Patanjali has

54

described asanas as postures in which one is steady and comfortable at the time of performance. If you are practising the shoulder stand or headstand, the body should be comfortable, steady and immobile in the final posture. So Patanjali has incorporated the concept of steadiness of the body in the practice of asana. But apart from that, even when we are not practising asanas, there should be comfort and steadiness in the body. That is the concept of dehasamya.

Dehasamya develops the awareness of our physical posture in different conditions. There are many people who sit for a long time on chairs and have lower back problems and shoulder problems. In dehasamya, automatically, no matter what you are doing, even if you are working in the garden, in some industry, or in the office, body awareness is there. It is balancing your body structure from top to bottom, making you aware of the needs of the posture and correcting any defect which may arise due to poor posture. So, the development of the feeling of stillness, balance and comfort in normal physical activities is also an aspect of yogic discipline.

Drishtisamya: stillness of vision

The last principle is *drishtisamya*, stillness of vision. *Drishti* means 'vision' or 'eyesight', and *samya* means 'stillness'. All the areas of vision have to be understood. Vision is an activity of the eyes. It is also an activity of the receptive power of the mind and it is also awareness. Becoming more and more aware is developing a broader vision in abstract terms. Vision can also mean distraction and dissipation of the senses and mind. So, drishtisamya is fixing the senses and mind on one point of concentration. When working, when reading, when enjoying anything in life, when involved in any activity, the mind has to be firm and one-pointed.

In the fifteenth century a master went to a fair where there was an archery contest. He was with his disciples and they goaded him into joining the archery contest. Each

55

participant was given three arrows. One arrow had to hit the bull's-eye, which was quite a distance away. Everyone was trying very, very hard and the master stood there watching them trying to hit the bull's-eye. Some were nervous, some were overconfident and all were trying to hit the bull's-eye in their various states of nervousness and overconfidence.

When the master's turn came, he picked up an arrow, stood up with an air of overconfidence, straightened his hat, checked his pants, straightened his shirt, picked up the bow, twanged it two or three times and shot the arrow with full force. The arrow went wide of its mark. All the disciples behind him started to snicker, "Our master can't even shoot an arrow." One disciple asked him, "Why did you shoot that way? You could have done better than that. We have seen that your aim is always perfect." The master said, "Yes, but I put myself in the shoes of the person who was overconfident. Now watch and see what happens next."

Again he picked up the bow and the second arrow. He took very careful aim and released the arrow gradually, checking the wind direction as he let the arrow fly. This time the arrow went only half way, falling far short of the mark. Again there was sniggering behind his back. He turned to the disciples and said, "Look, I put myself in the shoes of a nervous person who is unsure of himself and who takes care of every minute detail before performing an action. But because he is unsure of himself, he can never hit the target. The arrow always falls short."

Then he took up the third arrow, released it and straight away hit the bull's-eye. He picked up his prize, which was a big straw doll, and started to walk away with it. The entire group at the carnival, who were waiting for his explanation, said to him, "Don't go yet, tell us who the third person was who shot the arrow." He looked back at them, smiled for a moment and said, "That was me." That is known as drishtisamya: perfection in action, perfection of mind, perfection of vision.

THE SIX YOGAS

These are some points of yogic discipline as described in the Upanishads. The different literature has also mentioned six yogas. They are karma yoga, jnana yoga, hatha yoga, raja yoga, mantra yoga and laya yoga. Karma yoga is the yoga of action. Jnana yoga is the yoga of knowledge and wisdom. Hatha yoga is the yoga of attaining physical and mental purity, shuddhi. Raja yoga is the yoga of awakening the psychic awareness and faculties. Mantra yoga is the yoga of freeing the mind by utilizing a sound vibration. Laya yoga is the yoga of conscious dissolution of individuality.

Why have these six yogas been prescribed in the upanishadic tradition? First of all, you have to remember that this tradition is based on evolving an awareness of the divine, without duality. They say that in order to become part of the ocean, the river has to lose its identity. In order to become part of the ocean, the drop of water has to lose its identity. In order to realize the divine consciousness, the individual consciousness has to lose its identity. This is the concept of *advaita*, 'non-dual experience'.

This concept of advaita has been expressed by practically every realized master who has walked on this planet. Christ said, "My father and I are one." Krishna said, "I am what I am." This has been the sentiment and feeling of all realized beings, a drop becomes the ocean. In this process of becoming one with our higher nature, we experience many facets of ourselves which are not only confined to the experiences of the body and senses, but also related to our samskaras and karmas, with the unmanifest side of our being, with the elements that control our body and mind. All the areas of experience, from gross to transcendental, have to be covered.

Therefore, in order to have different realizations and understandings and to have a complete picture, these different yogas have been prescribed. Karma yoga is the yoga of being aware of our actions in the world, and also being aware of the karmas and their influence on our personality. Jnana yoga is a means to develop awareness and interaction in the world of objects as well as to have the knowledge of the experiences possible in the unknown dimension. Hatha yoga is a means to purify the tattwas, the elements of the body and mind. Raja yoga is practised to enter the realm of psychic awareness. Mantra yoga cuts the bondage of ignorance, and finally laya yoga allows our consciousness to dissolve in the higher identity.

Someone once asked Paramahamsa Satyananda, "Is it possible to attain realization in one lifetime?" His answer was "No, it is not possible to attain realization in one lifetime." The questioner asked him, "Do you mean that our efforts to practise yoga, or the techniques of other spiritual traditions, and to follow the precepts of our religion are all in vain?" He said, "No, they are not in vain, but you have to understand one thing – a transcendental reality cannot be understood by an untranscendental mind and personality."

In order to understand that reality, first you have to convert this untranscendental self into a transcendental being. The aim of spiritual practices is to convert the self into a transcendental being. Their aim is not to provide realization. Once your being becomes transcendental, the mind, the brain, the body and the senses all become transcendental, and then the transcendental awareness will merge with your self. The practices provide the means to become transcendental.

In the following six chapters we shall look independently at the different yogas: karma yoga, jnana yoga, hatha yoga, raja yoga, mantra yoga and laya yoga.

6

Karma Yoga

Karma yoga is the first yoga described in the Upanishads as being necessary in order to understand the state of perfection. Karma yoga is one of the main aspects or angas of the yogic discipline, as described in the vedic tradition. Karma is literally translated as 'action', which is something everyone in this world performs, whether consciously or unconsciously. When the word yoga is added to the word karma, it means that karma yoga is any action performed with meditative awareness. So karma yoga is actually the yoga of dynamic meditation.

Concept of karma
Karma can mean many things. Every aspect of creation is governed by the law of karma. Karma is the basic pattern of one's individuality and of the knowledge that one experiences in life. It is also action performed by the intellect, the thoughts and the senses in order to enjoy the fruits of the material world. As an analogy, the soul can be compared to a baby playing in the playground of the world. The toys that it plays with are the karmas – thoughts, desires, ambitions, circumstances, roles and other related items. This baby plays with everything in the playground of the world and the karma becomes an integral part of its nature, because karma is also an action of the unmanifest dimension.

In philosophical terms, karma means the primal seed of desire. The concept of karma which has evolved is that this primal seed of desire guides the destiny, thought, action and behaviour of every individual. To be able to understand this primal seed of desire in the context of abstract karma is very difficult, because it has to be understood in relation to the unmanifest nature, the ego principle and the antah-karana. Before trying to understand the concept of karma on that dimension, however, it must first be understood on a physical level. The different areas of the physical dimension in which we experience karma have to be identified.

One area of karma is action performed by the senses. The concept of the senses includes the organs of perception, the jnanendriyas, and the organs of action, the karmendriyas. The legs, hands and head move. This movement of the body parts is action performed by the karmendriyas. The input of the sensory organs is action being performed by the jnanendriyas: the eyes see, the ears hear, the tongue tastes, giving us an understanding of the external environment. These types of karma are physical in nature.

The senses are also mental in nature and have been described as the different activities of the mind that make us aware of the body and its relationship with the world of objects and the senses. These different aspects of action represent karma being performed through the senses, which are physical and mental, through the mind, which is an analytical process, through the intellect, which is a comparative process, through the samskaras, which are impressions carried from past experiences deep within the consciousness, and through the karmas, which are inherent, primal seeds of desire that influence our patterns of thinking and behaviour.

Process of transformation

We function on all these different levels simultaneously without any awareness, knowledge or understanding of them. When there is awareness of the actions being performed, internally as well as externally, then that awareness becomes a meditative process. Karma yoga can be classified as the true psychological aspect of yoga because in this process of dynamic meditation we have to become aware of the subtle areas of our personality. This dynamic aspect of meditation involves the awakening of latent mental faculties as well as new dimensions of awareness.

For example, a caterpillar lives at ground level and cannot fly, but when it becomes a butterfly it leaves the ground and begins to fly. Human beings are like caterpillars, living at ground level all the time. The body of a caterpillar represents bondage. When the time comes for it to undergo a transformation, it builds a cocoon around itself; then it goes through a period of trauma and transformation and emerges as a beautiful butterfly. That is the principle of karma yoga.

This caterpillar represents the individual identity, known as *jiva*, which is subject to the limitation and bondage of karma. In order to become free from karma, to exhaust karma, to become a butterfly, one has to withdraw into oneself, into one's own personality. This withdrawal can be compared to the state in which the caterpillar builds a cocoon around itself. Within that cocoon, it changes itself, its body, its abilities, so that when it leaves the cocoon, instead of crawling, it begins to fly.

The state in which we find ourselves right now is the state of bondage, represented by the caterpillar. By the practice of karma yoga we go through a state of transformation. With persistence and understanding of our present state, we eventually break down the old body and adopt a new one which becomes the means of attaining light and freedom. This is the aim of karma yoga, harmonizing the actions of the self and attaining union with the higher self. When karma yoga is looked upon as meditation, then it becomes a process of awareness, concentrated action and mental one-pointedness. Dissipation of energies and consciousness is controlled by karma yoga and this eventually brings about a state of purity and transcendence.

LEVELS OF KARMA YOGA

Karma yoga means performing action with meditative awareness, from moment to moment. Not only must the actions be performed consciously, but one's attitude towards the actions must also be observed. Physical karmas are performed by everyone and are motivated by a desire for self-satisfaction or gain, whereas the motto of karma yoga is 'give, give, give', not 'take, take, take'. The attitude and awareness related to an external action changes the outlook towards it, and the vision broadens. While performing an action on the physical level, there has to be total meditative awareness.

When we are involved in activities to sustain and nurture our personality, mind and emotions, even those activities have to be observed. We have to see whether the actions are ego-centred or egoless. Ninety-nine point nine percent of our actions are ego-centred. This kind of action is known as *sakama karma*. Actions performed with a purpose or desire which has been guided by the ego principle are ego-centred actions. In order to experience egoless action, initially we have to use our intellectual ability to analyze the situations and experiences that we are having, and eventually try to stabilize ourselves at one point which is not guided by the ego.

For example, suppose you write down a page of your thoughts and leave it lying on the table. You may be a highly evolved soul who is aware of karma yoga, meditation, viveka, vairagya and many other things, but if someone walks into the room, picks up the page and says, "Who is the idiot who wrote this?" how will you feel at that time? There will be a momentary feeling of shock and anger because your pride has been hurt. If that can happen even to a person who has developed his awareness, imagine the effect on a person who is not practising karma yoga. That person will snap back immediately, "What do you mean, who is that idiot? That idiot is me." At that point, a clash of egos, a clash of

62

pride, will take place over a very small incident – someone's comment on your writing. In karma yoga it is not the surface reaction that is important but the subtle reaction that has to be observed. By observing the subtle reactions, it may become possible for us to convert the ego-centred actions into egoless actions, the egoless expression of our being.

Interaction: level of speech

The traditional literature speaks of karma as being performed through speech, through mind and through intellect. Interaction concerns the karma of speech. When we interact with other people, we are very aware of our own personalities, of where we stand and what kind of image we would like to project. In order to fulfil this ideal image, we may have to make certain changes or modifications in our thinking, reactions and behaviour. For example, if I want to project an image of myself as a nice person, then despite what anyone may say – that I am bad, crooked or false – I will swallow my anger and try to be nice. My whole awareness will be on projecting myself as a nice person and not on observing my own inner reactions. How are the words and feelings of other people affecting me? How am I able to convey my feelings and words to other people without affecting them in a negative way? So the interaction of personalities is actually the testing ground of karma yoga.

Even in family life, this interaction often becomes very difficult. Take, for example, the interaction between husband and wife. At first they think they have come together out of love, but later on, after one clash, distancing and aversion begin. The distance becomes greater and greater until, after a couple of years, the love that was felt on that first day of marriage is converted into intense dislike and incompatibility, ending in divorce. This is also an example of ego-centred behaviour. If we can somehow find a balance in our own behaviour and expression, and convey that to the partner and the family, then such splits can be avoided.

Someone once asked Paramahamsa Satyananda, "What is the reason for so many divorces in the world today?" and he said, "It is because families do not share the same aim in life." If families do not share the same aim, then a split is bound to take place. This is because one partner is not willing to come out of his cubicle and the other is not willing to come out of her cubicle. Both take a rigid stand; he has his aim and she has hers. Through the process of karma yoga one can understand the way to balance one's expression and needs.

Stimulation: level of mind

Karma is also performed though the mind. Karma at the mental level relates to motivation and stimulation. When there is a lack of stimulation, boredom sets in. Another aspect of karma yoga, therefore, involves overcoming boredom, which is one of the hardest jobs to do because it is the nature of the mind to seek stimulation. Once one type of stimulation loses its power, the mind seeks further stimulation. After some time, one job becomes tedious and seems like a routine, doing the same thing day in and day out. We experience boredom due to repetitive action and to the lack of stimulating new input.

If there is observation of the self, then the desire for stimulation can be observed. Often stimulation becomes the motivating factor behind our creativity and positive qualities. When there is no stimulation, we tend to lose creativity; our mind becomes stagnant and loses its positive nature. Yoga has described this deficiency of mind as a state of inaction within a state of action. While performing an action, one reaches a state of inaction, and in a state of inaction there is boredom. It is said in the *Bhagavad Gita* that if you can maintain a balance between the states of action and inaction, then you are a yogi.

What is this state of inaction and action in relation to one's life? Before going into this theory, first we have to know the basic principles involved in karma yoga. With a lack of stimulating input there is boredom, lack of a positive mental attitude. This is a state of mental deficiency because the mind is not in harmony and balance with itself. Thoughts go in one direction, desires go in another direction, our weaknesses take us in another direction and the result is a split in the personality. In order to remove this deficiency of mind, the dissipation has to be understood and stopped.

Social conditioning: level of intellect

Intellectual karma yoga is trying to know the reason for something and thinking about whether or not this reasoning fits with our own understanding of life. Intellectual understanding relates to beliefs, ideas and concepts that we have imbibed from our culture, from the society in which we live and from our religious background. The concept of intellectual karma yoga is based on the way we compare a new idea with an idea that is already within us, and then either accept or reject it. Acceptance or rejection of an idea is motivated by our beliefs and our likes and dislikes of particular ideas, thoughts or situations.

The following example will give you an idea of the cultural programming or social conditioning that we carry within us. If an Indian goes to a restaurant in Italy and begins eating spaghetti with his fingers instead of a fork and spoon, everyone in the restaurant will turn around and stare at him. Similarly, if a foreigner goes to a village in India and starts eating chapattis with a knife and fork instead of his fingers, people there will begin to stare. In both cases that initial question mark, that initial aversion, will definitely arise because there is no understanding of the other social or cultural conditionings. Intellectual action which motivates our thoughts and affects our expressions on the physical level, for example, facial expressions, is a form of intellectual karma yoga.

Impressions: level of samskara

The next aspect of karma yoga is on the level of samskara. Samskara is a very peculiar thing. It is the library within a

DNA molecule, containing everything that we have imbibed. One DNA molecule contains the total information of all the libraries in the world combined. Samskaras are like that too. Samskaras are the inputs of volumes and volumes of books which we carry within us and which have been accumulated over millions of years. When these samskaras come to the surface of the mind, they are very powerful. They can manifest in many ways, as a desire for food, a desire for sleep or in the form of a sickness. They are known as impressions.

The tradition says that there are many ways to become aware of and to eliminate samskaras. One way is to relive the samskara and to experience the aspect of pain or pleasure contained within that samskara. Another way to eliminate samskaras is through the practice of karma yoga. While we are performing karma yoga with total one-pointed attention, the process of inner purification that we are trying to achieve brings deep-rooted samskaras to the surface of our consciousness in the form of likes and dislikes, ideas or concepts. When we see things in a different light and become more perceptive and creative, it is also a form of samskara.

It is very difficult to explain how samskaras manifest when they become ripe and how they can influence and affect our behaviour and actions. The practice of karma yoga helps us to become aware of the samskaras that are ripening and to remove their negative and disturbing influence from our mind, providing a state of purity, harmony, equilibrium and balance within. The same technique is adopted for purification of the karmas, because karmas are the original seeds of desire.

Experiential realization

Karma yoga is a very effective and valid yoga for experiencing the total self. When karma yoga is complemented by other yogas, when the awareness of the action evolves along with the practices of other yogas, purification is spontaneous. Someone came to the ashram in the early days and he saw everyone working very hard. He said to Paramahamsaji,

"You don't teach your disciples any sadhana or scriptures. What will they gain through all this karma yoga?" Paramahamsaji replied, "That state of purification and harmony my disciples can gain through karma yoga, no other person can gain, even after twenty lifetimes of sadhana and learning."

This challenge is still open today. Paramahamsaji was very straight about it. He said, "Purification has to take place from within at all levels." We may be unable to understand how the purification begins from inside, but it is very simple. If we have a bad experience in our sadhana, then we do not look forward to that sadhana anymore. If we have a bad experience with somebody, we try to avoid that person. At the same time we are trying to be pure and accepting, which is a contradiction. On the one hand we are saying, "Everyone is equal," and on the other hand we are saying, "I know more than you, so who are you to tell me what to do?" That is a very contradictory philosophy. It is an intellectual realization or concept, but not an experiential realization. According to Paramahamsaji, karma yoga is a process of experiential realization, a stepping stone towards developing and attaining spiritual awareness.

ATTITUDE TOWARDS ACTION

In karma yoga, it is not the actions themselves which are considered to be important, but the frame of mind with which the actions are performed. Actions happen without our knowledge anyway, and they will continue to guide our life whether we wish them to or not. Action is a continuous process which keeps on happening, and over which there is no voluntary or rational control. It is the attitude towards action and work that is most important. It is the awareness of action and work that is important and not the work itself.

It is this change of attitude which eventually creates the change within. It is similar to the analogy of a knife, which in a murderer's hand can be used to take away someone's life and in a doctor's hand can be used to save life. The

67

instrument is the same, a knife is a knife, but it is the attitude of the person holding the knife which is important. The same knife can take a life or save a life, depending on the frame of mind of the person holding it. The right frame of mind has to be a positive, bright, optimistic attitude towards life and the actions involved in life. With this positive action and attitude that we are trying to develop there should also be a drive, a motivation towards realization. This attitude must lead us to a meditative experience.

Karma yoga is definitely not philanthropic or charitable work. Many people compare karma yoga to charity work. Providing food and shelter for those in need is a form of karma yoga, but it is sakama karma yoga, action performed with the desire of gaining merit, status or name and fame. This kind of charity work will not lead the practitioner to a meditative state. It is an external action which is performed with a social view or understanding in mind. Social work cannot and should not be considered as *nishkama karma* yoga, action performed without any desire or personal motive.

The whole aim of karma yoga is to lead one into a meditative state of awareness, an awakened state of consciousness, where we become observers of what is happening and how these actions and interactions influence, bind and limit our expressions and personality. This change also has to be understood in relation to the other yogas. Combining the practice of karma yoga with other yogas, such as jnana yoga, bhakti yoga or hatha yoga, is necessary because karma yoga becomes a powerful tool only when it is combined with other yogas.

Action and inaction
As an aid to further experience, a state of egolessness needs to be developed. A change in one's attitude to and vision of life will help one to become egoless. Therefore, it is said that one must perform action with full intensity, by becoming as egoless as our present condition and circumstances permit. Egolessness means leaving aside the idea that "I am

68

performing", "I am achieving", "I am doing". This is also the theory of the *Bhagavad Gita*, because in the *Gita* two kinds of yogas have been explained. One is the yoga of action and the other is the yoga of inaction. These two words seem to contradict one another. How can there be action and inaction at the same time?

Action and inaction are related to our attitude. For example, in some schools of yoga, when people are initially exposed to spiritual ideas, it is stipulated that karma should not be performed because karma is binding, whereas in other schools it is stipulated that through karma it is possible to attain mukti, liberation. A person who has no concept of karma becomes very confused by this. What should he do? On the one hand, he is being told not to perform any action, in order to become free or to come closer to the state of realization. On the other hand, if he has to perform actions day in and day out, again the thought arises, "How can I attain realization by performing actions?" This confusion arises due to lack of spiritual education.

At no time in life can we say that we are inactive. We may be inactive externally, but internally we are certainly active. Is it possible to be inactive in mind, to be thoughtless, emotionless and desireless? No, it is not possible even in the state of realization. Even God, who is supposed to be a combination of omniscience, omnipresence and omnipotence, is not actionless, thoughtless, emotionless or desireless. How then can the stopping of every kind of physical activity help us to practise the yoga of inaction?

Selfless action

It is the belief and experience of those people who have attained higher awareness that by removing the identity of 'I' through karma yoga, it is possible to be inactive. 'I', as the body and mind, as an individual, am not the performer, am not the enjoyer of the karma or the results of the actions; I am simply an actor. An actor goes on stage and plays his role from beginning to end, but while he is playing the role, despite his identification with it, he is still a different individual. Though he may be acting in a Shakespearean play, the concept, attitude and awareness that an actor has on stage is that he is still John Smith, that awareness is always there. When we have the awareness that we are fully active in the world but at the same time not the active agent, that our nature is not to be active externally but to be aware and observant, then this concept or notion of 'I' loses its grip over our personality and the actions become selfless. They are no longer motivated by the concept that 'I' am performing an action, but become different.

How do they become different? Actions performed with the concept of duty or obligation take us away from inharmonious expression. At present our expression in the world is not harmonious. There is no harmony in our thinking, so how can there be harmony in our action? We are subject to positive and negative influences. Even after being involved with yogic disciplines for many years, people are still unable to grasp such concepts. That motivation of selfishness, of 'I' superimposes itself on everything.

Car and driver analogy

Selfless action is something that has to be worked towards gradually; it is not something that can be understood or attained in an instant. There has to be awareness attached to it. This is the concept of the *Bhagavad Gita*. Who performs the action? Is it the body, the mind, or the self? The *Gita* says that it is not the body or the mind but the self which is sitting inside and performing the action.

Consider the analogy of a car and a driver. Who drives the car? A car is just a metallic structure with gears and an engine. The mind is like the ignition, which, once turned on, makes the car move forward. It is that initial spark coming from the spark plugs that ignites the engine and propels the whole machine forward, but it is the self, the driver sitting inside, who controls the ignition, brakes, clutch, lights, etc. That driver is separate from the car, from the gears, from the metallic structure and from the movement that is taking place within the whole structure. The driver is actually unaware of what is happening inside the engine. He is just observing the dashboard, the console, the instrument panel in front of him. The driver is not there to observe how the gears are changing or whether or not the cylinders are firing sequentially. He has only to monitor and observe the dials in order to know whether or not the car is working properly. In the same way it is the self which guides our actions. The thrust of the *Gita* is that we have to experience that self within and not identify with the actual movement of the car. The movement of the car is irrelevant. It is the driver sitting inside that is important.

So who is performing the action? It is the driver who is performing the action. Who is that driver? The driver is the self. How can an individual mind become aware of that driver or self? By following the process which is described in the different attributes of karma yoga.

ATTRIBUTES OF KARMA YOGA

Efficiency

The first attribute of karma yoga is efficiency. Actions performed by the body and mind happen spontaneously and should be done with total efficiency. This efficiency involves full concentration and awareness of the mind. If there is no concentration and awareness, then you can be sure there will be no efficiency either. You may ask yourself how one can become efficient. It is not necessary to have extraordinary skills in order to be efficient, but it is necessary to be keen, to have awareness and concentration, to be one-pointed and not distracted. You must be able to observe the whole event or situation in order to become efficient.

Equanimity

The second attribute of karma yoga is equanimity, which means that there is balance of mind in both success and failure. If our mind becomes disturbed by failure and success, then we swing like a pendulum, from one side to the other, from a positive and optimistic approach during success, to a negative and pessimistic approach during failure. This swing of the mind from success to failure and failure to success is very disturbing and distracting. According to yoga, this change of attitude over which there is no control is a very dangerous thing.

This mind swing will produce a sudden burst of energy and action, but at the same time the possibility of withdrawing into a shell will also be there. Why should one withdraw into this self-created shell and claim, "I am trying to practise karma yoga but it is so difficult?" In order to maintain mental balance, one has to practise the other yogas as well, and abandon attachment and the desire for a result and achievement. Abandon any self-fulfilling expectations which enrich the ego, or which create a loss of self-image. Equanimity, balance of mind, is one of the important aspects of karma yoga.

Absence of expectation
The third attribute of karma yoga is not to renounce action under any circumstances. There is a very beautiful sentiment given in the *Bhagavad Gita*: "It is not possible for embodied beings to renounce action, but it is possible to renounce the results of action." Just the use of the word 'embodied' conveys a very deep meaning to the whole concept of karma yoga. 'Embodied' includes everything – body, mind, intellect, ego. So, never think of renouncing action, only think of renouncing expectation of the results of the actions performed.

Egolessness
The fourth attribute of karma yoga is egolessness. "He who is free from the feeling of ego, and who is not swayed by the feeling of good and bad, walks the path of righteousness and righteous action." This is another beautiful sentiment

from the *Bhagavad Gita*. Egolessness, not being bound by ego, or being free from the bondage of ego, takes us on the path of righteousness, which is the sinless path. The yogic definition of sin is 'disharmony'. A disharmonious state which takes us away from realizing our true nature and direction, which diverts the awareness and attention away from righteousness, is known as sin in yoga. The *Gita* states that by being egoless, one can follow the righteous path and avoid the sinful path of disharmony. Egolessness also implies that one has to be simple, sincere and desireless. To cultivate egolessness, two important qualities are essential: sincerity in our commitment, goal and direction, and simplicity in thought and action.

Renunciation of limited desires

The fifth attribute of karma yoga is renunciation. One who is in control of the self and who is devoid of desire is a true renunciate. A true renunciate attains enlightenment. The first point of the statement is being in control of the self and the second point is being devoid of desire. Both points are abstract terms dealing with the last aspect of karma, the seed of desire.

It is understood that when we begin our journey, the motivating factor is a desire. 'I wish to' is the form of our desire. It is not elimination or renunciation of this desire but the renunciation of other limiting desires that is necessary. We must know which are the limiting desires that hold us back and which are the propelling desires that push us forward. This can be done by combining karma yoga with raja yoga, by following the processes of pratyahara, dharana and dhyana.

Throughout this whole structure of karma yoga, we are simply trying to convert the negative attitude into a positive attitude. Once the whole thing is converted into a positive attitude, then it is the sattwic quality which takes us beyond the realm of the positive nature. It is like using a thorn to remove a thorn that is stuck in the body. The positive nature is also limiting. Of course, it is better than the negative nature, but still it is limiting.

To deal with the positive nature is easy, but to deal with the negative nature is really difficult. In the whole process of karma yoga, we are attempting to convert the negative into positive. Once the whole thing has become positive, then the gunas will take over. Ultimately it is the guna, or the inherent nature, that will take us beyond the duality of the positive and the negative and into the state of transcendence.

Duty or dharma

The sixth attribute of karma yoga is considering every action to be a duty. Do your duty, for action is superior to inaction. When action is performed with the idea of duty it produces a very deep experience of bhakti, surrender, belief, trust and faith in a higher nature, a higher reality guiding us. This duty is to be understood in relation to one's individual, social, global and universal dharma.

When one develops the awareness of dharma as an inherent commitment, duty or obligation towards other beings, then one develops a giving or helping nature. Often people talk about and believe in giving a helping hand to others, but our actions, which may seem outwardly like helping, do not necessarily convey the same feeling to others. Often even the desire to help others carries with it some thought of gain or profit. Helping others is in itself a dharma. We should not be restricted by the idea of some kind of personal gain.

Initially, the practice of karma yoga is difficult because to combine the concepts of efficiency, non-expectation, equanimity, egolessness, renunciation and duty in one action is difficult. The thrust of karma yoga is to have these concepts combined in one thought, in one action, in one moment. Once these different ideas are combined, then we can say that we are practising karma yoga.

74

LIVE KARMICALLY

The more aware an individual becomes of the changes that are taking place in his or her attitude, performance, outlook and approach to life, the more unselfish that person will become. This person will also develop a universal vision. Christ stated very clearly, "As you sow, so shall you reap." This is a very clear reference to karma yoga. Action leading to an expanded vision of life is what we are trying to sow. The ultimate result is an expanded vision of life. That is the law of karma, which applies on subtle dimensions as well as on scientific levels.

Science accepts the fact that every kind of action creates a result, a reaction, which may not necessarily be in the same context as the initial action. It could be subtle, it could take a different form or be a different experience. The clapping of two hands produces a sound; striking two material objects together creates a sound, a spark, or some other reaction. Each action creates a different result. The reactions are not always similar to the actions and can have a different nature altogether.

What we think and experience on both the physical and subtle dimensions creates different kinds of karma. It also creates different types of reactions in our personality which are not perceived immediately. A childhood experience can manifest later on in life in the form of a fear, a complex or an inhibition. The experience we have today will manifest later on in life in a different form. The reactions are always different. These reactions may be negative and limiting or positive and open. By being aware at the time of performing action or karma, we are initially trying to see how the action is performed. Later, when we have developed awareness, we can see which reactions can be experienced from a particular type of karma. It is here that karma yoga stops being a physical process and becomes a meditative process.

Gunas or qualities

In order to achieve this meditative process in karma yoga, one has to be aware of the *gunas*, which are the aspects, qualities or nature of the phenomenal world. These aspects have been divided into three categories: *tamasic*, meaning a state of inertia or ignorance; *rajasic*, meaning a state of dynamism and activity combined with full ego involvement; and *sattwic*, meaning simplicity and equanimity in action. Simplicity in action is the sattwic karma that we are trying to evolve. In the course of our growth we begin from the tamasic pattern or frame of mind. Tamasic actions are deluding in nature. They are performed for self-satisfaction and many times harm another individual. They are actions with limited vision and concept and are subject to the state of ignorance or avidya.

On a higher level the next form of action is known as rajasic. These actions are performed for the fulfilment of a personal desire with ego, effort, drive, motivation and expectation of a result which is self-satisfying. Most of the world population works on the rajasic level of karma. To go one step beyond the rajasic nature should be the main thrust of a positive ashram type environment, where karma is done without any dislike, hatred or disturbed feelings, and where the karmas or actions flow from one state to the next. Such karmas uplift the whole group; they do not just satisfy or fulfil the ambitions of one individual.

Actions done without any kind of expectation, hatred or dissipation of mind, and which flow from harmony to dedication to compassion and to the integration of our personality, are known as sattwic. It is this sattwic karma which we have to evolve and strive for. Once we are able to strive on this path, then we can achieve different states of awareness and realization.

The final statement that the yogas make is to live karmically. Do not try to reject the karmas, or to build upon them, but live karmically. Flow with the karmas that come in life, flow with the nature of life, with total awareness and detachment. The statement, "Live karmically", is not only yogic. In different traditions such as Tao, Zen, Buddhism, Hinduism or Christianity, the same concept of flowing with life has been emphasized.

Generally, what happens is that instead of flowing with life, there is a struggle. If there is a struggle in anyone's life, then you can be assured that the karmas are not sattwic but rajasic. If there is a struggle in our mind, our thoughts or our beliefs, then we are living under the influence of rajas. At the time of struggle we are acting from our ego, which superimposes itself upon our ideas and beliefs and therefore upon our actions.

Total surrender

Once the ego is eliminated, the concept, feeling or idea comes that "I am not the doer, God is the doer." There is a statement, "My father and I are one, but my father is greater than me." The same sentiment has been stated in Sanskrit: "Na ham karta, Hari karta, Hari karta hi kevalam." It is a very beautiful concept. At first we are saying, "My father and I are one," meaning that there is no distinction between the two. 'I', as an individual, do not exist; I have merged myself into the divine consciousness. But in the same sentence it is also said, "Still my father is greater than me, and it is he who acts."

There is no sense of ego identity here. Na ham karta – "I am not the doer." Hari karta – "the supreme consciousness is the performer." It is He only who performs through me. It is a statement of total surrender of the karmas – "Thy will be done." When this kind of total surrender happens on the level of the karmas, without any ego-identification, self-identification, sense-identification or sense of gain, then purity of mind, action, speech and thought is experienced. It is this state of purity which ultimately takes us to unknown dimensions.

This is the whole concept of perfect karma yoga, because here the actions become pleasant. The idea of work or

77

action is not normally pleasant, but when action becomes a joy, when it becomes light and there is complete involvement, the difficulties are not felt along the way. It is to overcome the difficulties in our attitudes, thoughts and actions that karma yoga is emphasized in the vedic, tantric and yogic traditions. According to these systems, one should not escape from life but escape into life. That is karma yoga.

7

Jnana Yoga

The second aspect of yoga is jnana, which has been described in the Upanishads as a means to obtain the meditative state and intuitive ability. The name itself creates some confusion because *jnana* literally means 'knowledge and wisdom', thus it is known as the yoga of knowledge and wisdom. The definition of yoga that we are using here is the process of meditative awareness. Therefore, in this context *jnana yoga* means the process of meditative awareness which brings us closer to our inner nature and gives birth to our intuitive faculties. It is this intuitive or illuminative knowledge which is the end result of jnana yoga.

Intense self-inquiry

The confusion still persists, however, because jnana yoga has been taken as a yoga or means to awaken the intellectual faculty. Intellectual or mental analysis, where we use the intellect and mind to analyze different situations or to be aware of certain nagging questions and try to find answers to them, is not jnana yoga. This is something that we do every day. If a question bothers us, we try to find the answer through our own effort, by talking to someone or by reading certain books. This normal means of finding an answer to a question is not a part of jnana yoga.

What is that knowledge, understanding or experience that you receive when there is meditative awareness within?

In that frame of meditative awareness would the form of knowledge be intellectual? Would it be confined to past mental impressions or conditioning? No, because that meditative awareness focuses the dissipated energies of the mind and channels them to make the mind more concentrated and relaxed. In this concentrated yet relaxed frame of mind, intuitive flashes occur which give us an experience of another understanding or reality that does not fit in with the normal, rational frame of mind or with the accumulated experiences of the mind.

So jnana yoga is not a yoga where we become bookworms, where we turn our heads upside down trying to find an intellectual, written or rational answer to a question. Jnana yoga is a yoga of meditation in which the attitude is one of intense self-enquiry, where we become aware of our intuitive abilities and faculties. It is these intuitive faculties which remove the boundaries of the pre-conditioned mind, thus bringing us closer to our own source. Therefore, jnana yoga can also be said to be a part of dhyana or meditation.

Non-acceptance and non-belief
The starting point of jnana yoga is to believe nothing and accept nothing, because what we accept and believe is often erroneous and non-factual. Of course, we also have to use common sense. Supposing I say, "Believe nothing and accept nothing", and you decide to follow that literally, then both of us could be in big trouble. If, for example, we see a snake and I ask you not to touch it because it is poisonous, and you reply that you will not believe or accept anything, what will happen? If the snake bites, you will go through intense agony. Supposing someone mentions that the food you eat passes through a large, rubbery intestine, and you question whether you possess one and cut yourself open to find out.

There are certain things about which you have to use your own judgement and common sense, realizing fully that other people have experienced it, that there is a scientific basis for it, although you may not have had personal experience of it yourself. If there is enough evidence to prove that such things really do happen, then that fact has to be accepted and believed. The concept of non-acceptance and non-belief is not to be taken in the context of our day to day life. It relates to the area or dimension where concepts become abstract, unclear and speculative, and have to be investigated. That is the aim of jnana yoga.

One must remember that initially the aim of jnana yoga is the removal of speculative knowledge, and later the aim is to have experiential knowledge. In this way the mind is emptied of preconceived ideas, dogmas and beliefs, which in abstract terms create certain expectations in life and do not give us an understanding of our life in terms of its strengths and weaknesses, needs and qualities. Given the opportunity, everyone would want to reach the moon, everyone would like to explore new things; that is definitely our desire. But have we ever thought about whether we are physically and mentally competent to embark on such a journey of exploration? Therefore, in jnana yoga all preconceived ideas and notions have to be removed and another set of ideas based on facts related to body, mind and spirit has to evolve.

Self-analysis

In this context the process of jnana yoga begins with self-analysis. This form of self-analysis is not abstract or abstruse; it is very definite. In fact, the practices of pratyahara and dharana may be classified as part of jnana yoga as well as raja yoga, because through these practices we analyze ourselves. What is happening at the level of our thoughts? How are we being swayed by the thoughts, emotions and feelings? Do we have the ability to stop them or to recall them at will? This kind of physical, mental, emotional and intellectual self-analysis is part of the techniques of jnana yoga. Something that gives us knowledge about ourselves is important because unless the basic principles of our personality are understood, we cannot progress on the path of jnana yoga.

Starting with the basic structure of jnana yoga, first the awareness of our needs has to be considered. What are the requirements of my body, mind and emotions? What are my social and family requirements? We need to have a clear-cut concept of these requirements. That becomes our personality, what we really need, apart from the ambitions. Then we need to observe and analyze what strengths and qualities we have and how they can help us to achieve our needs. This down-to-earth understanding of our personality will clear the dissipation of mind which is due to the influx of thousands and thousands of other ideas that are irrelevantly connected with our lives.

Therefore, in order to trim the various aspects of life, jnana yoga has been recommended in the Yoga Upanishads. This is how we have to trim our life. First we must know what our life is and have a clear-cut concept of our direction. Then we can begin our spiritual journey.

Experiential knowledge

Please remember that jnana yogis are not scholars. There is a beautiful saying in yoga: "Scholars gain every day and jnana yogis lose every day." What do scholars gain and what do jnana yogis lose? Scholars gain in terms of non-experiential knowledge. There are some scholars who have memorized volumes and volumes of texts and scriptures. They can easily refer to one text or the other, but if that is not applied in their actions, thoughts, beliefs and interactions, then what is the use of having that non-experiential knowledge? Jnana yogis, on the other hand, lose this kind of knowledge every day because they see the futility of learning something for which there is no use or practical application in their lives. If it cannot be applied, then why have it? If it is something that can be experienced, then try to have that experiential knowledge.

This is the yogic view of jnana yoga. This losing is possibly the most important aspect of jnana, which is opposite to what the word jnana implies. Generally, when we say 'jnana', it means knowledge which is to be received, but in yoga the concept of jnana is totally the reverse. You lose because the whole basis of the yogic thrust is to have experiential jnana and understanding. Once this process of analysis begins with the requirements of the body and mind, then it slowly becomes spiritual.

Who am I?

One of the most common spiritual enquiries is "Who am I?" It is not a question to which you can give an immediate answer. You cannot say, "I am John Smith", because John Smith is a label, a name which differentiates you from your neighbour, who is called Fred Smith. John Smith is the name you are known by at the post office for your pay cheque and correspondence. Our name is a social label. So the answer to this question "Who am I?" is not on the physical level or in social terms, but on some other level of enquiry. I have met many people who consider themselves to be jnana yogis. They say, "Swamiji, I ask myself the question "Who am I?" for five minutes every day before breakfast, then I go to work." Sometimes I have to laugh because such questions are not something you can ask yourself for five minutes before having your breakfast, lunch or dinner.

Ramana Maharshi was a great jnana yogi and, in fact, he was possibly one of the few jnana yogis who have existed knowing he was a jnana yogi. His whole quest was to find the answer to this question. Day or night, whether he was awake or asleep, his whole being was permeated with this question. He used to vibrate with the intensity of this question. It was as if he was standing on the edge of a precipice. The moment he lost body consciousness and fell into the hole, he was enlightened.

It is like the story of Don Juan jumping over the precipice into the void. This is a very interesting theory because when you stand on the edge of a precipice there is still a support, an identity, an idea. I am this and I am standing on the edge. But if you jump into the void, what is there to support you? Nothing! This void is known as shoonya, which means nothing, zero. Until one becomes nothing, one does not really understand what the spirit is. One does not find the answer to the question, "Who am I?" This relates to the final stage of jnana yoga, where one has to make that jump into the void.

Awakening of intuition

In the intermediate stage of jnana yoga there are flashes of intuition. Such flashes can be experienced in the scientific world, in artistic creation, in musical composition. This happened to Einstein, da Vinci, Michaelangelo and Beethoven. How did it happen? When there is an obsession in the mind about something, and there is total concentration at that point, then the deeper forces of our personality come into play.

If you are really worried or tense about something which has stirred your mind, you are aware of the problem or fault with full intensity. The dissipated nature of the mind which you had previously does not exist then. In that full intensity of the mind, the deeper forces of your personality manifest. That full intensity of mind becomes an obsession. The positive experience of that obsession is indicated in the lives of people such as Einstein. However, that same obsession, when experienced with our distracted state of mind, becomes a great tension.

Although Einstein, da Vinci or Michaelangelo did not know about jnana yoga, nowadays we can classify them as jnana yogis. They went beyond the existing limitations of predefined and preconceived knowledge and ideas, grabbed something and brought it back. That is what happened to Einstein. He went beyond the area of preconceived and accumulated knowledge. He picked up something from his intuitive dimension, brought it back and spent his lifetime rationalizing it. It is very difficult to spend one's life rationalizing an intuitive insight, but these flashes exist.

The mind is like a radio that is being tuned. In the process of being tuned it suddenly picks up a station that is broadcasting in a funny language, and we start thinking about it. What was that I heard? Usually we are not able to pick up the same station again because the radio waves become too weak or the transmission stops and we do not know when the next transmission is going to be; anything can happen. It is that tuning in to subtle frequencies which is the intermediate aspect of jnana yoga.

The questioning mind

We have discussed the three aspects involved in the process of jnana yoga. The initial aspect was practical self-analysis. The intermediate aspect was tuning into a particular frequency or vibration. The third aspect was jumping over the precipice into the void. That is the final answer. However, one point must be remembered and that is, if you want to follow the path of jnana yoga and you start thinking about which questions you should ask yourself, then you are not ready for jnana yoga. At that time the question becomes an urge which is not intellectual, mental or rational. With that urge or intensity of feeling, the question becomes a part of your being, not just something being thought about. The whole being is involved in wanting to know, not just the mind or intellect. This intensity of being will not happen with a mind that is experiencing anxiety, distraction or dissipation.

Therefore, jnana yoga has to be practised after you have stabilized yourself in a meditative state. In this meditative state the mind is tuned and charged. Many times the guru or teacher helps the aspirant to develop this kind of mentality. However, when we speak of guru we have to think in different terms. Many times a guru can guide a disciple to experience different states, whether directly or indirectly. Then the disciple unexpectedly begins to experience certain states which are considered unspiritual, or which are not in the same pattern of life followed before.

At that point the questioning begins in the form of intellectual analysis, followed by emotional analysis. Later, it becomes loss and gain analysis. What have I lost? What have I gained? Then it becomes analysis of one's own insecurities. Should I continue or not? No one told me that in three years this would happen. The negative trend of the mind pulls the aspirant away from the search.

When we are talking about a relationship between guru and disciple, where the guru is trying to induce the state of jnana in the disciple, it becomes a very complicated matter. What is definite, however, is that a guru can induce a change in the disciple's thinking, attitude and behaviour, ensuring that the intensity of the mind is awakened more and more. That intensity of mind has to be understood in the positive and not the negative sense.

Combination of practices

Jnana yoga is definitely not a path for everyone. It has to be combined with other practices of yoga, according to one's tendencies and nature. People who are dynamically inclined can practise jnana yoga if they combine it with karma yoga. People whose emotions are charged can practise jnana yoga along with bhakti yoga. Those who have potential psychic abilities can practise jnana yoga combined with raja yoga. Only those with an indomitable will can practise jnana yoga by itself. Jnana yoga is actually a supplement to meditation, dhyana. When combined with dhyana, it becomes samadhi later on because samadhi is experiential knowledge of spirit. In dhyana there is total identification and merger of the mind. In jnana there is full experiential knowledge of that merger. So jnana and dhyana combined give the experience of samadhi.

8

Hatha Yoga

In the Yoga Upanishads *hatha yoga* is described as a means of attaining physical and mental purification and balance. Although hatha yoga is the most commonly known yoga, there is a great misconception about its meaning. Hatha is generally translated as 'force', whereas in the yogic literature the word hatha is a combination of two mantras, *ham* and *tham*, which correspond to pingala and ida nadis respectively. In this context the term hatha yoga means the yoga through which these two forces are balanced. *Ida nadi*, a major pranic channel within the body, represents the passive aspect of prana which manifests as mental force or chit shakti. *Pingala nadi*, the other major pranic channel within the body, represents the solar, vital energy or the dynamic force which manifests in the physical dimension as prana shakti. According to this description, hatha yoga is the yoga of channelling the pranas in the body.

What is prana?
In order to understand hatha yoga, first we must understand what prana is and then we can take a closer look at the dual manifestation of prana. Despite the belief that prana is linked with the breath and that when we stop breathing we die, yoga says that *prana* is the inherent vital force that pervades every experience of matter at the level of the elements, from sky or ether, down to matter. Each element

87

is experienced in a different form, composition and combination of pranic force.

Matter is the densest form of pranic energy. Pranic atoms are compressed together so that they appear to us as solid objects, whether in the form of the body, which is animate, or a rock or a piece of metal, which is inanimate. The density of energy in different forms is the manifestation of pranic force in the different elements. This life force is responsible for the growth, maturity and decay of a particular life form in the manifest dimension. Prana is not linked with the mind, brain or physical activity, but has been given a separate identity apart from consciousness in yogic literature. Prana in its transcendental, unmanifest aspect is known as *maha prana*. The various manifestations of this vital energy are known as the sub-pranas.

Maha prana is linked with shakti/prakriti in its unmanifest nature. From the merger of maha prana with shakti emanates another aspect of prana, which is known as the manifest life force. The manifest life force or *vyakta prana* is responsible for the governance of the elemental, causal and subtle stratas of creation. This vyakta prana has been further divided into two categories. One is known as ida, the lunar force, governing the manifest, subtle (*sukshma*) dimension, and the other is known as pingala, the solar force, governing the manifest, gross (*sthoola*) dimension. The manifest, subtle dimension or ida represents the experiences of the greater mind. The gross dimension or pingala represents the manifestation of the physical and material world of objects. From pingala comes the five sub-pranas, or *upa-pranas*, which control the physical attributes of creation. These are known as: prana, apana, samana, udana and vyana, which are situated in different parts of the body.

The elements, the mind and the body all have their own structured personalities. How the structured personality is maintained with the awakening of prana is the beginning of the theory of hatha yoga. Hatha yoga represents the balancing and awakening of the gross and subtle pranic vibrations.

The two mantras comprising the word hatha correspond to the ida and pingala force. *Ha* or *ham* is the sound of pingala nadi and *tham* or *ksham* is the sound of ida nadi. This is also the symbology of ajna chakra. The two petals of ajna contain these sound vibrations. *Ha* represents the pranic force and *tha* represents the mental force of the one energy which governs creation. In the process of hatha yoga, purification and synchronization on the physical dimension as well as the mental dimension is achieved.

TRADITIONAL STRUCTURE

The practices of hatha yoga were originally divided into six groups or shatkarmas known as neti, dhauti, basti, nauli, kapalbhati and trataka. These are the six traditional shatkarmas of hatha yoga, *shat* meaning 'six' and *karma* meaning 'action'. The structure of hatha yoga is systematic and the sequence of practices is very precise.

First comes physical purification, which has been divided into three practices. The first cleansing practice is the technique of neti or nasal cleansing, which deals with the head. The second cleansing practice is dhauti, which involves the region from the throat to the stomach. The third practice is an excretory cleansing technique known as basti or yogic enema, which begins with the small and large intestines.

These three aspects of hatha yoga are physical in nature. The aim is to eliminate toxins and impurities which accumulate within the body due to incorrect dietary habits. Once the toxins are eliminated, the body reaches a state of purification which helps to bring about a state of balance in the functioning and performance of the internal organs and systems. Yogic texts also state that the diseases we experience are actually caused by imbalances and misuse of the vital energy within the body. In order to avoid this condition of imbalance, the practices of the first three aspects of hatha yoga have been prescribed.

Neti
The first technique is *neti*, which translates simply as nasal cleaning. However, neti originated, not as a practice of nasal cleaning, but as a technique for awakening the centres related to ajna chakra. When the sinuses are blocked, one can feel the tension near the eyes and forehead, where the pressure and blockages are experienced. Due to blocked sinuses, one may have watering and reddening of the eyes, and ear blockages. Yogis considered this part of the head to be very sensitive, so they put cleaning of the general nasal area, which affects the eyes and ears, first.

Two forms of neti are commonly known: jala neti, in which warm saline water is used, and sutra neti, in which a catheter is used to clean the nasal passages. The water neti that we practise in the Bihar Yoga system is an innovation of Paramahamsa Satyananda's to facilitate the process. The original form of neti involved drinking a glass of cold water through the nose and expelling it through the mouth. This was a very common practice in Indian villages, called *usha paan*. Every morning after brushing their teeth, the elders of the family would drink a glass of water through their nose. The neti lota came much later when Paramahamsaji started making the yogic practice more accessible, acceptable and easier for all.

Neti becomes a very simple process with a neti pot or lota. You just put the spout into one nostril and the water flows out through the other. Jala neti is the first practice to be done in order to cleanse the nostrils. Later, the viscosity of the liquid used to clean the nostrils can be increased. For example, some hatha yogis practise neti with oil, ghee, milk and even yoghurt. Each practice gives a different benefit. If oil is used, the effect will be different to using water. If amaroli is used, the result is different to using milk. It has been said that once the sinus passages are cleared and optimum functioning of the optical and auditory nerves is achieved, ajna chakra can be activated.

90

Dhauti

After neti comes *dhauti*, which means gentle washing. There are many forms of dhauti, each having a specific purpose and reason. Dhauti can be done with air, water, cloth or a stick. This group of practices includes danta dhauti, cleaning the teeth; jihva dhauti, cleaning the tongue, and karna dhauti, cleaning the ears. There are dhautis for cleaning practically everything, from the top of the head to the anus. These practices came into use long before the invention of such things as toothbrushes.

Vaman dhauti is cleaning the stomach by voluntary vomiting. There are two methods of vaman dhauti: kunjal kriya and vyaghra kriya, in both of which warm saline water is used. Kunjal is done on an empty stomach to remove excess acid or mucus, while vyaghra is done on a full stomach in order to empty out undigested or toxic food matter before it passes into the lower digestive tract.

Apart from water, a cloth can also be used. This practice is called vastra dhauti. The cloth is swallowed and kept in the stomach for a short time and then gently taken out through the mouth. As the cloth comes out, it brings all the mucus with it and the entire tract is cleaned. It is a very effective therapy for any kind of respiratory ailment, especially bronchial asthma. Kunjal is easy to practise as it is done with water, which is easily swallowed, but the swallowing of cloth can create a gagging reflex which throws the cloth out. However, in the case of respiratory disorders, where there is excess mucus in the throat, the cloth is able to slide down more easily.

These are the more commonly known forms of dhauti. One lesser known form is danda dhauti in which a wooden stick is used to clean the oesophagus. Vatsara dhauti is another process of cleaning the stomach by swallowing or drinking air through the mouth. The air is held in the stomach for some time and then expelled slowly by belching. This practice helps to eliminate many stomach ailments.

91

Basti

Basti is a process of cleaning the intestines and colon. The yogic theory is that disease originates in the intestines and not in the stomach. The food that we eat is passed down from the stomach to the small and large intestines for absorption. In the course of its travels from one end of the intestines to the other, which takes many hours, some of the digested food particles remain stuck in the folds of the intestines. As these food residues begin to decay, they emit acids and a foul smell. This decay of the food particles in the intestines produces toxins which cause illness in the body. Therefore, special care has to be taken to cleanse the intestines of decomposed food particles, to permit the proper absorption of fresh nutrients without the contamination of toxic build-up in the system.

For this purpose, yogis devised two main methods of purifying the intestines. One method is the natural enema called basti, which can be done with water or air. In this technique water or air is sucked into the anus using the contraction of the anal sphincter muscles. The water or air is retained inside for a short time, which creates a reverse force or vacuum, allowing it to flow back out again. This practice is effective for cleaning the large intestine, especially when the stool has become dry and hard. This practice may be performed while sitting in a tub full of water, or while immersed waist or neck deep in a river or pond. However, it should not be done in a chlorinated swimming pool. If the practice is done under impure conditions, it can be damaging instead of cleansing and purifying to ensure optimum health.

The other method is the practice of shankhapraksha-lana, which cleans both the small and large intestines. Shankhaprakshalana is the modern method of basti, in the sense that it is acceptable to and can be practised by everyone, providing there is an awareness of the appropriate climatic and dietary restrictions that have to be followed after the practice. There are two variations of this practice. One is called laghoo shankhaprakshalana, the short form, in which six glasses of warm saline water are drunk, two at a time, followed by the performance of five asanas which loosen up the intestines and allow the water to pass through. The second variation is called poorna shankhaprakshalana, the full form, in which sixteen or more glasses of water are drunk. It is the saline water which flushes out the whole system by creating pressure, and thoroughly cleans out all the accumulated particles from the intestines. This process also removes the entire mucus lining from the intestine, which makes the digestive system very sensitive and also increases mental sensitivity.

The effects of shankhaprakshalana and basti include stimulation of the nervous system, improvement of the digestive function, elimination of toxins from the entire system and sensitization of the nadis that link the chakras together. The state of physical purification also helps the pranamaya kosha to reorganize and restructure the flow of prana in the body. The increased sensitivity in the mind and energy is due to the effect of the practice on the pranic body. For this reason we find that many people are physically tired after performing shankhaprakshalana, but still have a lot of energy within them. There is no heaviness in the body; the whole body feels light, as if it is floating.

Nauli

After the intestines have been cleansed and their optimum health guaranteed by the practice of basti, the next shatkarma is nauli, rotation of the stomach muscles. Nauli is a kriya, and kriya is a part of bandha. Bandhas are postural contractions of the body, such as the chin lock, the stomach lock and the perineal lock. Kriyas are moving contractions, both preparatory and advanced techniques of bandhas. One example is agnisar kriya. Agnisar kriya is a very simple practice of emptying the lungs and holding the breath outside while pumping the stomach in and out as many times as possible, then inhaling deeply and relaxing. The rapid contraction of the lower abdominal muscles strengthens the diaphragm and the lower stomach region, and prepares the body for the practice of uddiyana bandha.

Nauli is an advanced version of uddiyana bandha. In nauli the muscles of the abdomen are pulled together at the centre of the lower abdomen and can be seen externally in the form of a vertical cord. These muscles are then rotated from side to side and it is this movement of the muscles and ligaments which causes the nerves to send a different kind of stimulation to the chakras. Nauli has a very powerful effect on the physical body and is especially beneficial for the awakening of manipura chakra. So, in this series the order of practice is: agnisar, then uddiyana and finally nauli.

Nauli is a combination of bandhas and kriyas together which stimulate the pranic centre known as manipura chakra. In different traditions it is said that manipura chakra is the source and seat of kundalini energy. Buddhism regards manipura chakra as the seat of kundalini, while yoga says that it is mooladhara chakra. When the kundalini awakens, until it reaches manipura, there is always the possibility that it will again return to mooladhara chakra, where it will remain in a state of dormancy. However, once the kundalini crosses manipura, there is no possibility of it descending, it has to continue its upward journey.

From this point of view, manipura is a very important chakra. According to the hatha yoga traditions, manipura is the seat of the sun in the body, the source of vitality and energy, the storehouse of prana. Prana is generated in mooladhara and stored in manipura. The generating station does not store the energy; the energy is stored in manipura chakra. Nauli is practised to clear manipura chakra of impurities and to remove the blocks in the channels of pranic force.

So we have moved from the physical to the pranic body. Now we will move on to the mental body, the dimension of consciousness. This dimension of consciousness is experienced and made manifest through the practices of kapalbhati and trataka.

94

Kapalbhati

Just as the pranic nadis have to be cleared, mental awareness also has to be freed from the fetters that bind it to the world of senses and objects. For this purpose, we use kapalbhati, a technique of pranayama and the fifth practice of hatha yoga. It is not the same kapalbhati that we may know and practise but a different kind of kapalbhati, the purpose of which is to raise the pranic energy of the body and concentrate it at ajna chakra. Once this pranic energy is centred at ajna chakra, it can be redirected to awaken the other psychic centres. The practice of kapalbhati is also taught as a part of the technique of prana vidya.

Nowadays this method of kapalbhati is not generally taught or practised by yoga students. In fact, very few people know what the technique is. It is not the bellows breathing that is usually performed in pranayama practice, although the name is the same. The same breathing is used but certain mudras and bandhas are also combined with it. The reason for practising kapalbhati is to focus the dissipated mental energies and to clear the mind and awareness of mental toxins. The practice of kapalbhati has an influence over the first three koshas. It begins as an annamaya practice using physical movements, the breathing process, the bandhas and the mudras. However, the aim is to awaken the pranic energy, pranamaya kosha, and to tranquillize the mental activity, manomaya kosha.

In this technique, as well as being aware of the physical activity, one has to become aware of the *swara*, or rhythm of breathing. *Swara yoga* is knowledge of the breathing cycle in the nostrils and how it influences the right and left hemispheres of the brain, and thereby the functioning and performance of the body. It is generally said in the yogic traditions that every ninety minutes the flow of breath changes from one nostril to the other. Externally the breath is seen to change, but yoga says that it is the flow of prana in ida and pingala that changes, and that change is then experienced externally in the form of the breath.

95

There are moments when the body, mind and prana all reach their peak at the same time, like the biorhythms which are calculated from the date of birth. According to the yogic concept, there are physical, mental and pranic biorhythms. When these three waves reach a certain point, there is harmony in the different koshas. This harmony is experienced in the form of a clear mind, thought and expression; increased nervous, emotional and mental energies; good health, physical fitness and mental relaxation.

Our biorhythms undergo many changes in the course of our daily activities. Knowledge of these rhythms at the time of kapalbhati practice makes us deeply aware of the pranic and mental states. Kapalbhati helps to control the mental state by influencing the physical level, by altering the experiences, the input and output of the nervous system and the brain, and speeding up the metabolism. In the context of hatha yoga, kapalbhati is practised to achieve a totally one-pointed state of mind. For the sake of our understanding, we may compare the practice of kapalbhati to the state of pratyahara. In pratyahara we try to divert the mind from external distractions and focus it at one point, and then in the practice of dharana we try to intensify the concentration. In kapalbhati, like pratyahara, we try to relax the dissipation of the annamaya, manomaya and pranamaya koshas. The aim of kapalbhati is to awaken ajna chakra.

Trataka

With the awakening of ajna chakra, the dormant layers of the mind are stimulated. With the awakening of these dormant areas, the distinction in the perceptions of what is conscious, what is subconscious and what is unconscious disappears. This change takes place at the level of ajna chakra. Bodh, enlightenment, mental awakening, takes place at the level of ajna chakra. That state of awakening has to be channelled, and that is done through the practice of trataka. The sixth practice of hatha yoga is trataka, which is a way of achieving optimum concentration of awareness and mind.

96

We can say therefore that the first three practices, neti, dhauti and basti, purify the physical structure in preparation for the awakening of the subtle energies in the body. The fourth practice, nauli, stimulates the source of energy and balances the entire pranic body, the pranamaya kosha. The fifth practice, kapalbhati, is a way of cleansing the mind, the psychic body and the pranic body from impurities and the accumulation of samskaras and impressions that clutter the mind. The sixth practice, trataka, is a technique of dharana which focuses the mind on one point or one object of concentration.

After the relaxation of the uncontrolled and unchannelled physical, mental and pranic activities, we go into a state of concentration with the practice of trataka. *Trataka* means 'to see', 'to look at'. Visual perception is the most powerful indriya or sensory organ in this manifest world. The range of vision extends beyond the physical dimensions. It is possible to see for miles and miles, to perceive what is happening many miles away without actually being there. It is the vision that is focused in the practice of trataka. The visual distractions that affect our concentration and awareness must be minimized, and this is done through the practice of trataka, steady gazing.

The hatha yoga texts describe many forms of trataka of which the simplest and most commonly used is gazing at a candle flame. Other forms of trataka can be practised by using different objects for concentration such as a yantra, chakra or mandala. Different objects from nature can also be used such as the moon, a star, a flower, a leaf or a point. Through the practice of trataka one can develop the ability to focus the mind at any time, which is necessary in the higher practices of yoga.

There is also a very deep meaning behind the practice of trataka. Patanjali's *Yoga Sutras* declare that even in the highest state of meditation or samadhi, certain impressions, ideas or experiences remain in the consciousness, and thus they disturb the concentration of mind. These deep impressions

97

or ideas which do not disappear, even in samadhi, are known as *pratyaya*.

When the mind has not been taught to concentrate and we have practised concentration only superficially, then when these pratyaya manifest in deep meditative states, their pull or attraction is very powerful because there is nothing on the other side of the mind to balance it. The ability gained through trataka becomes useful at that moment. When the visual distraction is stopped, we are able to experience a quiet mind which is like a still pond or lake. The different forms of trataka, such as concentration on the moon, a star, a candle flame or a crystal, also help to focus and channel the pranic energies. When these energies are channelled, the entire mental framework is influenced. The mind becomes stable and balanced and begins to function more efficiently.

In trataka, apart from concentrating the mind, you have to witness what is happening in the mind, from moment to moment. Concentration of mind is an external act which we are trying to perform. We force ourselves to sit straight and still, to gaze until the eyes begin to water, then we close the eyes and try to hold the image inside. That is an effort of concentration, but apart from that effort there is the aware- ness that one is trying to align oneself. It is this awareness which enables us to hold onto that point of concentration and witness what is happening within the mind. Ultimately that is the result we are looking for in trataka.

Incorporation of asana

Some yogis have also incorporated certain advanced asanas into this group of hatha yoga practices. They have the specific purpose of awakening or stimulating a particular chakra or pranic field. For example, when practising mayur- asana (the peacock posture) we put pressure on the stomach with the elbows. That pressure also stimulates nerves which help to awaken manipura chakra, and the state of physical balance attained is also an aid to focus the mind.

In this way, certain postures have been incorporated into the body of hatha yoga to induce mental and physical stability. This is probably the reason why many people consider hatha yoga to be the practice of advanced asanas. However, these asanas were added much later by teachers who felt that, in the changing world scenario, the original practices of hatha yoga were too intense and difficult for most people. These practices become techniques of introversion, which, if we do not prepare ourselves for them first, can alter the state of mental and conscious perception.

This is the traditional structure of hatha yoga as it is described in the Yoga Upanishads.

RULES OF HATHA YOGA

The traditional system of hatha yoga involves several rules which have to be understood and followed. The hatha yoga texts say that, if one's environment and habits remain impure, one cannot obtain purity just by practising the prescribed techniques. In hatha yoga there are many rules about living conditions and the place of practice. What kind of environment should there be within the house and around the house? What kind of attitude must we maintain in order to perfect the experience of hatha yoga? Rules are also given about diet. It is necessary for an aspirant to observe these rules in order to progress in hatha yoga.

Shaucha: cleanliness

One rule that is part of both hatha yoga and ashtanga yoga is *shaucha*, cleanliness of the body. This is a niyama or discipline. Cleanliness of the body, cleanliness of the environment in which we live, is necessary to maintain a tranquil mind. One cannot live in a cluttered house or environment and expect to have a sense of mental well-being, tranquillity and relaxation. Try to keep everything as clean as possible and try to maintain an orderly system in the house. Don't just throw everything here and there, put it in its proper place. That external discipline induces a sense of internal discipline. The idea of external cleanliness makes us aware of internal cleanliness in the dimension of thought, behaviour and feeling.

Natural environment

A proper locality is important in which the environment is pure and the air you breathe and the water you drink are unpolluted. There should not be a lot of noise pollution either. Try to live in a natural environment as much as possible without any kind of pollution. That natural environment should fulfil all the requirements of water and food. Have a farm where you can grow your own organic vegetables rather than depending on canned foods or a supermarket, except for a few items. Have plenty of clear spring water.

In the *Hatha Yoga Pradipika*, a treatise on hatha yoga, these points have been described. There it states that the house of the hatha yogi should be beside a river where there is plenty of clear water. This is further described in the *Gherand Samhita* and *Goraksha Samhita*, which are also treatises on hatha yoga. Every book dealing with hatha yoga has such references with the idea of inspiring people to lead a natural kind of life, free from pollution and distraction. The environment should be conducive to attaining purity of mind. When you live amongst nature without sounds and noise to distract your attention, you can achieve meditative states easily.

Diet

A proper diet which is pure, simple and as natural as possible is essential for progress in hatha yoga. If one eats pure food, then the system is revitalized again and again. It is like the theory: "Feed the earth and the earth will feed you." Feed the body so that the body feeds you, but do not overload it. Feed the body with pure foods in a disciplined and regulated way. Yoga has very definite ideas about eating habits and how they affect the digestive system. In our day to day life, we often go to the kitchen for snacks. We eat snacks all day long, whether it is a piece of cake, a cookie, a sweet or something else.

Each time we ingest food, even if it is only a tiny grain of rice, it has to be digested. Unfortunately the stomach does not measure the quantity of food that has been put into it. It will secrete the same quantity of digestive juices each time you drop something into the stomach, whether it is a snack or a large meal. If you eat a full meal once or twice a day, so that the digestive juices flow only once or twice, then the digestive system retains its strength and vitality. But if you eat snacks twenty times a day, which requires a continuous secretion of enzymes, then the stomach becomes very overworked and the digestive prana depleted. This misuse of the digestive system is experienced later in the form of digestive ailments or other diseases.

Therefore, yoga advises structured, disciplined habits in relation to food and diet. Whether you eat five times a day, three times a day or once in a day, try to maintain that routine throughout your life. Do not misuse your digestive system by eating irregularly and overloading the stomach. This is a principle of hatha yoga. Hatha yoga is a science which makes one aware of the maintenance and preservation of our body as a means of attaining the awakening of energy, kundalini and prana.

So, the living conditions and eating habits have to be structured properly by following certain rules. By living in a suitable environment which is free from distractions that divert the attention, the mind and energy can grow in a positive and constructive way. By regulating the diet and establishing fixed meal times, the pranas can be purified and the body and mind made more stable. After obtaining physical harmony and balance, the energy in the body starts to move and awaken. That awakening is felt at the level of the chakras and the pranas.

101

LATER ADDITIONS TO HATHA YOGA

The original practices of hatha yoga, as we have said, were the shatkarmas, the group of six purificatory techniques. However, many writers and thinkers have broadened the outlook of hatha yoga by incorporating other aspects to make it a complete system of yoga in itself. These yogis felt that every type of yoga practice dealing with the purification of the mind, the programming of our mental behaviour and attitudes and the awakening of the chakras and kundalini should also be a part of hatha yoga.

In fact, several Upanishads have incorporated many of the raja yoga techniques into hatha yoga. One Upanishad even describes some of the yamas and niyamas as being a part of hatha yoga. The yama known as *mitahara*, meaning 'balanced diet', and the niyama, *ahimsa*, which means 'absence of violence from within', are mentioned. This same text also describes four meditation asanas as being part of hatha yoga: siddhasana (adept's posture), padmasana (lotus posture), bhadrasana (gracious posture) and simhasana (lion posture).

Apart from yama, niyama and asana, this text has also incorporated practices of pranayama, pratyahara, dharana, dhyana and samadhi – the eight steps of raja yoga from yama to samadhi. Shatkriyas make the ninth group of the hatha yoga practices, bandhas the tenth, and mudras the eleventh. Amaroli is also considered to be a part of hatha yoga, and finally, literary or scriptural knowledge was also included. This has been the broad spectrum of hatha yoga in much of the yogic literature. We can also say that apart from the shatkarmas, these later additions were included with a view to making hatha yoga a complete yoga in itself. Now let us look at these other aspects individually.

Mitahara: balanced diet

Both ayurvedic and the hatha yoga theory state that in order to maintain proper digestion and stimulate the digestive

102

organs, to break down the proteins and minerals contained in our diet, we have to consume food in certain quantities or proportions. The proportions prescribed, according to the size of the stomach, are fifty percent solids, twenty-five percent liquids and twenty-five percent empty. This is the rule that yogis are supposed to follow, and it is what a yoga practitioner should aspire for. There should be no over-loading of the stomach, so that proper space is provided for the digestive process. By following this simple rule, digestion is regulated and problems of constipation, gas, acidity or loose motions are avoided.

This rule also leads to control over the mind. We have to keep our greed in check. So, apart from the physical benefit, there is also the aspect of self-observation and mental control. We must control the desire to eat more and more because after a certain point, when the food consumed has fulfilled the physical requirement, whatever we eat is just to please our taste buds. If it is something nice, we want to have more. We want that feeling of satisfaction – "Yes, I have really enjoyed my meal. Even if I suffer from constipation or dysentery tomorrow, I will manage it, but today I have enjoyed my meal!" This kind of attitude has to be kept in check. Proper dietary habits will also increase stamina and vitality and help to eliminate toxins from the body, ensuring a proper state of purification.

Ahimsa: non-violence
The niyama or discipline to be followed in hatha yoga is ahimsa. Ahimsa here does not mean non-injury, that is the dictionary definition. The yogic concept of ahimsa is removal of violence from within so that it is not experienced in thought, speech, action or behaviour. Just saying, "I follow ahimsa; I do not kill or injure," has no meaning in yoga as long as negative and harmful thoughts continue to play in the mind. If you are injuring yourself or someone else mentally through your thoughts or behaviour, then the shade of violence has not yet gone from your personality or

life. You have only stopped the external action of violence, but that is not absence of violence from the personality.

Therefore, ahimsa has been defined as one of the niyamas to aspire for in hatha yoga, where there is total harmony and coordination between mental functions, behaviour patterns and actions. Ahimsa can only be achieved with the help of awareness. As soon as we become aware of harmful thoughts being reflected in our behaviour or actions, as soon as we realize that we are hurting someone emotionally, intellectually or physically, it has to be stopped then and there.

Asana and pranayama

The third aspect is asana. The four practices that have been prescribed in the upanishadic texts belong to the meditative group of asanas. Siddhasana, padmasana, bhadrasana and simhasana are used for higher practices in order to create spontaneous bandhas or pressure in different parts of the body. These bandhas permit the pranic flow to move in a specific direction and to awaken a particular chakra. The practice of simhasana referred to here is not the lion pose in which you stick out your tongue and roar; that is a variation of simhasana. Here simhasana is the posture in which you sit in vajrasana with the knees apart and the palms flat on the floor. The purpose of these different meditative postures is to maintain the upright position of the spine, keep the head straight, prevent energy blockages from forming in any part of the body and allow for the free movement of the pranas within the body.

Some yogic texts have added advanced asanas such as mayurasana, the peacock posture, and other difficult postures that are not generally performed. These practices were later incorporated into the hatha yoga group in order to provide greater awareness of physical balance, coordination and harmony. The number of practices varies from text to text and from thinker to thinker, according to their own experience and understanding of the human body and personality.

Pranayama was the next aspect to be added to the original hatha yoga structure. In addition to pranayama, as mentioned in the *Raja Yoga Sutras*, pratyahara, dharana, dhyana and samadhi were also included. However, these practices will be discussed later in the chapters on raja yoga.

Bandha and mudra

The group of bandhas or psychic locks was added next. The three bandhas described in the yogic texts are jalandhara (chin lock), uddiyana (abdominal lock) and moola bandha (perineal lock). Again, the purpose of these bandhas is to awaken the chakras that are responsible for the awakening of the pranas and the ascent of kundalini. In moola bandha, mooladhara chakra is stimulated and the pressure of the mooladhara contraction is spread into the area of swadhisthana as well. In the practice of uddiyana bandha, manipura is directly stimulated, but at the same time the pressure is directed towards anahata by pulling up the diaphragm. In jalandhara bandha, vishuddhi is directly affected, but there is also pressure created in the head region to stimulate ajna, bindu and sahasrara chakras. So the purpose of these three bandhas is to provide the experience of *pranotthana*, or awakening of the pranas, in the different chakras.

After bandhas come mudras. There are many kinds of mudras, but broadly speaking there are the natya or dance mudras, which express a particular state of mind, emotion or event, and the yoga mudras, which channel and reverse the flow of prana in the body. Five yoga mudras are mentioned: khechari mudra for the stimulation of vishuddhi and bindu; maha mudra and maha bheda mudra, two kriya techniques; vajroli and sahajoli mudras, contraction and release of the urinary passages in the male and female bodies respectively, which help to stimulate swadhisthana.

After mudras comes *amaroli*, which is the auto-urine procedure, drinking of one's own urine in order to detoxify the body and develop stamina and vitality.

Literary knowledge

After amaroli comes literary knowledge. Literary knowledge here does not imply that one should become a bookworm but that certain texts are to be studied in order to gain an awareness and knowledge of the system and path being followed in hatha yoga. The rules associated with the practices of hatha yoga should be known. Hatha yoga should not be an unconscious or mechanical practice. When you perform the techniques of hatha yoga, you should know what kind of changes are taking place in the body, what kind of changes can be expected and if something new happens, how to go beyond or transcend that stage.

These are the concepts of hatha yoga as described in the later editions of the hatha yoga treatises.

9

Raja Yoga

THE ROLE OF THE VRITTIS

Raja yoga is presented here in a slightly different non-traditional way, the importance of which will become clear later on. The word *raja* means 'king', thus *raja yoga* is the kingly or royal yoga, the higher yoga or the supreme yoga. The term raja yoga came about as the result of an enquiry into the human personality by the different yogic masters and sages. The basic theme of raja yoga is to develop the dormant potential within the human personality. Yoga in general, and raja yoga in particular, has always advocated and recognized that the human personality contains a deep, dormant psychic potential within its framework. This potential is within the reach of everyone, provided they have knowledge of a particular system by which it can be tapped.

Personal traits

Yogis also recognized the different types of personalities found in different individuals. They realized that, according to the requirements and needs of these different personalities, a different approach had to be adopted. In our day to day life we express different aspects of our personality in the form of emotion, dynamism, intellect and deep inner awareness. These various forms of expression have become the personality types of modern psychology, known as the dynamic personality, the intellectual personality, the emotional personality and the intuitive personality. The

107

traits experienced in these different personalities vary according to our nature and conditioning of mind. Our social, cultural and religious conditioning becomes the basis for the expression of a particular trait.

Apart from this, the nature of each individual is different. Some people are more sattwic, some more rajasic, some more tamasic. Even this quality of our personality expresses itself in the form of a trait. No individual is similar to another, every individual personality is unique. These different personalities have their own levels of intellectual and emotional acceptance of the facts and events related to life, society, family and so forth. The basic desire to awaken the dormant potential, whether we call it kundalini or any other name, may be the same, but in order to achieve the target of this inner awakening we have to pass through layers and layers of our personality. The most effective method of doing this became known as the group of raja yoga practices, the supreme yoga, which aims at going deep into the dormant personality in order to awaken and experience the psychic potential.

Self-acceptance

According to the tradition, the theories and principles of kundalini yoga, kriya yoga and other advanced yogas, such as nada yoga, laya yoga and mantra yoga, all form part of raja yoga. You will find a great variety of yogic practices incorporated in the raja yoga structure. Despite the amalgamation of different types of theories, techniques and principles, the process of raja yoga remains quite simple. It teaches that in order to discover the dormant inner potential, one has to reach the level of self-acceptance, which is the first aspect of raja yoga. Self-acceptance means that we have to live in harmony with the dharmic principles, according to the role that has been assigned to us in life. We have to live life according to our karma. Self-acceptance and awareness of the self, or *swadharma*, are the two initial steps to be taken in raja yoga.

Let us look at self-acceptance first. The natural expressions of the human personality have to be accepted. If an elephant were to fantasize and try to live like a gold fish, or a peacock like a cow, then it would be a very disharmonious expression of their natural being. In fact, one would classify them as ridiculous. Do you see any such correlations in yourself? We are often like an elephant trying to become a goldfish or a weak mouse trying to become a roaring lion.

Such fantasies pervade the thoughts and lives of every individual. We all try to change our nature and the nature of others. In this way we create an adharmic lifestyle. *Adharmic* means 'disharmony', where two qualities or desires oppose each other and there is conflict. This has been the trend of human beings since time immemorial, because we have not been able to recognize or accept our nature as we experience it. It is very hard for us to accept the kind of person we are. We try to create a sugar-coated personality by ignoring our negative and limiting qualities, our detrimental expressions and actions. This is exactly the point that raja yoga makes. In order to reverse this process we have to be very observant and aware and realize our true nature. We have to open ourselves so that we can experience the harmony of life, and in order to open ourselves totally, there has to be a degree of self-acceptance. This self-acceptance is based on proper analysis and understanding of the qualities, weaknesses and strengths that lie within us.

Avoiding guilt

According to raja yoga, lack of self-acceptance is also the fundamental cause of ailments and diseases, whether they are physical, psychological, mental or emotional. Let us use the aspect of anger as an example. It is generally said by different moralistic traditions that one should not get angry, that it is bad to get angry. However, there are certain natural expressions in our life and anger is one of them. Anger is a safety valve for the pent-up energy that has to be realized at times in one way or another. If we do not open that safety valve and the energy remains bottled up inside, then the pressure will seek some other outlet. Maybe in the form of hypertension, heart ailments or anxiety.

There has to be a form of elimination, a process of release, otherwise physical and mental harmony and balance will be lost. This applies, not only to anger, but also to practically every ambition and desire that we experience. We have evolved strange concepts of right and wrong which often go against our nature, mind and body. Why do they go against our nature, mind and body? Because we are unable to come to terms with the realities of our personality. Self-acceptance has to be understood in a very positive, systematic and constructive way. We know that getting angry can be detrimental to our health, environment and relationships. The yogic approach therefore advocates that one may become angry and also not become angry. Both ways are acceptable according to the situation and the nature of the individual.

What happens, however, is that with the expression of a negative emotion like anger, a feeling of guilt is attached. That guilt should not be experienced in a harmonious life. If life is disharmonious, then guilt arises, then inferiority or superiority complexes arise, then the idea of high class and low class living and working arises, then the idea of being overburdened with worries and anxieties arises. It all comes from the aspect of guilt. According to yoga, sin is defined as a disharmonious way of living and acting. Guilt is a result of that disharmonious way of living and acting. We are constantly influenced by the events and circumstances that mould, shape and guide our actions. These distractions, dissipations, worries and anxieties hold our minds down like a weight. They do not allow the creative nature to manifest.

You can do twenty hours of meditation every day and make no progress if there is no self-acceptance. You can practise kundalini sadhana and not experience an awakening if there is no self-acceptance. So self-acceptance is the first step in raja yoga. It is linked with avoiding the feeling of guilt. If there is anger or negativity, it has to be expressed,

110

but we should express it with awareness and mental clarity, without guilt. We should not get caught up in the flow of that force of negativity, anxiety, frustration or depression. In the course of time, anger, negative thoughts and any limiting aspects of our personality will be transcended by this process of conscious, wilful expression.

Awareness of one's dharma

After self-acceptance comes dharma, the second aspect of raja yoga. Dharma is the natural role we have to play in life. The natural role is being what one is and not wanting to be what one is not. That is the concept of the dharmic, harmonious, useful way of life; being what one is and not adopting different roles at different times. Once we are able to allow the naturalness of life to manifest from within without any superimposed concepts or ideas, then the actions and qualities of life will not oppose each other. Right now our thoughts oppose our actions, our ambitions oppose our present day to day realities, our desires oppose our achievements. There is conflict within our nature.

ROLE OF THE VRITTIS

To enable us to become aware of ourselves, of our mind and nature, the different mental modifications have been described in raja yoga. The first modification is known as pramana (direct knowledge), the second is viparyaya (wrong knowledge), the third is vikalpa (fancy), the fourth is nidra (sleep) and the fifth is smriti (memory). The *Yoga Sutras* of Patanjali have described these five modifications as vrittis, which permit us to observe and accept ourselves and to enquire into the depth of our personality. The vrittis have to be understood, controlled and transcended, because it is the vrittis which bring about the experiences of pleasure and pain, which create confusion and conflict, which dissipate our energies and thoughts and prevent us from living according to the natural laws of nature, mind and body.

Other aspects play an equally important role. Ambition combined with pramana, viparyaya, vikalpa, nidra or smriti becomes a very powerful vritti. Ego or arrogance, negative desire or thought, combined with any one of these five, can become a very powerful vritti. These things are like spices added to food to make it tastier.

The thoughts and ambitions, emotions and behaviour, actions and awareness are external by nature. Why are they considered to be external? Because everything is dependent on the sensory and sensual input received through the agency of the body and mind. The senses belong to our external personality, but our inner personality uses them differently. The craving for sensual pleasures is also considered to be external because it is an activity of the manifest mind. The same craving in its positive form is utilized differently by the inner awareness. It is like the two sides of a coin. Just as work can be mundane and also divine, in the same way, the experiences of the senses and sense objects can be mundane and also divine, provided you are able to flip the coin to see the other side.

If we throw a pebble into a body of water, we will see ripples extending outwards towards the shore from the point where the pebble hit the water. Those circular ripples are manifestations of one single event, one single stone hitting the water and creating many ripples; it will not create just one ripple. In the same way the vrittis give birth to many different expressions, attitudes and visions of life. They are the different coloured glasses through which we perceive the world. Sometimes the world looks very beautiful and pink, sometimes it looks very drab and dull. Sometimes we get carried away by the force and sway of a thought, or we begin to wonder about the rationality of a thought we have had. That is the role of vritti.

Pain and pleasure
The five spices or vrittis belong to the realm of consciousness or more precisely to the realm of the manifest mind, the

antahkarana, the four aspects of mind we have looked at before: manas, buddhi, chitta and ahamkara. The *Yoga Sutras* state that, according to the intensity and quality with which these vrittis have been mixed, and according to our perception, understanding and circumstances, we can have two types of experiences, that of pain and that of pleasure. The experiences of pain and pleasure are known as maya. So the vrittis are aspects of maya, wrong or false notions about self-identity.

The pain and pleasure that one experiences in life is transitory. Despite that transitory nature, there is total identification; we are under their total influence. We can become negative, subdued and withdrawn. We can become expressive, creative and open. We can become joyful or depressed to such an extent that we want to commit suicide. Pain and pleasure equal maya. On the plus side, these five vrittis give the experience of pleasure and on the minus side, they give the experience of pain. These are the modifications of the manifest mind.

In raja yoga we want to go back to awaken the dormant potential which is the nature of spirit, the seed of the unmanifest, invisible energy. Just as we cannot see the nucleus of the atom, we cannot see the potential that is inherent within us until there is an explosion, a release of that potential. So, in raja yoga all the practices and techniques are aimed at releasing that potential. It happens on different levels, not just on the physical, mental, emotional, psychic or pranic levels, but covers the entire spectrum of the human personality, the whole range of bodily experiences. These five attributes of consciousness or vrittis have to be channelled, controlled and experienced in their true form in order to release that dormant spiritual potential.

Vairagya: non-attachment

The word *vritti* comes from the Sanskrit *vritta*, which means 'circular movement'. Circular motion takes us back to the example of the ripples extending to the shore. It also represents a beginning without an end, or an end without a beginning. One is always caught up in that circle. There is no escape until you use a sharp instrument to cut through it. According to the *Bhagavad Gita*, vairagya, non-attachment, is the sharp instrument that will cut through the vrittis and the roots of our material and sensual life.

Non-attachment is an important ingredient if we are considering the process of self-acceptance. There can be no self-acceptance without non-attachment. It is like spring-cleaning. When we go to the attic and see all the old clothes and bits and pieces lying around, we say to ourselves, "I will dispose of this useless old thing but keep that one." One or two things always seem to remain. We know these things are useless, but there is some emotional link. We say, "This piece of furniture was my great-grandfather's so I must keep it." It has been rotting in the basement, but just because it belonged to our great-grandfather, we keep it. That is because of attachment to an idea, to an object or to anything.

In the process of self-purification there has to be proper self-acceptance, which will lead us to a realization of our inner personality. There should also be non-attachment in order to come out of this circle. As Krishna told Arjuna in the *Gita*, vairagya, non-attachment, is the instrument that will cut through the bondage of maya, through the bondage of pain and pleasure. There is attachment to both pain and pleasure. Some people are attached to pain and some to pleasure.

Pramana: right knowledge

In raja yoga the first vritti is known as *pramana*, which is knowledge based on direct experience or awareness of the existing facts, circumstances and events which are perceived by us and which do not create any kind of false notion in the mind. Knowledge considered to be correct and true is derived from the following sources: (i) direct cognition, (ii) inference and (iii) testimony.

In order to understand pramana we have to analyze the different grades of acceptance of the existing facts or reality, because often what we accept as pramana can also be false. For example, we see smoke, but smoke does not necessarily mean there is a raging fire. We see one fact or piece of evidence such as smoke and we infer that there is fire. Here, direct evidence is also linked with inference; they have merged and become one. However, when we see that there is no fire, just a smoke bomb, then the inference we had made becomes baseless. So we will have to look more closely at the different aspects of pramana before we can understand it.

1. Direct cognition, or *pratyaksha*, the first aspect of pramana, is related to perceptions or experiences that we gain through the senses. It is the senses that create an understanding of right or wrong, just or unjust, the duality of opposing poles of experience. This first aspect of pramana is also a sub-vritti because it gives birth to different kinds of thoughts, experiences and perceptions. These thoughts and experiences are very much influenced by the input received through the agency of the senses. The knowledge of heat around the body is received by the sensors of the skin. This physical experience of heat creates the thought, "Yes, it is hot. I am feeling the heat. I am perspiring." This conversion of an actual physical experience into a thought pattern will later create the reaction, "I need to get out of this situation in which I feel hot, in which I perspire."

This reaction, which is mental in nature, will affect and stimulate the karmendriyas. This reaction is motivated by the desire element. When the desire element affects the karmendriyas, then it is natural for us to get up and walk out of the room. This is an example of how a sensory experience will convert itself into a mental thought and create a reaction within the mind. If this experience opposes the nature of the body, the physical condition, the state of harmony and equilibrium in the body, then other physical parameters will come into play in order to balance the first experience.

There are certain experiences which take place through the eyes; for example, we see smoke or fire in the distance. This experience of sight is a form of direct cognition, direct evidence, which will create the thought, "There is smoke, so there must be fire." This thought will also create a reaction that the fire needs to be put out. If the fire is far away and we are unable to reach it, then further transformation of that sensory experience into a physical activity will not take place. We may not be able to get there in time, or maybe someone else will already be putting the fire out. If there is a fire in the house, the eyes will see it and convert that experience into action. We will try immediately to put out the fire. So, sensory evidence affecting manas, the analytical process affecting buddhi, the intellect, and affecting the karmendriyas, the organs of action, is one form of sub-vritti.

2. Inference, or *anuman*, the second aspect of pramana, is guessing a fact which could follow a cause. There is smoke in the distance, and we know that where there is smoke there is fire. If there is lightning in the distance and the sky overhead is clear, we can guess or infer that there are thunderclouds in the distance creating the lightning. So we perceive a result and, in analyzing this result, the conclusion we come to regarding the cause is known as inference. This is also a sub-vritti.

3. Testimony, or *agama*, the third aspect of pramana, is based on the understanding of another person whom we have come to know. Who was the murderer of Mr John Smith? The testimony says the butler did it. Nobody saw the butler actually murder Mr John Smith, but from the testimony we are led to believe that the butler actually committed the murder. That testimony is the accumulation of different facts and events leading up to the actual murder in question, and seeing the link between these different facts and events.

A very good example of testimony is what we are doing now. I am speaking about yoga and you believe what I am saying, although no one here has actually experienced it.

116

We have not experienced the state of samadhi or dhyana, but there is an understanding in our mind that there is a process, a system through which we can have that kind of experience. We follow that system in order to have the experience of samadhi, dhyana, kundalini and so on because we feel deep inside ourselves that it is right.

We may cite examples of different yogis and masters who have had the experience, but even citing those examples is strengthening further our own belief. They are testimonials to a process that we are trying to complete. So in this third aspect there is no direct cognition, but there is belief in facts. We have not seen atoms but we know that they exist, we believe in their existence. We have not seen nitrogen or electrons or neutrons, but we know that they exist. How do we know they exist? Because scientists have proved that they do exist and we believe that proof.

So, this third kind of right knowledge, known as testimony, is also a sub-vritti because it creates changes in the pattern of our thinking, believing and acting. However, this refers to a very superficial state of mind.

4. Intuition, the fourth aspect of pramana, is also a sub-vritti but one which is not external or sensorial. Flashes of intuition convince us that our idea is right and we have to follow it. This type of pramana comes from the depths of our conscious mind, from our psychic personality, and we believe it to be true and correct. This is the right knowledge towards which yogis aspire, because yoga is a science in which one tries to experience the internal being, the internal structure of life and not the superficial structure.

So, by overcoming, subduing and channelling the three sub-vrittis of pramana, there is diversion of attention from outside towards inner experiences. When the intuitive ability becomes a spontaneous expression of the personality, the external, sensory and factual evidence ceases to play any role in the functioning of the human mind and one begins to live intuitively. The moment one begins to live intuitively, a link is formed with prakriti, the individual nature. That nature is an internal experience which can be converted into a meditative experience, an experience of samadhi. The intuitive experience can be used to unite the individual mind with the spirit.

So, the aim of raja yoga is the overcoming or controlling of a vritti which distracts the faculties of mind. This is expressed in the *Yoga Sutras* of Patanjali in the form of the second sutra, *"Chitta vritti nirodha"*, which means 'stopping the flow of mental distractions'. These distractions affect not only one single aspect of our personality but the totality of our personality from a sensory experience to the final action of the individual passing through manas, buddhi, chitta and ahamkara.

Viparyaya: wrong knowledge

The second vritti is *viparyaya*, which means 'wrong knowledge' or 'false understanding'. Viparyaya is also known as avidya, ignorance. This is false knowledge or understanding which is not based on true identity. It is knowledge based on wrong conception and false ideas about name and form. One story that illustrates viparyaya is that of the four blind men who wanted to see an elephant. They had each heard about the elephant and were keen to know what an elephant was like. So they went to a zoo and said to the zoo keeper, "We wish to feel the elephant since we cannot see it." The zoo keeper opened the gate and took them inside. One blind man touched the leg of the elephant and said, "Now I know, an elephant is like a pillar." The second blind man touched the tail of the elephant and said, "Now I know, an elephant is like a rope." The third blind man held the trunk and said, "Now I know, an elephant is like a python." The fourth blind man felt the tusk of the elephant and said, "Now I also know, an elephant is like a pointed rod."

Each blind man had a different idea of the elephant. Now, was each idea true or false? The zoo keeper knew that an elephant is not a pillar, a rope, a python or a rod; it has a different shape altogether. This is an example of false

118

knowledge which is not based on the awareness of true identity. Another example is that of seeing a snake in place of a rope. There is no light and you are walking along in the dark when you happen to see a snake on the road, and you jump back ten feet. Then when you shine a torch on the snake you heave a sigh of relief because what you saw was in reality not a snake but only a piece of rope. So, you have seen something, you have experienced something, but that experience is not true, it gives a false identity to a form.

There is a term in Sanskrit, 'tadroopa pratishtha'. The word *roopa* means 'form', *pratishtha* means 'awareness of identity' and *tat* means 'that'. I can see that a certain swami has a form and I identify that form with his name. When I keep recognizing that form with the help of the name, that is *tadroopa pratishtha*, recognition of an actual form. But if I look at someone else and call that person by the name of the swami, that means there is something wrong with my perception. I am not linking the name, the identity, with the correct form. This is known as *atadroopa pratishtha*, knowledge of false identity. This state of viparyaya or avidya happens when false preconceived ideas superimpose themselves upon factual understanding or knowledge.

Most people fall prey to viparyaya in their lives. The rumours we here are an example of viparyaya. This viparyaya, combined with our own self-imposed idea, is a very powerful vritti, because it deludes the awareness and creates a totally false concept about something that is not true. When we begin to believe that false concept without knowing all the facts and circumstances behind an event, it is pure avidya. This is how rumours are spread, because once an idea superimposes itself on a real life event, it begins to multiply.

Another example of viparyaya can be found in the story of Nasruddin. Once Mulla Nasruddin wanted to travel to a distant town and he needed transport. So he decided to visit his neighbour who had a bicycle. The next door neighbour was sitting inside his house and saw Mulla approaching. He knew Mulla to be someone who was always looking for

119

things he could use for himself and then taking them away. Mulla used to say to him, "Look, whenever you go out of your house you are not going to use the things that are kept there, so let me use them."

When the neighbour saw Mulla walking in through the gates of his garden he said to himself, "Okay, he is coming to ask me for something and I will tell him that today I am staying at home and using everything." As soon as the neighbour opened the door, he said, "Sorry Mulla, I'm staying at home today. I can't give you anything." Mulla said, "That's all right, since you are staying at home I will take your bicycle."

Vikalpa: fancy

The third vritti is *vikalpa*, which means 'unfounded belief', 'imagination' or 'fancy'. Vikalpa is the absence of any kind of object. It deals with the realm of thoughts which are self-made in our own mind. This is a very interesting vritti because according to Patanjali vikalpa is the symptom of a dull mind. Some people may raise an objection here and say that imagination can be used creatively and can be a very constructive process. We can give the example of scientists who have fantasized or imagined something and later on converted their thought, concept or idea into reality.

According to Patanjali, however, fancy, fantasy or imagination is the product of a dull state of mind. Following the theory that an idle mind is the devil's workshop, he says that when the mind is not attached to a real fact (not an imaginative fact), then it begins to fantasize about what it would like to be, what it would not like to do, what it desires. It becomes a self-centred mind; thoughts become self-centred, trying to fulfil aspects that we lack in our life. In the process of fulfilling these fantasies often we are led away from achieving the real goal. We know we can fantasize about going to the moon or to another planet and we know that it is a useless fantasy because we do not have the ability or training to be an astronaut. If we have the training and we fantasize, then there is a possibility of the event turning into reality but not otherwise.

Every child fantasizes about becoming an airline pilot or a policeman. These fantasies are very strong and children pursue them in their childish games. They fly model planes, imagining they are the pilots. However, it would take many years for the idea to be converted into reality and by that time their life has changed totally. The one who originally wanted to be a pilot begins to work in a stone quarry and to make menhirs like Obelix. However, if there is pursuit of a fantasy or imagination based on practical experience, then it can be fulfilled. Take the hobby of the Wright brothers, for example, who had the theoretical, conceptual knowledge of a machine that could fly. They started imagining and experimenting, and ultimately made a machine that could fly. The same thing happened with Edison and the electric bulb, and with other kinds of inventions that have worked.

Those people who have followed one train of thought without distraction or dissipation and have fantasized about their idea have achieved a breakthrough. But to achieve this kind of breakthrough one needs to follow a direction. So the first aspect is pure fantasy, which has no base, no preparation. The second aspect is fantasy with some kind of understanding or knowledge that certain things are possible. Patanjali talks about the first aspect of fantasy, unfounded belief. In the *Yoga Sutras* it is said that fantasy is trying to gain knowledge through words without the actual presence of an object. I can imagine that there is a box here, but there is no box; it is just my imagination creating a concept, an idea, without the actual presence of an object. Pure fantasy is an expression of your own mind creating things, whereas in the second kind of fantasy you see something, then you create something from it, superimposing another idea.

The first aspect of vritti is pramana, seeing something directly. The second aspect is seeing something and superimposing something else on top of it. The third aspect is the mental creation of something that does not exist, hallucination. This hallucination is a vritti and it is also related to desires. There was a swami who decided to take sannyasa because he could not get enough to eat at home. One day he had the idea that he would leave the ashram and beg for a couple of rupees. With these rupees he would buy flour, make some chapattis and sell them for four rupees. Then again he would buy flour, make chapattis and resell them for six rupees. He worked in the ashram kitchen and this is where he got the idea. He began imagining that ultimately he had about ten thousand rupees. With this ten thousand rupees he began to purchase a tiny flat, he got married and had sons. He said to himself, "Well, when my sons come to me, saying 'Papa, Papa, I want this, I want that', I will just give them a good slap." As he reached out to slap them, he hit the earthen pot full of flour, which broke, scattering the flour everywhere.

This is a story about fantasy or hallucination which is the result of a dull mind. If you are involved in your fantasy head, heart and hands, like the swami in the story, then it is the result of a dull mind because that mind is not accepting the realities of present day life. It is for this reason that Patanjali says fantasy or imagination is the result of a dull mind. If there is no identification and you know that you are just passing your time, fantasy may take the form of a nice story, but there is no ambition, desire or even action attached to that hallucination. There is a modern saying about vikalpa that, "Lunatics build castles in the air, psychotics live in them and psychiatrists collect the rent." That is vikalpa.

Nidra: sleep

The fourth vritti is nidra. The first three vrittis are extrovert by nature. Nidra, the fourth vritti, is introvert by nature. In the state of nidra the perception of the outside world is introverted and there is sensory, external blockage. The perceptions of the external environment, of the body and mind are not recognized consciously or unconsciously. The sleep that the *Yoga Sutras* talk about is not the state of dream but the state that goes beyond dream, deep sleep where there is no vacillation and no experience of any kind of mental faculty. This state of deep sleep in which there is total blockage of every kind of stimulation is known as a vritti. In this state it is believed that all the jnanendriyas or sensory organs of the mind become self-contained and there is no necessity for them to receive input from any external source.

In the *Mandukya Upanishad* it is said that sleep is known as *prajna*, where the knowledge, awareness or consciousness is withdrawn into the state of unconsciousness, where the consciousness does not extend beyond its boundaries or interact with any of the external senses, whether physical or mental. This state of prajna is awareness of the 'one' without a second, the state of non-duality. The *Mandukya Upanishad* further states that this state of nidra is similar to the state of samadhi for the same reason. The only difference is that in nidra there is total introversion with sensory and mental blockage, whereas in samadhi there is not total introversion. The mind is alert and aware, yet it is contained within itself.

Vritti is the term given to the state of sleep. Why is it known as a vritti? Because there is no awareness in nidra, and this lack of awareness creates a disturbance in the pattern of consciousness, of mind experience. This lack of awareness does not give the feeling, the knowledge or the understanding of time, space and object. This state of deep introversion is a spontaneous withdrawal of the externalized mind, it is not voluntary. In meditation there is voluntary introversion, where there is awareness of the different states of experience, while in sleep there is no voluntary introversion, it comes as a natural state. So there is always a jump from this state of wakefulness into the state of sleep. It is a jump from an extrovert, dynamic and active state of mind to a passive and dormant state of mind.

Yoga does not accept either the active or the dormant state of mind as being the final answer to mental awareness. Yoga says that in the active state of mind there are distractions and in the dormant state of mind there is total introversion or withdrawal of the senses and unconscious experience. The aim is not to reach the unconscious dimension, but to be aware while we are in the unconscious state. For this reason sleep has been recognized as a vritti of non-activity whereas the others are vrittis of activity.

The point which says that sleep is similar to the state of samadhi has to be understood not from an experiential viewpoint but from a rational viewpoint. In the state of deep sleep one does not dream and one is not aware of the physical identity, of the mental experiences, of time, space or object. This state of unconsciousness is the last point that rational perception can reach. It is also understood that there is a state of sleep which is so deep that nothing exists.

However, what happens in the next state which is said to be beyond sleep or the unconscious experience? This is known as the fourth state of turiya, or superconsciousness. If the unconscious is the last state to be perceived and experienced by the mind, then how can the fourth state of turiya be perceived as something different to the unconscious? It is something like going deep into the ocean. When we are on the surface of the ocean there is plenty of light. As we go deeper, the light becomes less and the darkness more prominent. As we go further and further down, there comes a point where there is no light whatsoever, only total darkness.

In this process of diving into the ocean we have gone through three different experiences: light, twilight and darkness. These three states flow into one another, from *chetana* (consciousness) into *avachetana* (subconsciousness), and from subconsciousness into unconsciousness. It is one continuity of perception. In this context the superconscious state should be similar to, but much darker than, the unconscious state. According to yoga, however, it is not similar because immediately after experiencing the unconscious mind one experiences the spirit, the atma. The entire range of human perception extends only as far as the unconscious level, which is the final state of introversion, where the concept of time, space and object is absent. The moment you pass through this state of nidra you establish yourself in the atma or spirit.

The atmic experience contains in itself all the three states that have been experienced before. It is the atmic experience that is known as turiya or the superconscious. So when we speak of superconsciousness or the supermind, we are using these terms wrongly. The correct term is actually the atmic experience. The turiya state is atmic and not mental. In this atmic state the mind does not see, think or feel, the mind is bypassed. Another concept has evolved here, that the mind is the medium which flows into the atmic experience and that is the experience of our inner spirit, the concept of turiya.

In order to reach that point of turiya there has to be a process of knowing the unconscious or the introverted state which is experienced in nidra. This concept becomes clear when we discuss the different stages of dhyana. Each stage of dhyana deals with a particular state of pratyaya or door of perception to our conscious, subconscious or unconscious mind. One door opens and we see a view, another door opens and we see another view, and so on. This is the aim of dhyana, to open the doors of conscious, subconscious and unconscious perception. Each door is known as a pratyaya or an impression in the field of our consciousness. These impressions or pratyayas are different to samskaras or karmas.

So sleep is a vritti in which there is absence of external awareness, and after this comes smriti or memory.

Smriti: memory

Memory or *smriti* is the fifth vritti. Memory is generally classified into two categories: conscious memory and subconscious memory. Yoga adds one more form of memory, the unconscious. This aspect of memory is related to the sensory experiences. The *Yoga Sutras* have defined memory as a faculty which does not allow the experiences received by

125

the senses and the mind to escape from the field of perception. Whatever we experience in our day to day life, from the time we are born till the day we die, is stored, photographed and retained. When we consider memory or smriti as conscious activity, then buddhi or intellect plays an important role. Not in the sense of processing the information consciously, but in the sense of recognizing an event, how it affects an individual and whether an immediate action has to be taken by the individual.

The process of filtering, processing and classifying the information received by the mind and senses is a subtle buddhi activity. These events are stored in the form of memories that are brought up by the mind according to circumstances and situations. There are times when we remember an event from our childhood because the external situation demands that we remember it. If you were to tell a story about your childhood, then immediately that impression would come up. We do not remember those stories at every moment, but they are stored in some place and when needed we can bring that information up to the conscious level and express and analyze it.

These memories that are stored and brought up later on to the conscious level are the subconscious memories. For example, you have lived with your brother and sister or with your parents. You have had wonderful times and also bad times. You may have wanted a toy and asked your parents for it but they refused. You insisted persistently and ultimately they became a little angry and slapped you. The event shocked you, as you never expected it from your parents. You went to bed crying and afterwards did not speak to them for three days. The memory of the slap is active, not the memory of the good times you have had together. Later on in life, if something happens then immediately the thought occurs that you were deprived. It is a hard impression which shatters the normal expectations.

The most difficult form of memory to understand is the unconscious memory. According to yoga the consciousness continuously experiences and retains those experiences which are not only of this lifetime but of many lifetimes. Strong impressions of previous lives manifest in the form of samskaras. The samskaras are unconscious by nature. It takes time for them to come to the subconscious and conscious levels, and it takes time to recognize them. Samskaras are a form of unconscious memory which the rational mind does not necessarily recognize when they come up. The rational mind may attribute them to some aberration in our personality, some peculiar tendency or trait in our nature, or to the influence of our stars and planets.

Many times when something peculiar happens we say that it is because that person is a Leo with an Aquarius rising or something similar. But in one way it is actually due to samskaras and in another way it is not. The basic trait or form of our personality can be attributed to our star or planet, but within this basic trait there are many different kinds of manifestations and expressions of our experiences and reactions. These changing reactions are known as samskaras, the unconscious memory. Everyone has the same body, but different races have different skin colours. The colour of the skin is not the same for the whole of humanity. It changes for different reasons: pigmentation, genetics, climate and so on. In the same way the human personality is one, but the reactions experienced by the various personalities are different because of the different samskaras that are manifesting.

Yogis have maintained that samskaras are the unconscious memories. These memories are not rational in nature and they can be experienced as imaginary, false or real. The mind revolves around these unconscious memories and they are possibly the strongest vritti in our life. These memories even include some impressions received in this life which have receded into the background beyond the subconscious level. For example, in early childhood there is no rational recognition of an event that is happening and so these impressions are stored in the unconscious memory.

127

Every action and thought pulls some form of information from smriti, the memory field. In fact, we can say that human life is just memory and nothing more than that.

Anything new that we do now will be stored as memory. What we are expressing now is being pulled out from the source or bank of memory. What we desire, what we like, what we dislike, our failures and achievements, are all being regulated by the impressions pulled out from the memory bank. Even in the deepest states of meditation and samadhi, memories pull the mind back again and again and make it extroverted. So this vritti of memory is the strongest mental modification and it has to be dealt with in a positive way.

We should understand the difference between an ordinary memory or impression and a samskara. Let us look at this from two different angles. One way of recognition is through the emotions; this is a door through which the impressions may pass. The intellect is another door through which the impressions may pass. Another way is through the door of chitta, recognizing what is needed now and what is not needed. When an impression or an experience goes beyond every kind of rational perception, it becomes a samskara. In the sphere of rational perception we have thoughts, intellect, emotions, desires, ambitions, etc., everything that we can experience now in our life and manifest now in our own activity. If something does not fit into any of these categories, it becomes a samskara.

All impressions have to go through the maze of memory. What we are doing right now is also being received by the memory through the door of intellect. If we start doing kirtan now, the impressions will be retained at a vibratory level. If something traumatic happens which causes the tears to flow, that impression will be retained at the emotional level. If some subtle vision or experience happens and you have an out-of-body experience, that will be retained at the psychic level. These levels are like different files, 'A', 'B', 'C', 'D', etc., and each type of experience is classified in a different file. Something that does not fit into any of the recognized patterns of our present personality is classified as miscellaneous and becomes a samskara. It is something beyond recognition with which you cannot deal.

Recently a man came to me and said that he was terrified of going mad. I asked him what had happened. He said that thirty years ago, when he was attending college his room mate had suddenly gone mad, and for the past month he had been seeing the friend in his dreams and this was disturbing him greatly. For thirty years he had not thought of that friend. Why was this happening all of a sudden?

I interpreted that he had retained this experience thirty years ago when he saw his friend going mad. Then due to the drive that was propelling him to become something, to achieve recognition and status, that event was pushed into the background. As soon as he had attained whatever he wanted to achieve – status, recognition, good family and a position of respect, the back files started opening, and the file in which his friend had gone mad opened up.

So there are some things which come up and have to be dealt with even thirty years later and there are some things which will not come up in this lifetime at all. These impressions are known as samskaras. Later on as life evolves, certain events, situations or conditions arise which awaken those impressions, then they will come up. If nothing occurs to awaken them, they will remain in the unconscious memory in the form of impressions or samskaras.

Every kind of experience which creates a shock to the normal frame of mind is considered to be a trauma. That trauma brings about some radical change in our perception of life. That radical change is a stamp which has impressed the consciousness at some level. Psychology deals with the negative impressions of trauma, whether it is a childhood trauma, sexual trauma or any other type of trauma, through different forms of analysis. They take the different negative manifestations of the trauma and work with them. The personality is like this, therefore, the person is behaving like this or reacting like that.

129

In yoga there is one more step. The painful impressions we receive, which are called trauma in modern language, become powerful or hard samskaras. Apart from these, other impressions are received which do not create traumatic or radical changes in the personality. These impressions simply enter into the miscellaneous file and become known as soft samskaras. So we have hard and soft samskaras. Hard samskaras are the worst kind because when they manifest the whole personality is affected. However, when soft samskaras manifest we do not feel them because they do not have the same intensity.

The practices of raja yoga all tend to touch and alter different states of mind so that awareness of the different vrittis can be developed and the aspects of the vrittis which are limiting in nature can be eliminated. In this way full experience of the effulgence of consciousness can take place. Raja yoga, as described by Patanjali, is the science of the mind. Every aspect that we have dealt with in theory is related to the mental modifications, starting from pramana right up to smriti.

10

Raja Yoga

BAHIRANGA – EXTERNAL STAGES

Raja yoga has been further divided into two groups: bahiranga and antaranga. The first group is known as external or *bahiranga* yoga, which consists of the first four stages: yama, niyama, asana and pranayama. They are known as the external yogas because they change and alter the external personality, behaviour and actions that are related to interactions in the world, to the concepts of name, form and idea. So the four initial stages of raja yoga are the external aspects through which we are able to control the vrittis or modifications which are affected by external stimulation and the environment.

The last four stages of raja yoga: pratyahara, dharana, dhyana and samadhi, constitute internal or *antaranga* yoga. In antaranga yoga one is supposed to work with the mind and experience the full mind from the initial state of sensory withdrawal to the state of samadhi, which is unity of all the faculties of mind. It is a mental process of observation, analysis, reflection, contemplation, meditation and achievement. These last four stages stop the input of further impressions or vrittis into the field of consciousness.

YAMA

The first aspect of raja yoga is known as *yama*, which is generally translated by the layperson as 'moral code of

131

conduct', but which actually means 'yogic self-control'. The five yamas or external disciplines are: (i) *satya* (truthfulness), (ii) *ahimsa* (non-violence), (iii) *asteya* (honesty), (iv) *aparigraha* (non-possessiveness) and (v) *brahmacharya* (celibacy).

1. *Satya*, or truthfulness, is reflected in the external behaviour during the interaction of an individual. Abiding by the nature of truth or the law of truth, one is able to purify and remove the conflicts from the mind. People think it is easy to speak the truth. It is easy to say that white is white and black is black. However, truth here does not refer only to what one speaks. It refers to awareness of what is correct, right and true, as it is manifesting from within, and the ability to express it. When we are able to observe the true manifestation of a vritti, thought, desire, or the influence of some external situation on our life without it being filtered, affected and altered by the agencies of our intellect, self-image and ego, then that truthful state of mind represents the purity and harmony of our inner expressions and experiences.

2. *Ahimsa*, or non-violence, is not an external act of eliminating violence from our actions, but the absence of the violent nature in our personality. This violence is expressed not only in one's interactions with other people, but also with oneself in the form of an emotion, thought, desire, feeling, motivation or ambition. Anything that disrupts the natural flow of human perception and consciousness is known as *himsa*, which is the quality of tamas, of ignorance.

Ahimsa means the total absence of violence from our nature, which is a sadhana in itself. It is not just an act of accepting some abuse or pain. There should be a totally non-reactionary state within us. One should not react negatively or violently. This absence of violence in our personality transforms the tamasic personality into a sattwic personality.

3. *Asteya*, or honesty, is the third yama. Yogis have known that we are not honest with ourselves because there are

many strings attached to our mind and they pull it in different directions. The honesty, simplicity and sincerity of our nature tend to be lost because of the different ideas, images or ambitions which are superimposed upon it and which become predominant in our lives. So, honesty has been incorporated into the aspect of yama as a way to experience the sincere quality of life where the true nature of the personality is seen and experienced without any kind of superimposition of external ideas.

4. *Aparigraha*, or non-possessiveness, is non-attachment. When there is attachment and self-motivation, then there is a feeling of possessiveness. We tend to become possessive about things to which we are attached, objects, environment and people that we like. That possessiveness manifests later as a form of our own ego satisfaction drive. Possessiveness is a good thing to have but it should not be influenced by the ego or by the selfish nature. Possessiveness should become a process of caring or nurturing and maintenance, without the attitude of selfishness attached to it.

So, to develop the quality of non-possessiveness means to become non-attached. Attachment means craving and detachment means cutting off. Non-attachment means not being affected by whatever happens or wherever one finds oneself. Aparigraha allows us to perceive the attachments which bind us to rajasic or tamasic states of mind or to the world of the senses and objects, and which do not allow our perception to rise beyond the selfish qualities. So, aparigraha, the reverse of attachment, is an effort to rise above all the things that hold us down.

5. *Brahmacharya*, which is generally translated as celibacy, actually means 'one who is established in higher conscious-ness'. The word *Brahma* means 'higher reality' and *achara* means 'the follower of' or 'one who is established in'. This higher reality is definitely not the sensual, sensorial or carnal reality. Later, brahmacharya became known as celibacy, but the original meaning of brahmacharya was to establish oneself in the awareness of higher consciousness.

133

NIYAMA

After the yamas come the niyamas, which are again five in number. The yamas are meant to harmonize one's social and external interactions, whereas the niyamas create a sense of discipline in one's inner life.

The niyamas are: (i) *shaucha* (cleanliness), (ii) *santosha* (contentment), (iii) *tapas* (austerity), (iv) *swadhyaya* (self-study) and (v) *ishwara pranidhana* (generation of faith). *Niyama* means 'inner discipline'. What are these disciplines which, according to yoga, it is necessary to cultivate in one's life?

1. *Shaucha*, or cleanliness, is the first niyama. Apart from physical cleanliness, environmental cleanliness and cleanliness of one's living area, shaucha is also geared to create the feeling of cleanliness within the mind. If one lives in a clean environment, it affects the frame of mind and helps one overcome the different mental conflicts and dissipations. This aspect of cleanliness is also found in the shatkarmas of hatha yoga, where there is purification of the toxins or impurities contained within the body and purification of the different conflicting inputs that clutter the mind.

2. *Santosha*, or contentment, means to be happy with whatever one has, to enjoy living in the present moment without craving or desiring anything more. The aspect of contentment is to maintain a constant state of self-satisfaction and fulfilment. There has to be a sense of satisfaction in spiritual life. Once there is satisfaction then the craving aspect of the mind is transcended.

3. *Tapas*, or austerity, means following a process of change and transformation for the better. Tapas is generally defined as seeking out the pure essence of matter, like the process of firing gold to remove the impurities and extract the pure gold. We melt gold and other metals in order to separate the impurities and obtain the pure metal. So in yoga there is the process of tapas by which the impurities of the personality are burnt off so that the true essence can manifest itself.

4. *Swadhyaya*, or self-study, in this context means the analysis and knowledge of our own personality, being aware of our individual qualities, strengths and weaknesses in order to know who we are. Swadhyaya is sometimes understood as the reading of scriptures. However, this is not the yogic concept because one can read and read and still have the same closed, limited mind, still maintain the same idiosyncrasies and false notions. One can read a book and say that what is written there is true. However, intellectual study is no use unless one is able to apply that knowledge in one's life. Without practical application, there is no logic in swadhyaya. The word swadhyaya means self-study. *Swa* here means 'self'. Therefore, swadhyaya is the study of our own personality in order to make our life an open book. To be able to read our life as we would a book, to be aware of each and every page that is written in the book of our life, is swadhyaya.

5. *Ishwara pranidhana*, or cultivation of faith, is the fifth niyama. Here the word *ishwara* means 'higher reality' and *pranidhana* means 'to believe in'. Sometimes it is also translated as surrender to God but again there is a difference of opinion here. If you understand the background of Patanjali, then this concept will become clear. Patanjali was a knower of Samkhya philosophy, which does not advocate belief in God. Buddha was a knower of Samkhya philosophy and, therefore, in the Buddhist teachings there is also no mention of God. Raja yoga was very influenced by Samkhya and therefore in the *Yoga Sutras* of Patanjali there is no mention of God anywhere, except for this one word, Ishwara.

Ishwara means something different from the normal concept of God. From the Samkhya point of view, reality is perceived as having two aspects, nashwara and ishwara. *Nashwara* is the decaying principle, whatever is created is bound to decay, and *ishwara* is the non-decaying principle. Nashwara can be described as appearance, what appears to be externally, and ishwara can be described as reality. We can also say that nashwara relates to the manifest dimension

135

of existence and ishwara to the unmanifest. This is the concept of the Samkhya system, which talks of one reality having two forms. In one form the process of growth and decay takes place continuously: creation, preservation, transformation and destruction. In the other form there is one continuous state of being. So we can say that nashwara is 'becoming' and ishwara is 'being'.

What is that reality which manifests, which becomes and which is? That reality is known as *chetana*, meaning the unmanifest aspect of consciousness and energy. The unmanifest aspect of cosmic intelligence, having the faculty to know, to create and to manifest, is chetana. The chetana principle is a beautiful concept, a combination of consciousness and energy in continuous motion within itself. It is like a vortex, a whirlwind. On the periphery of the whirlwind there is the awareness of speed, of movement, but at the centre of the whirlwind there is total stillness. So the aspect of total stillness in the centre is consciousness and the motion is energy. It is all contained within itself and moving around within itself.

When that chetana manifests in one identity or form, it becomes nashwara, changeable. When it remains in its true form, it is ishwara, the unchanging, unmanifest, non-decaying principle. So ishwara is the final term. Nashwara continues right up to the end of human evolution; even in samadhi there is the feeling of nashwara until the final merger takes place. Nashwara is the link that connects the entire process of evolution, and the final achievement is ishwara. Ishwara pranidhana means cultivating faith in the non-decaying reality, being aware of, accepting the existence of the non-decaying reality which is beyond the realm of appearance, beyond the experience of name, form and idea.

No system of thought in India has advocated the existence of God. Later, however, when the aspect of faith was incorporated into these different systems, it was stated that one should believe in a form of one's own choice. It was left open to the individual, and so there are thirty-three million gods and goddesses in India because of the idea of openness. This means that everyone is free to choose an image, an aspect of divinity, that they like and give it a name, form, colour and dress. Then one has to attune the mind to that image and concentrate on it.

Out of these thirty-three million gods and goddesses, the groups that became powerful and strong in the course of time were known as the Shaivas, who believed in the image and different manifestations of Shiva, the Vaishnavas, who believed in the incarnations of Vishnu in the form of Rama, Krishna, etc., and the Shaktas, who believed in the manifestations of Shakti in the form of Kali, Saraswati, Durga and others. They all came together and formed different systems of thought, sects, traditions and religions. However, there is nothing in the basic philosophical structure about a form of divinity. Therefore, in the *Raja Yoga Sutras* we find only the concept of ishwara pranidhana, surrender to the unmanifest reality, which has the possibility of taking on any form, but which in itself has no name, form or attribute.

ASANA

The concept of *asana* is a physical posture in which one is at total ease and in perfect harmony with oneself. This has to be understood properly. As Patanjali and other yogis referred only to asanas which are static or which are used for meditation, many people believe that the other asanas, in which the body does not remain still, are not part of this classification. Many people have classified asanas as either non-traditional dynamic postures or traditional static postures, but actually asanas cannot be classified in this way. A much broader range is encompassed.

Aspects of posture
Non-traditional dynamic postures refers to asanas performed as fast movements, which do not allow the practitioner to

137

remain quiet and comfortable due to the involvement in continuous movement. Surya namaskara is an example of a dynamic asana in which one is constantly moving from one posture to the next. However, this actually represents one stage of asana practice, and there are five stages which should be understood. The body has to undergo different kinds of changes; it is not static or stable by nature.

First, from the normal state in which we use the movements of our body in a limited way, it moves into the second playful, dynamic state where we run, jump and stretch. From there it moves into the third state where we are able to touch our toes or to bend backwards without straining any part of the body. Then the fourth state follows where we are able to maintain our physical balance in the balancing posture. The fifth stage is where we can adopt a posture for an extended period of time during which the body remains perfectly still, motionless and at ease, without any type of discomfort or pain. These are the five stages of asana practice.

Patanjali's statement regarding asanas refers not only to meditative postures, as is the belief of the commentators, but also to the various states of flexibility, adaptability and comfort in the body during asana practice. There is a lot of evidence available to prove the point that asanas are not only meditative, as described in the traditional literature.

Many of the Yoga Upanishads speak of various postures such as mayurasana (peacock pose) as being asanas in which the body is in perfect harmony with itself. Mayurasana is not an easy posture to perform as there is a lot of pressure, tension and discomfort due to the constriction of the chest, the pressure in the region of the diaphragm, the weight of the body being placed on the wrists and the effort of balancing the body. So, if such a posture is referred to in the Yoga Upanishads, it is necessary to think about whether meditation posture is the true meaning of asana.

There are other asanas described in the Upanishads such as vrischikasana, (scorpion pose), surya namaskara,

138

which is described as the final state of asana, and vashishth-asana, a balancing asana invented by Sage Vashishtha in which he would spend a minimum of three hours every day. These are the types of asanas that are considered to be perfect postures, in which the total body is in harmony. In these postures the body is comfortable and there is no disturbance or tension in any part, there is concentration of mind and also blissfulness during the practice.

Looking at the various asanas that have been described, we can see that in the five stages that have been discussed, the body is taken from a normal state to a highly tuned and balanced state. Therefore, no matter which asana we perform, even if it is the most dynamic in which we are pulling, stretching and pushing every ligament, muscle and nerve of the body, there should be awareness, balance, comfort and stillness.

Effect of posture on the body

The effect of posture on the body is very deep and subtle. The common aches and pains due to bad posture can be experienced practically every day. Those office workers and executives who sit in chairs, bent over desks for extended hours, generally tend to have stiff backs and shoulders, which later on become the source of back pain and the cause of stiffening and hardening of the joints, eventually culminating in chronic spondylitis.

This is a very common situation that we encounter every day in different intensities. Many times due to bad posture while sleeping, one wakes up feeling stiff and tight in the morning. Often due to incorrect sitting posture there is pain in the spine and one has to get up and stretch the body. Sometimes one feels pain in the neck and shoulders due to stooping and has to expand the chest again in order to feel better.

It is definitely not possible to awaken the pranas in certain physical conditions over which there is no voluntary control. It is not possible to clear the blockages from the nadis when

139

there is recurring bad posture which creates continual pain and suffering. So, the first thing that yoga says is to observe the posture that you are using every day and to correct it. When you sit down, sit properly; that is asana. Performing the lotus posture, the headstand and salute to the sun is not the only way to practise asana. These postures are a means of aligning the body and creating a particular condition in which there is the experience of harmony.

If asanas only work when we are performing them, then their purpose is incomplete. It may be that our pranas become active while sitting in the lotus posture and practising meditation, but what about the times when we are not sitting in the lotus posture and our position is all wrong? At such times, the stimulation or awakening that we felt during the practice of the lotus posture is gone. So situations like these have led to the belief that asanas are definitely not just meditative postures, with due respect to the commentators on the different yogic literature.

When you begin to gradually coordinate and harmonize the different body systems, such as the skeletal, muscular, nervous, glandular, respiratory and digestive systems, through various positions and movements, that is asana. When physical harmony is achieved through this practice, that is the culmination of asana, the apex that can be achieved during asana practice. Once we reach this apex, there is no limit to what our bodies can do and to what we can do. Even difficult asanas such as vashishthasana, dynamic asanas like surya namaskara and the simplest group of asanas such as pawanmuktasana become a meditative process when performed properly. So, asanas are those positions or movements whereby perfect coordination of the body is attained.

Range of asana

The tradition also maintains that the benefit achieved through the practice of asana is knowledge of the three dimensions. Any layperson trying to study traditional literature will begin to wonder how one can achieve knowledge of the three dimensions by the practice of asana. The three dimensions can be understood in any sense, such as physical, mental and spiritual; gross, subtle and causal; waking, dreaming and sleeping states, and so forth. However, looking at the different descriptions of the three dimensions we can see that these dimensions are best understood in terms of the koshas: annamaya, manomaya and pranamaya, because the extent of experience of the physical body is limited to these three dimensions, and asanas are physical in nature.

1. *Annamaya kosha* is the physical aspect, the bones, muscles, nerves, blood circulation and the internal organs, such as the lungs, heart, kidneys, liver and pancreas. Everything that is physical in nature is included within annamaya kosha. The practice of asana is never unconscious or mechanical. It should always be done with awareness and concentration. For the practice of each asana, the yogis have described where we have to concentrate, which chakras and what kind of sensation and feeling we have to be aware of, and also what kind of pain we may experience. There is a wide range of experiences of which we have to become aware and observant.

This faculty of awareness or observation will increase our sensitivity to our own body. Therefore, through the practice of asanas we must first learn to observe our own body. What the body needs, what type of stretch, what type of release the muscular system needs, what kind of tension underlies which system, whether there is any disturbance being experienced anywhere in our physical body. What is the physical experience in the state of comfort, in the state of stillness and quietness? This in-depth awareness of the body is the first benefit of asana practice at the level of annamaya kosha.

2. *Manomaya kosha* is the mental aspect. At the level of manomaya kosha the effort made to still the mind is very important. While making a physical movement, we are adding awareness and trying to concentrate. We are trying to practise asana pratyahara by withdrawing the mind from the

141

distractions that pull it outside and merging it with the physical posture. So, asana pratyahara is the experience of manomaya kosha, where one begins to know the movement, nature, quality, strengths and weaknesses of the mind through the practice of asana.

3. *Pranamaya kosha* is the energy aspect. When the body and mind are attuned with each other, pranamaya kosha is definitely affected. This is because prana relates very much to physiological experiences such as muscular stiffness and tiredness, and different pranic blocks are experienced in the physical body in the form of discomfort, energy depletion or disease. If there is dissipation of mind, one cannot be aware of this pranic energy or direct it into the right channels, where it can become the tool for the awakening of the subtle and dormant potentials. Awareness of prana requires intense sensitivity of mind. If the mind is not sensitive enough, there cannot be an experience of prana. Without concentration and awareness there will be no experience of prana.

This knowledge of pranamaya kosha, which is awakened through the practice of asana, prepares the practitioner for the techniques of pranayama, which deal specifically with the field of prana. So, asana becomes the stepping stone to the practice of pranayama. The purpose of asana is to remove the pranic blockages and regulate the flow of prana throughout the body. The purpose of pranayama is to awaken the pranas, and this is where the range of asana ends. This is the meaning of the statement from the Upanishads that knowledge of the three dimensions dawns through perfection of asana. To continue beyond this physical range, techniques of pranayama, pratyahara and dharana are required.

PRANAYAMA

Pranayama is the fourth aspect of raja yoga, which follows the sequence of asana. Through asana one transcends the limitations of the body and mind and gains an in-depth awareness of the koshas up to pranamaya. The techniques of pranayama further intensify and develop awareness of pranamaya kosha. They awaken the different pranas within the physical structure and also remove blockages from the chakras, thus paving the path for the awakening of kundalini.

In Sanskrit the word *prana* means 'vital energy' and *ayama* means 'to expand'. So, the actual meaning of the word *pranayama* is 'expansion of the range of vital energy'. However, before the practice of pranayama there is another stage, known as prana nigraha. The word *nigraha* means 'control', so *prana nigraha* is the 'control of prana'. These are the two aspects of pranayama covered by raja yoga.

Initially, when we begin the breathing practices, it is not actually pranayama we are practising. Pranayama is the result of attaining full control over the functions of the upa-pranas or sub-pranas. After attaining harmony in the physiological structure, when prana is awakened in the realm of the chakras then pranayama begins. It is in this context, because of these subtle aspects of which we were previously unaware, that we have to clarify our precon-ceptions about pranayama. Therefore, we will take up the subject of prana first, second, prana nigraha and third, pranayama.

1. Aspects of prana

Prana or vital energy is the essence of all created, manifest forms, whether animate or inanimate. It is the essence or the force which determines the existence of matter and other elements. In chapter 8 (Hatha Yoga), it was explained that the original prana is known as maha prana. Maha prana is the transcendental aspect of prana which is unmanifest and does not come into the categories of either sthoola, gross, manifestation or sukshma, subtle, manifestation. When the maha prana is combined with the attributes of prakriti or nature, then it is simply known as prana.

This second stage is actually the combination of prakriti and maha prana working together to create the gross and

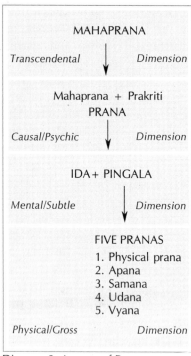

MAHAPRANA

Transcendental   Dimension

↓

Mahaprana + Prakriti
PRANA

Causal/Psychic   Dimension

↓

IDA+ PINGALA

Mental/Subtle   Dimension

↓

FIVE PRANAS
1. Physical prana
2. Apana
3. Samana
4. Udana
5. Vyana

Physical/Gross   Dimension

Diagram 2: Aspects of Prana

subtle manifestations. From this prana comes ida, the sukshma or subtle pranic experience, and pingala, the sthoola or gross pranic experience. Another name for ida is *chit shakti*, the force that governs the subtle dimensions, while for pingala it is *prana shakti*, the force that governs the dimension of matter.

From this manifest, pranic force, there are five further manifestations. The first is the physical prana or upward moving energy. The second is *apana* or the downward moving energy. The third is *samana,* the lateral moving energy that balances and distributes. The fourth is *udana,* the circular moving energy. The fifth is *vyana,* the all-pervading energy.

In brief, these five pranas belong to the dimension of matter, to the physical realm of experience. Ida and pingala belong to the mental realm of experience. The result of the merger of prakriti and maha prana is the psychic realm of prana. So, the first aspect, the group of five pranas, is physical; the second aspect, ida and pingala, is mental; the third aspect, prana, is psychic or causal, and the fourth aspect, maha prana, is transcendental.

Five pranas – the physical aspect
Beginning with the body, these five pranas have different functions and flows.

144

1. *Sthoola prana*, the upward moving force, is situated in the thoracic region between the diaphragm and the throat. The physical organs associated with this prana are the lungs, heart, oesophagus and trachea. Control and regulation of the functioning of these organs is attributed to the physical prana. Inhalation and exhalation of air are functions of the physical prana, and without these two aspects of breathing we would not survive. If the heart or the blood circulation were to stop, it would be difficult to survive. So these two major organs which are necessary for survival are controlled by prana.

2. *Apana*, the downward moving force, is situated in the pelvic region between the navel and the perineum. This energy is responsible for the elimination of waste matter and toxins from the body. Apana controls the functioning of the kidneys, bladder, large intestine and the urinary and excretory organs. Expulsion of faeces and urine, which is necessary for the survival and fitness of the body, is regulated by the apana force.

3. *Samana*, the lateral moving force, is situated in the abdominal region between the diaphragm and the navel. This balancing force controls the entire digestive process. The physical organs associated with samana are the stomach, liver, pancreas, spleen, duodenum and small intestine. All the food that we eat is broken down and the nutrients necessary to maintain the fitness of the body are distributed by samana. The word *sama* or *samana* means 'equal', and is the prana which distributes equally the nutrients necessary to preserve the annamaya kosha.

4. *Udana*, the circular moving force, is responsible for the functioning of the jnanendriyas, sensory organs, and the karmendriyas, organs of action. Udana is situated in the legs, arms, neck and head. It coordinates and controls the movements of the legs, arms and neck and directs the activities of the brain and sensory organs, which are situated in the head region. These include the eyes, vision; ears, hearing; tongue, taste; nose, smell; and skin, tactile sensation.

145

The organs of action controlled by udana are three in number: hands, feet and speech; the other two – the excretory and urinary organs, are under the control of apana. 5. *Vyana*, the all pervasive force, is the reserve tank of annamaya kosha. When the pranic petrol is empty and there is no filling station, then the reserves of vyana are used. Vyana is the reserve force which becomes active whenever there is a lack of energy in any of the other pranas. It is what is known as the second wind. Often when we overexert ourselves physically and feel extremely tired, a rush of energy comes which enables us to continue. This is the vyana experience.

Apart from the physical aspect, these five pranas are connected to the chakras. Apana is responsible for the functioning of the two lower centres of mooladhara and swadhisthana. Samana is responsible for the manipura experience of vitality and dynamism. Anahata and vishuddhi are controlled by prana. Ajna, bindu and sahasrara are controlled by udana. Vyana is all pervasive. These are the physiological locations and aspects of the five pranas.

At the physical level, these five pranas, and more specifically the prana located in the thoracic region, are said to be related to the in-going and out-going breath. The breathing techniques, which are known as pranayama, aim at stimulating and awakening these five pranas through a process of controlled inhalation, exhalation and retention. So, the breath is linked with prana in the physical sense.

Ida and pingala – mental aspect

Let us move on to the mental aspect of our life, which is dominated by the experience of ida and pingala. Ida is the mental force, which is represented by the moon, the lunar energy. The traditional name for ida is chit shakti, the force of chitta. All the mental experiences that we have in life and the functions of the four aspects of mind: manas, buddhi, chitta and ahamkara, are controlled by ida, as long as they remain mental in nature, without manifesting

146

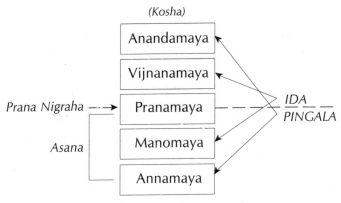

(Kosha)

| Anandamaya |
| Vijnanamaya |
| Pranamaya |
| Manomaya |
| Annamaya |

Prana Nigraha ——→

Asana

IDA
PINGALA

Diagram 3: Range of Ida and Pingala

physical interaction. What you are experiencing right now: the thoughts, sensations, vibrations, creation of different ideas and images, are the work of chit shakti, the ida force.

The ida force is the subtle energy that controls manomaya and vijnanamaya koshas, whereas pingala controls annamaya and anandamaya koshas. Please remember that asanas influence annamaya, manomaya and pranamaya koshas, and pranayama influences pranamaya kosha. From pranamaya kosha, the ida and pingala forces reach out in both directions.

The thoughts and mental experiences that remain confined to the manomaya kosha or the mental dimension until they become physical are known as ida activity. Desires, thoughts, emotions and feelings are given form and vitality by the force of ida. Vijnanamaya kosha, the intuitive ability and knowledge one gains through sadhana, is also a function of ida, the mental force. So, the range of ida covers manomaya and vijnanamaya koshas.

The range of pingala, or the vital force, is first experienced as physical vitality in annamaya kosha. Physical stamina and stimulation, the states of relaxation and tension, are the physical aspects of pingala energy. In anandamaya kosha the awareness which remains even in the deepest state of meditation, after the dissolution of all the samskaras and

147

karmas, is the result of awakened pingala. Even in samadhi, where there is awareness, there is pingala energy. This is the subtle aspect of prana.

Yoga says that even the subtle areas and experiences of mind can be controlled through the practices of pranayama. Please remember that pranayama is the expansion of the pranic range, it is not control of the breath. The techniques of nadi shodhana, bhramari, bhastrika or kapalbhati are techniques of prana nigraha, they are not pranayama.

Kundalini – causal aspect

After the subtle aspect of prana comes the causal aspect, the combination of prakriti and maha prana. This psychic area is where the kundalini manifests, because kundalini represents the manifest energy which has gone through different transformations, from the sublime to the most earthly form. The reversal of this process, which is known as kundalini awakening, is directed or motivated from the causal aspect of prana. When all the chakras are fully active and functioning, when the pranic passages are clear, then kundalini is awakened. When a spiritual awakening takes place and the kundalini rises up from mooladhara through the different chakras towards sahasrara, it is controlled by the dimension of maha prana combined with prakriti. The combination of maha prana and prakriti equals kundalini. Maha prana is the final state of effulgence in sahasrara.

2. Prana nigraha

The word nigraha means 'control of' and prana means 'vital energy'. Therefore, prana nigraha means 'control of the vital energy.' This vital energy can be seen from the physical as well as the pranic viewpoint. The physical aspect deals with control of the vital air and the pranic aspect deals with control of the movement of vital energy that takes place at the level of prana, apana and samana.

First we will deal with the physical aspect. When we talk about prana in the physical body as something which is manifest, then the attention is automatically diverted to the breath. There are certain traditions in yoga, including those of pranayama and swara, which say that the normal breath is the external manifestation of this vital energy. Therefore, it is imperative that we know how to breathe properly. Correct breathing will provide oxygen, strength and stamina for the whole body. It will also deepen the awareness of the pranic flow in all the channels.

In the physiological description of pranayama, the practices begin with (i) awareness of the breath, (ii) lengthening of the breath and (iii) directing the breath within a particular part of the body, for example, in the frontal passage from navel to throat, or from navel to ajna, or in the spinal passage from mooladhara to ajna. Once these three steps have been covered then we come to the fourth step, which is alteration of the flow of breath in the different nostrils. This fourth step is an important one.

Purification of the nasal passage so that there is no difficulty in breathing is one of the first considerations in pranayama. Therefore, as a general rule in pranayama it is always suggested that any kind of practice is begun with whichever nostril is open and flowing, and not necessarily with the right or the left nostril. Inhalation should be through the open nostril, whether right or left, and exhalation should be through the blocked nostril. Awareness, lengthening, direction and alteration of breath are all known as prana nigraha. Whatever practice we do, whether nadi shodhana, kapalbhati, bhastrika, surya bheda, chandra bheda, sheetali, seetkari, bhramari or ujjayi, the main purpose is initially to become aware of the breathing process and then lengthen it.

Lengthening the breath

Normally, due to the dissipated state of pranic energies, our breath is very shallow and short. We tend to breathe more through the thoracic cavity, rather than through the lower abdomen. This thoracic breathing is not acceptable in yoga because breathing in through the upper part of the chest does not utilize the full capacity of the lungs. However, by moving the diaphragm with the breath, there is access to the lower part of the lungs and a greater quantum of air. Using the full capacity of the lungs is an important consideration for yoga practitioners as well as for those who wish to improve their health and raise their energy levels.

Initially, in the yogic practices lower abdominal breathing is taught to develop the awareness of air filling the lower half of the lungs. The diaphragm and abdomen work like a pump which sucks the air inside and pushes the air outside. With this practice the process of increasing the inhalation and exhalation pattern of the breath begins. Later on, different ratios are added in order to gradually increase the length of the breath without discomfort at the time of controlled respiration. If we try to breathe slowly and deeply without any training, the lungs get tired very easily. So the breathing ratio is increased slowly one count at a time. At first, inhalation and exhalation are given the same count, for example, 5:5, as in nadi shodhana. Then the exhalation becomes twice the duration of the inhalation. In this way the ratio keeps increasing to strengthen the lungs and diaphragm, so that there is no tension, tiredness or discomfort felt when we come to the more advanced stages of pranayama.

It is said that a person who has perfected pranayama should normally breathe about one breath per minute. Now, we breathe approximately ten to fifteen times per minute. Ultimately, however, it should be possible to gain sufficient control over the process of breathing so that even in the normal waking state, whether sitting, walking or working, it will take thirty seconds to inhale and thirty seconds to exhale, and that should become the normal everyday pattern.

To reach this point of breath control, the final ratio corresponding to the Gayatri mantra is taught. This is performed in the following manner: one slow and steady inhalation, with one repetition of Gayatri mantra, which has twenty-four matras or counts, then internal retention with repetition of four Gayatris, which is ninety-six counts, then exhalation with repetition of two Gayatris, which is forty-eight counts, and external retention with repetition of two Gayatris, again forty-eight counts. This count of 1:4:2:2 is the ideal ratio of the breath: one: inhale; four: retain the breath inside; two: exhale; and two: retain the breath outside. To reach this level of control may take many years, but this is the final stage of breath control to which pranayama can take you at the physical level. This describes the process of lengthening the breath and how total control is gained over the breathing process, while still remaining at ease and feeling no discomfort.

Effect of pranayama on the three pranas

After this, we come to two more important aspects of prana, which are heat generating and cold generating. Samana, the force responsible for digestion and distribution of nutrients or energy to the different parts of the body, is responsible for the generation of heat. Most of the pranayama practices that generate heat in the body stimulate and activate samana. For example, bhastrika, or bellows breathing, pumps the stomach in and out continuously and there is direct stimulation of the samana force. Kapalbhati also directly stimulates the samana force. These pranayama techniques which can make us sweat and which increase the blood pressure, vitality and stamina in the body are concerned with the awakening of samana.

On the other hand, we have cold generating pranayama practices. These are the practices that lower the blood pressure and reduce hyperactivity. Here the process changes. The breathing is done through the mouth, which links the breath with the apana force. These cooling pranayama practices include sheetali, where the tongue forms a tube through which the breath is sucked in, or seetkari, where the breath is drawn in through the clenched teeth. So, the prana situated in the thoracic region is never used, stimulated or awakened in the practices of bhastrika,

151

kapalbhati, sheetali or seetkari. These pranayama practices work only with the energies of samana and apana. Activation of samana is activation of manipura and the solar plexus, which is related to manipura. Activation of apana is activation of mooladhara and the sacral plexus, which is related to swadhisthana.

Kumbhaka, or retention of the breath, whether internal or external, is the only method through which prana is stimulated or awakened. If we hold the breath and concentrate, after some time we will notice a build up of heat in the thoracic region. We will not experience this heat at manipura. The heat generated in manipura or samana dissipates throughout the whole body. But the heat generated at the level of prana, in the chest area, does not dissipate; it remains there. When this heat is experienced and intensified by the practice of kumbhaka, the activation of prana will also combine with the awakening experience of samana and apana.

In the *Yoga Sutras*, Sage Patanjali has spoken about different kinds of pranayama, but he has been very simple and brief in his description. He says that inhalation, exhalation and breath retention are the three kinds of pranayama. When people read this statement they think that the physical process of inhalation, retention and exhalation represent the three kinds of pranayama referred to, but this is not the case. These three actually represent the awakening of the three pranas. Retention corresponds to the force of prana, inhalation corresponds to the force of samana and exhalation corresponds to the force of apana. So, according to that sutra, the control of these three pranas is the real pranayama, which is called prana nigraha.

In kundalini yoga another reference to the relationship between these three pranas and pranayama can be found. Kundalini yoga describes the process of kundalini awakening as the reversing of the prana and apana flows and their meeting in samana or manipura. Normally apana flows downwards and prana flows upwards; they are being repulsed by each other. In the centre of the body is the lateral flow of

152

samana. So, when we reverse the flow of apana and prana, and the three forces merge in samana, then kundalini awakening takes place. This explanation is just a reference to explain more fully the process of inhalation, exhalation and retention as the three kinds of pranayama.

The breath plays a vital role in providing awareness of prana. Through the breath we can direct this pranic force to merge at one point. However, in the advanced stages of pranayama, the breathing technique by itself is not enough. There are different techniques, such as prana vidya, bandhas and mudras, and only when these are combined do they become the advanced aspect of pranayama.

Conductors of prana

The nadi system described in pranayama does not correspond to the nerve system of the physical body, rather it belongs to the bioplasmic body. The word *nadi* does not mean nerve, it means 'flow', something which is flowing. The nadis are the channels through which the energy or prana flows. The energy pathways of the pranic body are known as nadis. The system of kundalini yoga describes the *medhra*, or plexus of the pranic body, from which all the nadis emanate. This nadi plexus is situated in the region between mooladhara and swadhisthana. From this particular plexus, seventy-two thousand nadis emanate. These nadis are the conductors of the pranic force which is distributed throughout the various parts of the body.

Out of these seventy-two thousand nadis, which include all the major and minor flows, only seventy-two are considered important. Out of these seventy-two nadis, which are the carriers of prana and the corresponding vayus, the upa-pranas, only ten are considered to be major. These ten major nadis are situated in the spinal cord and pass through each and every chakra. Each of these ten nadis carries the ten different manifestations of prana, apana, samana, udana, vyana, and the five minor pranas, naga, koorma, krikara, devadatta and dhananajaya.

These minor pranas are responsible for such actions as sneezing, yawning, itching, belching and blinking of the eyelids. The autonomic activities over which there is no voluntary control are regulated by these minor pranas, which are known as vayus. So the five pranas and the five vayus flow along these ten channels which emanate from the medhra or the nadi plexus in the region between swadhisthana and mooladhara. They connect the seven chakras together and move continuously from mooladhara to sahasrara in one bunch.

Of these ten pranic flows, three are most important: ida, pingala and sushumna. Both ida and pingala are nadis but, at the same time, they represent the action of prana on the physical and mental levels. Thus we have ida nadi and ida force, and pingala nadi and pingala force. The channel and the force that it carries are two different things. So, when we speak about ida we have to clarify whether we are referring to the ida nadi or the ida force.

Ida and pingala nadis flow from mooladhara to ajna. The prana they conduct is both subtle and gross, mental and physical. So, when we speak of ida and pingala as being pranic force, we are referring to the two aspects of prana which are active and passive in nature. When we speak of ida and pingala nadi, we are referring to the pranic passages which emanate from mooladhara and terminate at ajna. The passive force flows in ida nadi and the active force flows in pingala nadi.

Effect of alternate nostril breathing
Yogis have said that the normal breathing process is connected with these two nadis and forces. This sounds logical because when we check the flow of breath, we usually find that one nostril is more open than the other. No physiologist has been able to say why we have two nostrils, when the function of both nostrils is to breathe in and out. No one has given an answer to this question so far, but it is something we should consider. If the purpose was only to

breathe in and out, then there would be only one nostril. But I do not think that was the consideration God had in mind when he made us. He somehow created an invisible link between the two flows of the right and left nostrils and the two forces of ida and pingala.

This speculation was made because each nostril flow creates a different mental or physical state. In scientific terms we refer to these activities as sympathetic and parasympathetic. This is something that we can experience at any moment. When we are sleepy or drowsy, we will notice that the left nostril is flowing. When we are active, physically or mentally, then we will notice that the right nostril begins to flow predominantly. Why does this changeover take place and what is the connection between this change and the physical or mental condition, for instance, in the state of drowsiness or in the state of activity?

Therefore, yogis have speculated that each nostril is connected with a particular nadi. When the breath flow is regulated in one nostril, it will stimulate, awaken and vitalize the corresponding pranic force. When the breath flow is regulated in the other nostril, again the same stimulation or awakening will take place in the corresponding pranic force. In order to manipulate the bioplasmic or pranic body, and in order to intensify the experience of the pranic body, the alteration and control of the breath in the nostrils is used.

Pingala, which flows in the right nostril, corresponds to the physical aspect of life. It is ruled by the sun and therefore is known as the solar force. Pingala is said to be positive in nature. According to the Tao, it relates to the yang or male principle. It is hot in temperature and is related to the sympathetic nervous system. Ida, the flow in the left nostril, represents the opposite polarity. The ruling planet is the moon, the negative force. According to the Tao, it represents the yin or female principle. Ida is cold in nature and is related to the parasympathetic nervous system. Ida and pingala represent the duality of the pranic forces.

155

With physical control of the breath, by lengthening and alternating the breath flow from one nostril to the other, certain pranic changes also take place. These pranic changes help to clear the pranic blockages which may exist in the nadis. For example, one pranayama technique is nadi shodhana. In this practice we begin to lengthen the breath and to alternate the breath through the nostrils at a slow and steady pace. Then we increase the ability to retain the breath.

Nadi shodhana means purification of the nadis. *Shodhana* means 'purification' or 'piercing', and *nadi* means 'the pranic flow'. So this practice, which is simple and easy in the beginning but becomes complex and difficult later on, has the function of clearing the pranic blockages from the passage of ida and pingala through alternation of the nostrils at the time of inhalation and exhalation. This creates balance in the two breath flows and in the corresponding mental and physical processes.

Awakening of prana and sushumna

When this balance is achieved, the awakening of prana can take place. Yogis have given a name to the awakening of prana which happens in prana nigraha. When the ida and pingala forces begin to flow regularly, rhythmically and continuously, and no blockages or physiological discomfort is encountered in the breathing process, then that stage is known as *pranotthana*, which means 'the awakening of the pranas', more specifically the awakening of the two pranas, ida and pingala.

When the awakening of the two pranas, ida and pingala, occurs, the third nadi or force, known as sushumna, awakens. This awakening of the third nadi is considered to be most important in pranayama, kriya yoga and kundalini. It is only when sushumna is awakened that pranayama actually begins. Until this occurs ida and pingala purification continues at the level of prana nigraha. With the awakening of sushumna, the practice of pranayama and the expansion

156

of prana takes place within the pranic structure. Therefore, the extent of our physical effort is limited to prana nigraha. Even with the purification of the nadis and the awakening and balancing of ida and pingala, there will be no expansion in the field of prana. The pranic field expands only when sushumna awakens, and actual pranayama begins after this.

3. Pranayama

The expansion of prana takes place in three stages. The first stage is the reversal of the flow of apana, the second stage is the reversal of the flow of prana and the third stage is the expansion of the pranic energy at samana. As mentioned before, in the prana nigraha group only three pranas are considered to be important: apana, the downward moving force, prana, the upward moving force, and samana, the lateral moving force. These three pranas are the ones directly affected when we come to the stage of pranayama which follows prana nigraha. Once we have achieved control over the breathing process and can lengthen the breath and retain it with full control, without any shortness of breath during the process of *pooraka* (inhalation), *rechaka* (exhalation) and *kumbhaka* (retention), then the first stage of pranayama, the reversal of apana energy, can occur.

Stage one: Apana energy, which flows downward, is wilfully reversed and made to flow upward from mooladhara to manipura. The yogic texts state that at this stage the inhalation and reversal of apana must happen through the ida channel. This is why it is generally said that we should begin pranayama with the left nostril, ida nadi. But in the prana nigraha stage, when we are simply trying to practise breath awareness, breath control and lengthening of the breath, it does not really matter through which nostril we begin the practice. The reversal of apana takes place through ida nadi, by inhaling through ida and feeling the flow of apana reverse and rise up through the passage of ida from mooladhara to manipura. However, to reach this level where you can sensitize the awareness to actually feel the upward

157

flow of apana from mooladhara to manipura may take many months of practice.

Stage two: The force of prana, which normally flows upward in the thoracic region, is reversed and made to flow downward from vishuddhi to manipura. This process takes place at the time of exhalation when there is awareness of the prana moving downwards through pingala nadi from vishuddhi to manipura.

Stage three: The merger of the three pranas: apana, prana and samana, takes place at manipura with the practice of kumbhaka or breath retention. When the forces of apana and prana merge in the region of samana, it is the culmination of pranayama. At the time of kumbhaka there has to be total awareness of manipura, not in the form of a chakra but in the form of agni mandala. *Agni* means 'fire' and *mandala* means 'zone' or 'area', so *agni mandala* means zone of fire.

When there is mastery over the process of kumbhaka and the aspirant is able to retain the breath for an extended period of time, say for the duration of four to eight Gayatri mantras, at that time dharana has to be practised on agni mandala. When concentration is practised along with pranayama, then the three pranas fuse into one and activate the other two pranas, udana and vyana. When the five pranas are activated simultaneously, the kundalini energy is awakened. This is the final process of the expansion of prana, the third stage of pranayama. There is no written practical instruction on how to practise this last stage. It is a verbal instruction given to the aspirant by the master who sees the progress and perfection of the technique.

Indications of perfected pranayama

The yogic texts describe the perfected process of pooraka, rechaka and kumbhaka in the process of pranayama. At the time of pooraka, inhalation, when apana is rising through ida nadi, there is an incredible cold sensation. It is as if the whole being is entering into a state of hibernation; there is a feeling of total withdrawal. It is the last stage of sensory withdrawal that a person can have on a psychic level. I have seen a few people who changed totally after a month or so of normal pranayama practice. They became withdrawn and quiet, as they went deeper and deeper into the pranic hole. That is a physical indication of apana reversing through ida nadi.

The yogic texts also state that at the time of rechaka, exhalation, when prana is being reversed, there is a feeling of total void, where nothing actually comes to the surface of the mind. The mind goes absolutely blank. There is no input of any kind from the world of name, form and idea. There is a feeling of total shoonyata, as if the entire energy is leaving the head, which is the active thinking centre, and merging itself in manipura. So, the normal mind which sees, experiences and thinks does not exist at that level. It is very hard to relate to any kind of thought, idea, desire or emotion. Whatever happens seems very far away. The body moves like a puppet, as if someone else is manipulating it.

The difficulty here is that since many of these practitioners are unaware of the physiological or psychological changes that may take place due to pranayama practice, they become afraid and stop the practice in order to return to the normal state. Therefore, pranayama practices have always been secretive techniques. Twenty years ago people were not aware of pranayama at all and even now no one is aware of these esoteric aspects of pranayama. We consider pranayama as simply opening one nostril and closing the other. However, it is not possible to go deep, where these kind of reversal processes and psychic manifestations occur, without proper guidance. If one tries to do so, it is possible to lose balance of mind and to lose control over the manifestations of energy, which may begin to run wild in the body.

In kumbhaka, when prana and apana are merged at manipura, at agni mandala, all the modifications or vrittis of the mind cease to function. The entire consciousness, the mental perception and the whole pranic structure cut off their connection with the physical body, and there is a total

159

stoppage of the vrittis. However, this cessation of the vrittis is not the aim of pranayama. It is an indication, a marker or milestone to let you know that you have come to the point where you have perfected the techniques of pranayama and it is now time to move on to the next practice.

Do not think that Patanjali's statement about controlling the chitta vrittis is achieved through pranayama. In the final practice of pranayama, the entire mind and all the perceptions of mind, the prana and all the manifestations of prana, are brought together at one point. Because of this merger there is no awareness of what is happening at other levels. One feels as if one is being moved like a puppet. One cannot rationally or logically see what is just or unjust, but this is a temporary phase.

This third aspect of pranayama, the merger and awakening of the pranic body, takes place within the span of a few weeks and then one comes out of it. It does not last for years and years, nor is it a condition to be aspired for. It is like all the spark plugs of a car firing at the same time to start the engine. Once the engine starts they stop firing and sparking. So, all these withdrawals of consciousness, energy, perception and other mental faculties are the firing or sparking manifestations which occur. Once the pranic generator begins to function, they again revert back to their normal states.

When this last stage of pranayama is perfected, there are physical, mental, psychic and spiritual experiences. On the physical level there are two major indications. Good digestion is one. As agni mandala becomes totally active, you can eat anything without experiencing any problems. Yogis who have perfected pranayama can even digest poison without ill effects. The second physical indication is lightness of the body, which manifests as the siddhi of levitation, or raising the body off the floor. These are the two physical indications that manifest when one has perfected pranayama.

On the mental level the vrittis are controlled but not stopped. To become the master of the vrittis, you see the changes and act accordingly. On the psychic level, it is said that the nada or psychic sound is heard. This sound can be heard even when one is walking, eating or talking to someone. The depth of one's being opens up and one becomes aware of the vibration that is controlling the whole body. When the pranas are activated one becomes aware of their movement and the sound they are producing at the time of their activity; that is the manifestation of nada. Therefore, pranayama is the technique that precedes pratyahara, dharana and dhyana. This last aspect of pranayama is very subtle, and if we go into it deeply then it is possible to have this experience in one split second.

11

Raja Yoga

ANTARANGA – INTERNAL STAGES

In the *Raja Yoga Sutras* of Patanjali there is a sutra describing the process of sadhana:

स तु दीर्घकालनैरन्तर्यसत्काराऽऽसेवितो दृढभूमिः ॥ १४ ॥

Sa tu deerghakaala nairantarya satkaaraasevito dridha bhoomihi (*Samadhi Pada*: 14)

This sutra can be translated as: "That (practice) becomes firmly grounded which is continued for a long time with reverence and without interruption." Here *sa tu* refers to the practice which is done, *deerghakaala*: for a long period of time, *nairantarya*: continuously without a break, *satkaara*: with faith, *asevitah*: which creates, *dridha bhoomihi*: solid foundation.

This is the main sutra that must be taught to every aspirant. Three qualities are necessary for the achievement or fulfilment of any sadhana, whether it be spiritual or material. The first is faith or conviction. Even if we are working in a factory, there has to be a conviction that through the work we will achieve our goal. Without that conviction there is no motivation to do the work. The same applies to spiritual sadhana. There has to be faith or conviction that, "Yes, through my sadhana I am going to attain the goal." Whether it takes a long time or a short time is irrelevant.

162

Nairantarya is continuity or regularity, which is the second aspect of sadhana. When we feel that we can fulfil our need through a particular sadhana, then we must try to become regular in it. During that period of regular practice, we try to ignore any distractions that come in the way. Once we set out on a journey, how long it takes us to reach our destination depends on our continuity. We can stop twenty times on the way or we can just go on continuously. If we stop twenty times on the way it will take longer to complete the journey, but if we go on continuously we will complete the journey sooner. Continuity without a break is necessary in order to obtain the full benefit of the practice.

Many times people come to me and say, "Swamiji, I have been practising this sadhana for so many years and nothing has happened." I ask, "How often do you practise it?" They say, "Oh, I practise once a week." So I tell them, "Practising one day a week is like taking one step forward and not practising for the remaining six days is like taking six steps back. How can you expect to make any progress?" In sadhana there must be continuity and regularity. Just as we find time to do those things we consider necessary in our life, in the same way we have to find time to be regular in our sadhana.

Deerghakaala means 'a long period of time'. This is the third aspect of sadhana. Practising over a long period of time is something that puts people off. If we have to do something for a long time, it is easy to get bored. In external awareness, the mind follows the senses, but when we are internalized, with the senses following the mind, then deerghakaala, the time factor, is not important. So, we have to be committed to our spiritual practice without any impatience or expectation of achievement within a certain time. If there is expectation of achievement within a certain time, it should be dealt with accordingly.

We also have to consider that our approach to sadhana begins, like a caterpillar, from one small leaf of a huge tree. To arrive at the centre of that tree may become the aim later on, but in the beginning we cannot just go straight to the

163

centre. For that, a different kind of awareness is needed. We have to start crawling from where we are, like a caterpillar with a leaf as its world. As it passes the leaf, it reaches a tiny twig which connects to a bigger branch, which connects to another bigger branch, which connects to the trunk of the tree, which goes down into the roots. Our mentality, our expectations, our life, our world, is our leaf, and we are all caterpillars nibbling away at our leaf. From this leaf we have to come down to the main trunk and eventually try to bore a hole in the centre. This is the process of sadhana that applies in the four internal stages of raja yoga – pratyahara, dharana, dhyana and samadhi.

PRATYAHARA

Pratyahara is generally translated as 'withdrawal of the senses' because at this stage we withdraw our mind from the external sensory objects and internalize it. In the normal state of perception, the senses become active first and then the mind follows. That is what happens in the normal state of feeling. If we see a scene that attracts the senses, then the mind will follow and recognize the scene as being nice, pleasant or beautiful. If we analyze this minutely, we will also notice that first there is sensory recognition of any kind of experience, then mental recognition follows.

Although these two forms of recognition are so close together that it is very hard to differentiate between what has come first and what has come after, minute observation will show that the senses go first and the mind follows. Therefore, in pratyahara the first step is not to withdraw the senses from the sense objects, but to withdraw the mind from the senses. Once you are able to withdraw, dissociate or disconnect the mind from sensory attraction and internalize it, the senses will follow the mind, and this is the secret of pratyahara. So, according to this principle, the definition of *pratyahara* is withdrawal of the mind from the senses, not withdrawal of the senses from sense objects.

164

Withdrawal of the mind has to be understood from different perspectives. Let us begin with the relevant sutra from Patanjali's *Raja Yoga Sutras*:

स्वविषयासंप्रयोगे चित्तस्यस्वरूपानुकार इवेन्द्रियाणां प्रत्याहार: ॥ ५४ ॥

Svavishayaasamprayoge chittasyasvaroopaanukaara ivendriyaanaam pratyaahaarah (Sadhana Pada: 54)

This sutra can be translated as: "Pratyahara is the limitation of the senses, of the mind, withdrawing them from their respective objects." The major points of this sutra in Sanskrit are: *sva*, which means 'one's own', *vishaya*, which means 'object', and *asamprayoge*, which means 'not coming in contact'. These words describe the state of pratyahara. Sva refers to what one is feeling, experiencing and observing, one's own experience. Vishaya is the object of experience. Everything we see is an object of experience. If we look at a person, what do we see? Do we just see the body, do we see the personality or do we see the mentality, behaviour and attitude? In one view we see the total picture of the person.

That objective awareness carries with it different experiences, physical, mental, emotional and psychic, all combined in one form. What do you think when you look at a swami, for example? If you just observe him or her as a material object and nothing else, then that swami will be only a body. There will be no feeling of happiness or joy associated with the body. But when you look at the swami you are experiencing all these things combined in one image.

So vishaya, although broadly translated as object, is the combination of the identity, the physical structure, an idea, the mental, emotional and psychic personality expressions contained within the name and form. Therefore, when we look at something we are seeing many different ingredients merged into one, and this is how we perceive the world in which we live. It is this perception that creates the understanding or knowledge of right and wrong, pleasant and unpleasant, comfortable and uncomfortable, and so forth.

The experience or the concept of duality arises from vishaya.

Now, forget about human beings and just look at any structure or statue. When you go into a museum and see an inanimate object for the first time, immediately there is an association and the formation of an idea. You see a statue of a person wearing a certain kind of attire and therefore you recognize it as a prehistoric image or an image of a warrior, for example. Association of ideas takes place and it is that association which is vishaya. When you know someone intimately, then it is not only association of imaginative ideas that takes place, but also the actual experiences that you have gained through personal interaction which gives you the total picture. It is not only name, form or idea; all three are combined.

The third Sanskrit word that is important in our understanding of the sutra is asamprayoge, which means 'not coming in contact'. 'Sva vishaya asamprayoge' equals pratyahara. Here 'not coming in contact' means that there is no personal identification or association with vishaya. How does one become aware of vishaya? Through the mind. The mind acknowledges or recognizes a vishaya through the senses. So when the mind is removed from the senses, there is no contact with vishaya. The organs of sight, taste, smell, touch and sound still exist and function, but the faculty that recognizes the messages conveyed by the sensory organs has been disconnected.

Dissociation of mind

When I was living in the ashram in America, I had a refrigerator with a little red light which would turn on when the fridge was not working. It was a very old fridge and every day I would see the red light flashing and have to go and check. When I could not find any reason for the fridge to malfunction, I thought that maybe the red light had gone berserk. After a month of constantly worrying about the fridge, I decided to remove the red light completely so that

166

I would not be aware if there was something wrong or not. From the moment I disconnected the light I had no more worries because that input was no longer there.

This is a practical example of dissociation of the mind from the mechanical activity of the senses which illustrates the state of pratyahara. When the senses are directed outwards we are constantly aware of our immediate environment. With the mind deeply associated with the senses, it is not possible to experience or recognize the mental faculties which have nothing to do with the sensory experiences. In order to go deep into the mental dimension in yoga, there must eventually be a dissociation of mental perception from the senses. Otherwise how will it be possible to experience our subconscious, our unconscious, our samskaras, our karmas or the archetypes of our personality?

One mistake we often make is trying to dive deep into the ocean, while still trying to retain the same vision that we had above water. This is not possible. We try to go deep into meditation while still retaining the same head space that we had in our external life. We try to analyze the experiences of deep meditation from the same intellectual and emotional space, which is external and sensorial by nature. This is a very common mistake due to lack of spiritual education, because our teachers have not been able to go beyond external, sensory perception.

Dissociation of the mind from the sensory field is not a negative state; it is a very beautiful experience. I will give you one example of dissociation. While daydreaming you are not asleep, you are not awake. The eyes are open but the mind is somewhere else, totally involved in the activity of the daydream. Often it also happens that when you come back to the conscious state and try to again recreate that daydream experience, it is not possible. If there was a feeling of happiness in that state of daydreaming and you try to think, "What was I feeling?" you will find it has gone and does not come back.

The daydream experience is similar to dissociation, where the mind becomes free from the influence of the sensory

167

fields; there is a very buoyant, light, happy, contented, out of this world feeling. Many times pratyahara is also associated with fantasy because in this state of dissociation one begins to see different kinds of visions through the mental eyes. The eyes may be open but they are seeing an invisible movie of flying over the mountains. That mental image is being created by the eyes, there is the sensation of wind touching the body, but it is happening internally, not externally.

Dissociation of mind is not a traumatic state. Dhyana is more traumatic than pratyahara because in meditation we have to work to overcome the influence and the attraction of the samskaras, the karmas, raga and dwesha. So dhyana is more painful, pratyahara is not. It is a very pleasant experience where only one simple training is given. Separate the mind from the senses and let the mind create its own world. What the mind does there is not important at this stage. What is important is to separate the mind from the senses. The mind can go deep, it can create its own worlds while the senses remain outside.

Once we are able to create this differentiation or distinction between sensory awareness and mental aware- ness, the mind can be directed to go deeper into other states where dharana becomes intense. Dharana, which is called concentration, is deepening of mental awareness. As the mental awareness deepens, when there is total absence of the external, sensorial awareness, then dharana takes place. Dharana can take place in any form.

We can compare dharana with the experience that two lovers have when they are together for hours and hours but it seems as if only a few moments have passed. However, if something unpleasant has to be done, then one moment will become like one whole hour. So the intensity which makes us aware of one moment as a long time, or a long time as one moment, is dharana. In the positive sense, dharana is defined as a deepening of awareness, where the concept of time is lost, where objective consciousness is lost and only awareness of space remains.

Removal of object awareness

In order to transcend the concept of time and remove the idea of object, a method is adopted. Idea, name, form is the area where we deal with our mind, our senses and our faculties. In the normal state the mind is fully involved with idea, identity (name), form (object) and time. This is the waking, active state of the self. In pratyahara we dissociate the mind, which is in the form of idea and name, from the objects of the senses. The experience of object or form does not remain anymore, but idea, name and time continue.

Idea will be active as long as the mind is active. Name, or awareness of an identity, will remain active as long as idea is active. But contact with form or object, which is external and experienced by the five senses, can be eliminated from the mind. So, if you simply remove the mind from the form or the object of the five senses, then that is pratyahara. Mind continues to create its own idea. What is an idea? It is a form of thought, desire, ambition and so on. Idea continues to create name or identity, but there is no actual grasp of this form. With my eyes closed I can imagine mentally that the microphone stand is in front of me, but that is mental perception. Whereas if I am able to feel it, see it and touch it, smell it and hear it, then it is awareness of the form or object. However, if I only use my imagination, there will be no awareness of form. What remains is only idea, name and the dimension of time. So, removal of object awareness is pratyahara.

Keep in mind that pratyahara aims to withdraw the sensory perception from the three levels of name, form and idea. These three levels also combine the physical (external), the subtle (self-created) and the causal (inherent) experiences. External, self-created and inherent are the three dimensions from which the sensory awareness has to be withdrawn and fixed at one point. That one point is the state of dharana, concentration, but fixation of the mind at one point within itself is where the mind becomes stable in its own identity. In order to reach this stage, there are many different

169

pratyahara practices. We will begin with some of the major external practices, starting with ajapa japa.

Practices of pratyahara

Ajapa japa is normally translated as 'continuous repetition', but the principles involved in it need to be considered first. In the beginning, after you complete the preparatory stage of body awareness there is awareness of the breath, which is an external activity. Using the external activity of breath there is a process of going within. Initially the breath is experienced as a flow in the nasal passages, next as a flow in the frontal psychic passage between the navel and throat, and then as a flow in the psychic passage, extending from mooladhara to ajna. Here the external movement, the external awareness of the breath is internalized and experienced in the psychic passage. Later, a mantra, which is a sound or vibration of power, is added to stop the self-induced dissipation of concentration, of the mind running after this thought or that sound or this sensory experience of the body.

So, ajapa japa covers the gross, external aspect, using physical activity, the breathing process, to internalize the awareness. Then mantra is added to stop the self-induced mental fluctuation. Later on, depending on the intensity of the practice, if there is deep concentration on the mantra then even the causal manifestations, inherent experiences of the senses and the world, tend to dissipate gradually. So there is also an advanced level of ajapa japa practices belonging to the dharana group.

Yoga nidra, a technique that induces deep relaxation, is another practice we will describe briefly from the pratyahara point of view. Although there are many stages in yoga nidra, generally few are taught because yoga nidra belongs to the pratyahara group, the dharana group and the dhyana group. There are clear divisions in yoga nidra.

The pratyahara group of yoga nidra practices includes awareness of the body, rotation of the mind through the

170

various parts of the body, breath awareness and the awakening of different physical and psychological sensations and feelings, such as heaviness/lightness, heat/cold, pleasure/pain. These sensations and feelings are different experiences that are accumulated and stored in the mind, and by this practice these impressions are released.

In the *Yoga Sutras* such impressions are termed pratyaya. Even in the highest meditative states or in the states of samadhi, pratyayas continue to exist. The three divisions of yoga nidra aim at removal of the pratyaya from the conscious or external plane, the subconscious or subtle plane and the unconscious or causal plane. Therefore, certain techniques of yoga nidra, which belong to the aspect of dhyana, become aids to experience that state of samadhi. In the pratyahara state of yoga nidra, however, there is mainly a release of stored impressions of sensory or mental experiences.

Trataka, the practice of gazing steadily at one point, is the next technique. Trataka falls into two groups: pratyahara and dharana. Pratyahara trataka is gazing at an external point, whether a candle, symbol, yantra or mandala, or the different forms of trataka that have been described in the traditional texts such as the *Hatha Yoga Pradipika*, *Gherand Samhita* or other yogic literature. Trataka aims to control the dissipation that occurs when we become aware of form. Form is seen by everyone and that form is recognized as something that is visible to everyone. That form symbolizes the state of mental dissipation.

Our eyes are very active. We constantly look at things, and we look at so many things that we are not actually aware of everything that we see. Even at this moment there is a lot of information going in through the eyes, but not all of it is being recognized. We only recognize the information that the mind acknowledges. The eyes are considered to be the most active sensory field. To have control over the visual sensory perceptions and to channel the impressions received through them is the aim of trataka, control over the aspect of form, the awareness of form.

171

Another form of trataka is *antar* or inner trataka. The process is similar, but instead of using an external aid on which to focus our visual perception, we develop and awaken our own internal visual perceptions. What is stored in the mind in the form of visual impressions is released through the development of this technique.

Antar mouna, the next practice of pratyahara, is translated as 'inner silence'. This technique is related to thought awareness: observation of the thoughts, stopping the thoughts, bringing a thought to mind, following an external thought and going to its source. The practice of antar mouna is related to awareness of the idea field, just as trataka is related to the form or image field. This idea field is both internal and external. It is not only physical or mental but relates to both dimensions of experience.

By following a thought we try to go to the source and ultimately remove the pratyaya which creates that thought. These pratyayas of thought are possibly the most complex ones to become aware of, because in thought there is the combination of an emotional identity, an intellectual analysis of something that is happening, as well as our personal input in the form of ambition, desire, need, strength, weakness and so forth.

Do this experiment yourself. Pick up a thought and then isolate its different components. Isolate the emotional aspect and go to its source, isolate the analytical, intellectual aspect and go to its source, isolate the desire aspect and go to its source, isolate the strength aspect and go to its source, isolate the ambition aspect and go its source. Separate the thought into many aspects and see what you ultimately find. When you do this kind of experiment then you will know the actual process of antar mouna.

Thought is like an onion with many layers stuck to each other. The onion seems very solid, hard and strong, but as you peel off one layer at a time the onion becomes smaller and smaller until nothing remains. That is how yogis view the thoughts. The process of antar mouna involves stripping the thought of its component parts, from the image which has presented itself to us. To become aware of the form of thought as it presents itself in the realm of idea is the purpose of antar mouna in pratyahara.

DHARANA

Dharana means to hold or bind the mind at one point. It follows the state of pratyahara in which the normal process of the mind following the senses is reversed, so that by internalizing the awareness, the senses ultimately follow the mind. Dharana is not just fixation of the mind on something. It is a very complex process in which the mind is taken right through the different states of external, internal and intermediate experiences.

When there is sensorial disconnection of the mind, then anything that manifests internally in dharana becomes more intense and powerful. We may have experienced this intensity in the form of an emotional outburst at the time of meditation. There are many people who become highly emotional as they go deep into meditative states. These emotional outbursts are often attributed to some kind of mental, psychological or emotional blockage, but beyond that there is another reason. According to yoga, when an intensity of thought, idea or feeling is experienced unconsciously in the deeper layers of the mind, without the distraction of the senses, at that moment the idea or thought form becomes a very intense experience.

Such an emotional outburst is also a state of dharana. The difference is that in this case there is no support or basis that we can latch on to. Therefore, the intensity is very strong and we feel it coming from deep inside. As that emotional outburst takes place, we relate it to some event, situation, circumstance or experience from the past. Childhood memories surface, images of happy or sad times that we have had come rushing up, and we go with the force of those feelings. That is the external reaction which takes

173

place in meditation when the mind is without a support. Therefore, it is quite common to see people crying, expressing their emotions and going through different spontaneous, physical movements in the state of dharana.

Right now, with the externalized mind we are conscious and aware of how our body has to react and behave. In the external state there is also an unconscious control of prana, whereas in meditation that unconscious control is not there. There is no control over prana. The mind is cut off from the body and the pranas begin to move and flow spontaneously. So the body adopts different postures according to the movement of the prana. When this disconnection takes place the pranas become free. The mental concepts become free from the conditioning of body, environment and even local mentality.

Intensity of concentration

The important thing here is to keep the mind fixed on one point only. Any point of concentration can be used, such as a mantra, symbol, thought, idea or any form. Intensity of concentration is generally regarded as dharana. There is a story in the *Mahabharata* that illustrates the intensity of concentration required for this practice. When Acharya Drona was teaching archery to the Pandava and Kuru princes, he asked his pupils to come forward one at a time in order to see a small clay bird that he had placed on a branch at the top of a tree, and to shoot an arrow through the eye of the bird. When each prince came forward, the guru asked him the same question, "What do you see?"

The first prince replied, "I see the forest, the sky, the tree, the leaves, the branch and the bird." The guru said, "Don't shoot, put your bow down." Then he called the second prince and asked, "What do you see?" The prince replied, "I see the sky, the tree, the leaves, the branch and the bird." The guru told him also to put down the bow. All the pupils who came forward failed to understand the teaching the guru was trying to impart, because he expected a very specific answer.

174

Finally Arjuna's turn came and the guru asked him, "What do you see?" Arjuna replied, "I see the bird's eye." Then the guru asked, " Do you not see the leaves of the tree and the branch on which the bird is sitting?" "No," said Arjuna, "I see only the eye."

The guru asked, "Do you not see even the bird's wings or head?" Arjuna replied, "No, I see nothing but the bird's eye." So the guru was satisfied and said to Arjuna, "You have learnt well." Arjuna did not have tunnel vision, nor was he blind to the scenery around him, but the intensity of his concentration was so great that all his faculties of perception were fixed on one single point – the bird's eye.

At the time of meditation, if there is oscillation in the mind, concentration will not be experienced. Dharana is a state in which there is total one-pointedness. It may come only for a second after a lot of practice. If you are trying to practise meditation with an oscillating mind which is moving from one point to the next, while different thoughts and ideas are coming and going, then it is not meditation or dharana, or even pratyahara, because there are too many oscillations and distractions. Just closing the eyes and trying to fix the mind on an image is not enough. Proper training has to be given to the senses, to the mind and also to the mental faculties as and when they manifest, in order to perfect dharana and to come to the meditative state of dhyana.

External stage of dharana

The yogic tradition describes three different levels of dharana: bahir lakshya, madhya lakshya and antar lakshya. The first is bahir lakshya. The word *bahir* means 'external', *lakshya* means 'aim' or 'goal' and dharana means 'concentration'. So *bahir lakshya* is an external aim which one should focus upon to achieve the state of concentration. Bahir lakshya involves different processes. The first technique is bhoochari mudra, gazing into space. First, the hand is held horizontally in front of the nose and you focus on the nail of

175

the little finger, looking at it intensely and fixing the position of the eyes. Gradually the hand is removed and the same focus of the eyes is maintained for as long as possible.

Bhoochari mudra is a practice of bahir lakshya. It is very difficult to keep vision fixed on space. The eyes need to focus on something; it is hard to focus on nothing, on space. However, the longer you maintain the focus of the eyes on the point of space, the easier it becomes to control the sensorial inputs and prevent them from distracting the mental attention. The yogic texts state that when this stage is perfected, a blue light is seen upon closing the eyes.

In addition to the first stage of frontal vision as practised in bhoochari mudra, there is upper vision as in akashi mudra, which is the second practice. In akashi mudra you bend the head back and gaze upward into space, keeping the eyes open. This practice can also be performed by combining shambhavi mudra and gazing at the space between the eyebrows at the level of ajna chakra.

Although these techniques are all visual in nature, different nadis are influenced by the position of the eyeballs. In kundalini yoga, for example, it has been stated that in order to awaken mooladhara chakra one has to practise nasikagra drishti, nosetip gazing. Focusing the eyes on the tip of the nose creates different sensations in the nadis which are connected with each other in the forehead region as well as to ida, pingala and sushumna, which in turn creates a certain stimulus at mooladhara. These are some of the techniques of bahir lakshya which stimulate the nadis and help to awaken the different psychic centres.

The bahir lakshya techniques aim at awakening the different nadis. Just as bhoochari mudra, the first of these practices, is known to be perfected when there is a vision of blue light, in the same way, the practice of akashi mudra is known to be perfected when there is a vision of golden light. What does the blue and golden light signify here? It signifies the awakening of ida and pingala; the blue represents ida and the gold, pingala. So, in the external aspect of dharana,

176

an effort is made to internalize the mind, to fix the mind on one point, to intensify the state of concentration and also to awaken the two nadis, ida and pingala.

Intermediate stage of dharana

The next aspect of dharana is madhya lakshya. The word *madhya* means 'intermediate', *lakshya* means 'aim', and dharana means 'concentration'. So madhya lakshya is the intermediate stage of dharana. In this stage an effort is made to focus the mind on the experience of space. In yoga, three regions of space are generally described which are within the physical body. These three physical spaces are:

1. *Chidakasha*: the space of chitta or consciousness, experienced in the head region, between vishuddhi, ajna and sahasrara chakras.
2. *Hridayakasha*: the space of the heart, experienced in the chest region, between manipura, anahata and vishuddhi chakras.
3. *Daharakasha*: the space of the lower regions, encompassing mooladhara, swadhisthana and manipura chakras.

The techniques of dharana meditation commonly described in the books on meditation are related to these three spaces which are seen and experienced physically within the body. These practices are called: chidakasha dharana, hridayakasha dharana and daharakasha dharana.

Chidakasha dharana is a meditation technique in which the awareness of space in chidakasha is built up in different ways: seeing the colours, shapes and symbols that manifest, creating and removing mental images, and allowing images to arise spontaneously. As the mind becomes subtle, different shapes, geometric figures, yantras and mandalas will be seen. These represent a state of perception in the mind. Sometimes nothing will be seen. In order to draw water from a well you need a long rope. If the water is eighty feet down and your rope is only forty feet long, you will never get water. So, although you may see nothing in chidakasha, it does not mean that nothing exists. There is

177

always some experience at every level; no level is without experience. However, it should be understood that the intensity of our effort will determine how far and how deep we can go. This principle applies to every technique and aspect of yoga.

Hridayakasha dharana, concentration on the heart space, is a vedic meditative process involving the three bodies of prajna, tejas and vaishwanara. In this process the light is experienced in the heart. There are many Upanishads which give descriptions of the hridayakasha dharana techniques. These are techniques dealing with the intensity of emotion and feeling, creation of an emotion, colours of an emotion, changing of an emotion and also the dimension beyond emotion. These are not the conscious emotions which we deal with normally in daily life, but the deep, subconscious feelings which are far more intense. These emotions have to be experienced and relived in order to break the conditioning of the mind. The psychotherapeutic aspect of meditation has its roots in hridayakasha dharana.

Daharakasha dharana, concentration on the space of the lower regions, is comprised of the techniques found in the kundalini literature. These practices involve concentration on specific images in the region of mooladhara, swadhisthana or manipura. Here one sees a lotus flower, a colour, a symbol, a deity, an animal or an element. This detailed awareness of the chakras is daharakasha dharana. In particular, one builds up an understanding of the active role of the elements or *maha bhootas* of earth, water, fire, air and ether or space.

Vyoma panchaka: five subtle spaces

Once one is established in the subtle awareness given by daharakasha, which gives insight into the way one's inner experience is influenced by the maha bhootas and their interaction with the senses, instincts, emotional and mental states, one comes to vyoma panchaka. *Vyoma* means 'space' and *panchaka* means 'five'.

In the Yoga Upanishads the vyoma panchaka practice forms part of *taraka yoga*, which takes one across the ocean of samsara into the transcendental unmanifest dimension, and is therefore part of laya yoga. However, this is for practitioners who experience the vyoma panchaka spontaneously, without effort. For aspirants who need to build up the experience in stages, the practice becomes part of the effort to perfect dharana and can therefore be classified as raja yoga.

Daharakasha, hridayakasha and chidakasha, the three gross spaces, are experienced in the conscious and subconscious. But the experience of the five subtle mental spaces, collectively known as the vyoma panchaka, is in the realm of the unconscious and superconscious. For the yogi who has developed the drashta, or witnessing consciousness, the 'unconscious' does not refer to absence of awareness but rather to the absence of vrittis, the previously known structures or modifications of the mind. The vyoma panchaka lead the practitioner through previously veiled realms of experience, through the unconscious and beyond.

These five spaces consist of: guna rahita akasha, param akasha, maha akasha, tattwa akasha and surya akasha.

1. *Guna rahita akasha* is the attributeless space. The word *guna* means 'attribute' or 'quality', *rahita* means 'without' and *akasha* means 'space'. The final experience in this akasha, taken literally from the scriptures, is that 'in the morning a complete ring of sunlight or flame of fire is seen'. This description gives some idea of what guna rahita akasha is. It is seen that after one has passed through the experiences of the three spaces and beyond the conscious and subconscious planes of life, then at the unconscious level prajna purusha or the prajna identity is perceived as a luminous body.

A ring of fire or sunlight, representing the luminous body, is beyond the known attributes of the manifest and physical dimensions. It is beyond the realm of physical and mental gunas. Maintaining this vision or visual experience for an extended period is the experience of guna rahita

179

akasha. The vision of prajna is not involuntary vision, it is voluntary vision. Just as we can imagine the image of a rose or of any other object if we wish, in the same way, this vision becomes a voluntary visual experience.

2. *Param akasha* is described as 'deep, dark space with a twinkling star-like light'. There is a state of perception known as shoonya or nothingness. Here total absence of light, cognition and knowledge is experienced, with just the awareness remaining in the form of a tiny star or point of light. It is self-contained awareness, not dissipated or expanded awareness, but a fixed, luminous point of awareness. From this, a meditative process has been developed known as shoonya meditation. There comes a point after this where there is total absence of external and internal awareness, and only awareness is active. That state is the experience of param akasha. *Param* means 'supreme', therefore, this is the 'supreme space'.

3. *Maha akasha* is described as a 'bright like the middle of the sun, which no eyes can see'. You cannot see the brilliance of the sun by going into the middle of it. This shoonya state is evolving. Initially there was total darkness with just a point of light, and that represented awareness. The recognition of that point of light is drashta, observing the awareness. But here the merger of drashta with that awareness takes place so that the whole personality is engulfed by total awareness. It is like being in the centre of the sun, surrounded by brilliance and light. That is known as maha, the great.

4. *Tattwa akasha* is the elemental space. The word *tattwa* means 'element', but here the experience is not of the five gross elements which we know as earth, water, fire, air, and ether, but of the seed or essence from which the elements are germinated. In this space, the tattwas exist in a dormant state, and so there is no activity, no motion which is expanding outwards. There is perfect stillness or quietness where each faculty is centred in its own being, so there is no action, nor is there any seed which creates action in the form of desire. In this space the concept of duality has

vanished, all experiences relating to name, form and idea have disappeared and there is absolute stillness.

5. *Surya akasha* is the luminous space of the sun or the soul which is pure and untainted. The word *surya* means 'sun', but it is also interchangeable with *atma* or 'soul', which is the internal, self-luminous principle and illumination. The space of surya or atma is considered to be the source of light which is manifest in every visible and invisible object of creation. It is both seen and unseen. This space is a permanent reality and it is illumined by the tattwas or elements. It represents the pure form of the tattwas at the time of their creation.

These are the vyoma panchaka or the five subtle spaces of which we build awareness in the intermediate stage of lakshya dharana. As the consciousness becomes stabilized in subtler perceptions, the practice takes on a new dimension, becoming part of laya yoga, where individual consciousness dissolves in the knowledge of the absolute.

Internal stage of dharana

The next stage of dharana is antar lakshya. The word *antar* means 'internal' and *lakshya* means 'aim'. Here an internal aim has to be aspired for. This stage can be considered as the preliminary state of dhyana because in this state the awareness and concentration of mind have passed beyond the experiences which arise out of the conscious and subconscious perceptions. One has acknowledged them and entered into another level of dharana where the psychic awareness becomes active.

Initially it was the mental awareness, knowledge and perceptions which became active while recognizing the visions arising in chidakasha. Experiencing the feelings and merging the mind with the feelings arising from hridayakasha, and recognizing the psychic structure of personality in dahar-akasha, are also activities attributed to mental awareness.

Up to this point, the mind was in a state of attention. Divide the word attention: at + tension = attention. Initially the effort made kept the mental awareness, the mental faculties, at their peak. In this peak experience of mind, going into the deeper aspects of the three akasha experiences and the final akasha experiences, the vyoma panchaka, the awareness was always in a state of alertness.

There is a lot of emphasis in dharana on being observant, and this observation faculty is gradually made subtle. Through observation it is possible to reduce the distractions which arise with the interaction of the senses and the outside environment. So when the mind is removed from a state of 'at tension', then psychic awareness, which is more natural and spontaneous, dawns. Being aware of focusing the mind on our psychic experiences is the last stage of dharana and the first stage of dhyana. Within this stage there are three demarcations or levels which have been described by the sages and seers. The first is darshan or visualization of sushumna, the second is awareness of nada or inner sound, and the third is vision of the blue light.

1. *Darshan or visualization of sushumna*: Antar lakshya dharana begins with awareness or vision of sushumna nadi. In intermediate dharana, we develop awareness of ida and pingala and the experience of blue and gold light. Beyond that, however, is the realm of sushumna. Although sushumna is generally considered to be one single psychic nadi, it is actually two. Sushumna nadi is like a tube, in the middle of which is another nadi, known as brahma nadi. *Brahma nadi* is the passage through which kundalini travels from mooladhara to sahasrara. Intensifying the awareness of brahma nadi and observing it in the form of a luminous thread in the middle of sushumna is the first stage of antar lakshya dharana.

Brahma nadi is visualized in sushumna in the form of a fiery, luminous thread and it is along this thread that kundalini rises. Here the process of seeing is not imagination, it is known as darshan. We imagine with mental awareness. Imagination is the process through which we divert our mind from one type of experience to another. If we try to

182

visualize a flower with our eyes closed, there is no real clarity. The image is not seen; there is just a mental idea that, "I am seeing a flower". However, when there is intensity of thought, that flower can be seen in the form of a vague, shadowy outline. So, imagination is used in order to pass through the first two stages of dharana. Then when the psychic awareness dawns, the process of seeing becomes darshan.

The word *darshan* means 'to see'. It is the actual vision or manifestation of a symbol or an object, like a flower, appearing in full colour and form. This process is known as visualization. In the process of visualization there is an actual experience similar to a holographic type experience, where the object of concentration, which does not really exist, can be seen clearly. In yoga this kind of experience is termed darshan or visualization. So, at this stage the luminous thread of brahma nadi is not imagined, it is seen in the centre of sushumna, extending from mooladhara to sahasrara. The movement of kundalini is also seen in the form of a point of light moving up and down along the brahma nadi.

The tradition also says that when the light of kundalini, which rises through brahma nadi, is seen in the head region, the colour of chidakasha changes. Normally when we close our eyes it looks black and dull, but at this time it will be white, as if the whole head is filled with light. Some texts also state that just by seeing this light in the middle of the forehead, the practitioner is liberated from the bondage of the conscious and subconscious dimensions.

2. *Nada*: internal sound: Another indication is a hissing sound heard by the ears at the time of deep dharana. One hears it but there is no external source, it comes from inside. This happens when the kundalini experience reaches the level of ajna chakra, for it is here that the nadas, the sound vibrations, are heard. One can hear many different kinds of sounds internally, like wind blowing through leaves and branches, crickets, frogs, animal and human sounds.

183

Yoga recognizes ten types of nada or internal sounds which are acknowledged as the milestones of kundalini awakening at ajna chakra. These are given in order as follows: (i) the sound of a fizzing sparkler, (ii) a distant flute, (iii) a large bell, (iv) a conch, (v) a lute, (vi) cymbals, (vii) a veena, (viii) pouring rain, (ix) double drum, (x) thunder clouds. While hearing the flute music many people have seen the darkness in chidakasha change to different, bright, flashing colours. Some people have also been able to reproduce these vibrant colours in beautiful three-dimensional artwork, or the flute music in celestial and enchanting compositions.

3. *Blue light*: The final indication is seeing the blue light at ajna chakra, the eyebrow centre, and at anahata chakra, the heart centre. This blue light which appears in the psychic experience or the kundalini experience represents the fulfilment of the akasha experience. Seeing this blue light signifies that you have gone as far as this technique can take you and that you are ready to move on to the next stage. This is the completion of antar lakshya dharana, which is subtle, psychic concentration, holding the mind to an inner experience and having darshan of it, not just imagining it.

DHYANA

After dharana, we come to dhyana, which is generally termed meditation. This meditative state is attained when one is established in psychic awareness. To facilitate the process of understanding, dhyana has been divided into three categories:

1. *Pratyahara dhyana* is a meditative state attained through the process of pratyahara.
2. *Dharana dhyana* is the transformation of emotion and feeling into a form of bhakti, not in the sense of devotion but in the sense of purity and simplicity of heart and nature.
3. *Dhyana* is the final meditative state which culminates in the experience of samyama.

Elimination of the pratyaya

Pratyaya is the seed of an impression which is received by the consciousness and experienced in the form of memory, knowledge, samskaras and karmas. These are the pratyaya or seeds of consciousness. Even in the last stage of illumination the pratyaya continue to exist in these four forms.

The *Yoga Sutras* state that the uninterrupted stream of consciousness is meditation. This has been defined by Paramahamsa Satyananda as the 'merger of three aspects of awareness into one at the time of meditation'. Until now we have been the observer, something has been happening and we have been watching it. We have been separate from that process which is happening. In pratyahara and dharana the state of mind is similar to sitting back comfortably and watching a movie. Sometimes there is identification with what is happening if it is connected to some deep aspect of our personality, and sometimes there is no identification whatsoever, because that experience does not trigger off a feeling which is recognized by the mind as 'mind'.

This is not the state that is achieved in dhyana. In dhyana, what is being seen, who is seeing it and the process of seeing become one, because this is the content of consciousness. The first content of consciousness is what I am seeing. There is total awareness, concentration and observation. The second content of consciousness is the knowledge or awareness that I am observing it. But this second content is not that intense. The total intensity of observation is objective, it is not in the self.

The third content of consciousness is the knowledge or awareness of practising a technique or a process. Just for a moment imagine that you are concentrating on a symbol. You become involved and intensify the awareness of the symbol, so symbol awareness is the primary field of awareness. At the same time there is body awareness in the background. When something happens to make us aware of the body, such as pain or a mosquito bite, then the mind

185

moves from the symbol to the area of pain, dissipation takes place and a break in awareness occurs. At that time there is a further aspect of which we are generally not aware, namely the following of a process, pattern or sequence. First, there is body awareness, then stillness of the body, then breath awareness and so on – these are the different stages in the process of meditation.

These three aspects are contained in the perception field of total consciousness. The first aspect, which is objective awareness, is more intense, let us say sixty percent; the second aspect, which is body awareness, is less intense, say thirty percent, and the third aspect, which is the awareness process, is the least intense, say ten percent. In meditation these three aspects become one, so that there is no distinction between the process, the body and what is being experienced. Here meditation is not just a mental process; it becomes a living experience.

There is a story which illustrates this point very well. Once a swami came to live in the guru's ashram and he asked the guru, "Tell me of a method through which I can concentrate my mind and experience the so-called God reality." So the guru gave him a mantra and told him to practise it every day with concentration.

After a couple of days he came back and said, "Swamiji, I can't concentrate on my mantra; many thoughts come and disturb me." So the guru asked him, "What kind of thoughts enter your mind?" The swami replied, "Well, I have a buffalo and whenever I sit down to do my mantra, the thought of the buffalo and the image of the buffalo appear in my mind and it is distracting." So the guru said, "Alright, forget about the mantra, just concentrate on your buffalo and say 'Om Namo Buffalo, Om Namo Buffalo', and so on."

The swami started his new meditation. Time passed, half an hour, one hour, two hours, three hours. He was sitting like a rock, immobile. Dinnertime came and he was still meditating. Someone thought, "Well, he is a real sadhaka; he doesn't care about dinner." Satsang time came and someone thought, "Swamiji is giving satsang so I should inform him." He went and knocked at the door and asked, "Are you coming for satsang?" The swami replied, "I would like to but I can't get out of the room." "Why not?" the other swami asked. "Because my horns won't fit through the door," replied the swami.

This has happened to people who have identified and merged their awareness with what they were seeing. This is the state of dhyana, where the consciousness becomes just one entity, where the mental experience becomes a living reality. One reaches the peak of human effort in meditation. This pratyaya which is just a memory, knowledge, samskaras and karmas can take any form. It can manifest in the shape of an idea, a sound or any imaginary object. The symbol that we see, whether a flame, a triangle or a yantra, is nothing but pratyaya that we are forcing to appear in front of us. Memory and knowledge are within us, but they have to be brought out. This is how pratyaya elimination takes place in the process of dhyana, when these memories and impressions are given a definite form, recognized and subsequently removed.

According to Paramahamsaji: "When visualizing a particular object, one should not visualize that object alone but also oneself practising dhyana simultaneously." At times one may become oblivious to the object, but the awareness known as the sakshi or drashta aspect should be there. Otherwise, if the mind slips away during concentration, one is not aware of it. This slipping away of the mind should not happen in dhyana. Thus dhyana includes the following three kinds of awareness: (i) an unbroken, continuous flow of awareness of a single object, (ii) awareness of the self and (iii) awareness of the process of dhyana. These three kinds of awareness go hand in hand. So the uninterrupted flow is experienced and the elimination of pratyaya takes place.

Now, although there is just one process of dhyana, changes that are experienced in the personality are divided into three groups. The first change happens at the level of karma. What kind of change takes place and of which karma? Initially, when the pratyaya or inherent seeds manifest in meditation, at that time the root or impression that can alter an emotion, a thought or a behaviour pattern is removed from the soil of the psychic personality. One can compare all the thoughts, feelings, behaviours and actions to blades of grass growing in the psychic soil. The only problem is that we do not know how to cut this grass. So, when the grass becomes long we find ourselves caught up in a very great mental conflict.

If you know how to push a lawnmower across the field of the psychic personality, then the grass that remains there looks beautiful. However, when the weeds, which also exist along with the grass, come up due to the gunas, the tamasic and rajasic traits of the human personality, then the beautiful lawn becomes a weed patch. The weeds manifest in human behaviour in the form of negativity and in the form of the four instinctive drives: (i) desire for food, (ii) desire for sleep, (iii) desire for sensual satisfaction, and (iv) fear of the unknown. It is there that our garden becomes totally overgrown and it is impossible to remove such weeds.

First of all, we do not know where they have come from. They could arise out of a single pratyaya. We know of people who have had intense psychological traumas, stemming from a very simple seed, a childhood memory. A trauma we experience in our life may be caused by a memory pratyaya. A mental conflict is caused by a pratyaya of knowledge which creates a different impression, a different condition of mind. The desire for food, the desire for sensual satisfaction, the desire for sleep, and fear of the unknown arise out of pratyaya, samskaras or traits deeply embedded in our personality.

Try to observe yourself and find out which of these four pratyaya play the most dominant role in your life: sleep, food, sensual enjoyment or the feeling of fear or guilt. You will notice that one, two, three or even all four are usually intense. That is a conscious recognition of your physical and psychological condition. There are some people who just like to sleep and despite all efforts they are unable to come out of that state. Other people are mad about food or sensual enjoyment. Most people have one or two traits which manifest as an intense aspect of their personality. These are also pratyaya.

How do we reach a point where these pratyaya do not become an obsession in our life? When there is no obsession, we are free. Obsession is the right word for pratyaya. An idea or thought of something comes and we desire it keenly. This can be something good or bad, positive or negative, in nature. Positive things can also become an obsession, which is also not good because life becomes unbalanced. There has to be some kind of awareness and alertness. Yoga tries to eliminate the extreme manifestations of pratyaya through meditation.

Pratyahara dhyana

The first step towards elimination of pratyaya is taken in the stage of pratyahara dhyana, which changes our mental attitude, mental environment, mental structure and transforms the way we act, think, live, speak and our whole approach to life. Pratyahara dhyana can also be defined as a process of self-psychoanalysis which aims to remove or lessen the intensity of the pratyaya existing within us in the form of memory, knowledge, samskaras and karmas.

Meditation is defined as a continuous flow of the contents of consciousness and here we have to understand that two processes are involved. Consciousness in general is activated. Our normal frame of consciousness of which we are aware can be termed utilitarian consciousness, which is experienced in the form of conscious, subconscious and unconscious experiences, in the form of memory, knowledge and samskaras, and in the form of the word, meaning of the word and knowledge of the word. Apart from this, there is also another aspect of consciousness which is not utilitarian but all encompassing. In this stage of dhyana, one has to move from utilitarian conscious, subconscious to unconscious in various stages.

The first aspect: Here is one example of how this meditation process can be utilized to improve our awareness of the utilitarian aspect of consciousness within our daily life. Pratyahara dhyana is awareness of the reaction of the self, when conditions or situations which exist outside are encountered. Take the word 'stupid', for example. What does this word actually mean or represent? We never dissect words; we understand them according to their common usage and we react accordingly. What does the word 'stupid' mean? It means to be in a state of stupor, which is a dazed state or a state of amazement.

The word stupid contains three aspects. The first aspect is the word as a combination of consonants and vowels which does not mean anything in itself; the second aspect is the meaning of the word, and the third aspect is knowledge. If someone calls me stupid, then instantly my mind will consider the word stupid from these three aspects. Stupid as a phonetic word does not mean anything in itself, but the conveyed meaning of the word is understood. After that comes the knowledge aspect, where I ask myself, "Am I stupid? No, I'm not, that is the other person's impression of me."

The second aspect: This awareness of these three aspects is the meditative process. If that meditative awareness is not there and someone calls me stupid, then there will be a very violent reaction, a conflict, a clash. This happens with a word and with situations and circumstances that we face in life. Therefore, in the other stages of pratyahara dhyana we begin to develop the awareness to the extent that both the environment and the interactions with other people are understood, opening of the mind takes place and reactions are avoided.

If someone says, "People have been saying this about you," and we react, then we are not in that meditative state. If, on the other hand, we say, "Oh well, let them say what they like, I know that I am not that," then we are not affected. In this way we maintain our peace, harmony and integrity. That is the meditative state. Therefore, in this second aspect, with the broadening of awareness and perception, we begin to see the subtle aspects of the environment or the vibrations that are constantly and continuously affecting us, altering our thought patterns, actions and behaviour. Once the negative input into the personality of the meditator has been curtailed, then the second stage, which is dharana dhyana, begins.

Dharana dhyana

We can practise pratyahara or dharana, but dhyana is a state of mind. With the practice of pratyahara and dharana, the meditative state is attained and then expressed at every step of our life. In this stage of dharana dhyana, a particular approach is adopted in order to expand the faculties of the mind. There are three aspects to the process of dharana dhyana.

The first aspect is to perceive the external cause of the sensations that we experience in our life, by themselves, whether they be physical, emotional, intellectual or psychic in nature. Each sensation we have has an outside cause as well. Take hunger and thirst, which are extreme examples. When we feel hungry, it is due to lack of food in the stomach. Food and water are not generated inside; they are the external means that we use to overcome the feelings of hunger and thirst. Anxiety and fear are also triggered off by external causes, which are the conditions of our immediate environment to which our mind, intellect, feelings, beliefs and knowledge are exposed. So, the first stage of dharana dhyana is knowing the external cause of sensations and feelings we are experiencing within on the physical, mental, emotional, intellectual or psychic level.

The second aspect is concerned with the internal movements of the sensations and feelings, due to the external cause. These act as a trigger to further expose what is within us. The consideration of those inner motions is the second aspect of dharana dhyana. For example, we may see a rope lying on the path at night and mistake it for a snake. The cause is outside, but it will bring up many feelings and sensations from within. Trembling of the body, partial paralysis of the limbs, skipping a few heartbeats, rapid breathing, sudden discharge of adrenaline and a state of intense fear will be experienced with the triggering of the body's flight and fight mechanism. So many changes take place inside. The observation of this multitude of internal changes, not just on the physical level but also on the intellectual, emotional, mental, psychic and spiritual levels, is the second stage of dharana dhyana.

The third aspect of dharana dhyana is to perceive the mental reaction isolated from the cause, to just become aware of the inner reaction. It is here that most of us encounter great difficulties and create blockages. We tend to suppress things that we do not want to acknowledge as existing within us. We do not want to accept the weaknesses or the other distorted aspects of our personality. We can feel the presence of these blockages and suppressions, but we are unable to go in and face them. This is because deep inside there is an unconscious knowledge that to encounter these suppressions would be exposing ourselves, which no one likes to do unless there is firm determination and conviction.

At the time of such exposure, very strong reactions come in the form of increased thought patterns and negativity. There is a desire to avoid that exposure by adopting different changes in lifestyle, perhaps in the form of constant eating or sleeping, in an attempt to forget these undesirable encounters. Many times there is an unconscious desire to leave the body, as seen in the condition of anorexia nervosa, where one stops eating. These are some of the negative behaviour patterns which can occur when we consciously begin to analyze the mental reactions by themselves, or when there is unconscious recognition of such mental reactions, which cannot be logically explained.

Therefore, meditation has always been considered to be the greatest form of psychotherapy, provided that it is properly guided. It clears many things. Further, the process of meditation has to be combined with intense externalized karma yoga. Paramahamsaji used to say quite forcefully that for one hour of meditation, eight hours of hard, physical work is necessary in order to balance the meditative process. This does not necessarily mean physical work in the sense of digging in the field, but certainly constant motion, where the energies of the body and the mind are fully utilized. These two energies of the body and mind have to be attuned in order to enter into the meditative state. This balance between body and psyche is necessary so that we can progress and have the strength to overcome blockages and suppressions.

Dharana dhyana takes us to a state of bhakti, not in the devotional sense, but in the sense that it opens up the heart and soul to experience the simplicity, harmony, unity and integrity that exist between the individual and God, between the soul and the experiencer. What do we experience in meditation? Things that are within us, the spirit, soul or God that exists within us. There is a saying, "The seed dies when the sprout comes and the 'I' dies when freedom comes." 'I' is the seed which dies with the attainment of bhakti. From the concept of duality we attain unity which is within the self. This unity is also microcosmic and macrocosmic in nature because here one experiences the totality of consciousness and not just the utilitarian consciousness.

Dhyana
After pratyahara dhyana and dharana dhyana, we come to the final stage, which is just known as dhyana. This meditative state culminates in and infuses the entire human expression with the experience of samyama. Initially, when we go through the process of dharana dhyana, purification of the mind and emotions takes place. With this purification

we are able to rise above the dualities of life and have a glimpse of the unity that exists between the individual self and the higher self. Although we use the word unity, the actual word is identification or non-distinction. It is the realization that we are not different or distinct from the divine energy that is manifesting within us.

This realization is not permanent. It begins as a concept, in the form of an idea, which slowly gathers strength and momentum and transforms the whole personality. This process of personality transformation is the process of dhyana. Within this process there are several gradations, which have been termed: brahman dhyana, pranava dhyana, trimurti dhyana, saguna dhyana, nirguna dhyana, savishesha dhyana and nirvishesha dhyana. Underlying all these aspects of dhyana is the concept of Brahman as a living reality or experience. The final achievement, that attainment and realization of Brahman, is the state of samadhi.

1. **Brahman dhyana** is meditation on the concept of Brahman. In yoga Brahman refers to the transcendental reality which does not undergo any form of change, whether it is in relation to the efforts of the individual or the influence of nature (in this case meaning prakriti or the force of manifestation) or of the gunas. This higher reality is a constant and continuous stream of knowledge which can be explained in the following three words: Omniscience, Omnipotence and Omnipresence. That is the meaning of Brahman.

The concept of Brahman can also be considered as the ever-expanding perception of life. Just as the perceptions of a child change with growth, in the same way, human perceptions, ideas, concepts and visions change with the growth of the mind. The mind must be utilized constructively and creatively to come to the realization that "I am that force, I am that power". Once this power is fully experienced within the mind and the self, then change and transformation take place in our life. Of course, this is just a concept, an idea, and it is not possible to live in this world with an idea until it is transformed into a living experience. When that happens, the vibrations emitted by a person can alter everything with which they come in contact.

There is a story about a swami that illustrates this point. When this swami first came to the ashram he was very much taken by the idea of Brahman. He thought it was something one could realize instantaneously. So he asked Paramahamsaji how he could evolve quickly to a state of spiritual experience where he could realize that Brahman. Paramahamsaji told him to begin with the simple idea of *Aham Brahmasmi*, 'I am Brahman.' He told the swami to practise this for at least one year in order to develop this idea with total intensity. The swami began the practice and towards the end of the year he came to Paramahamsaji and said, "I think I have grasped the idea. I am Brahman, you are Brahman, this ashram is Brahman, the person sitting beside you is Brahman. My whole perception has changed, all I can see is Brahman everywhere."

Paramahamsaji said, "That is very interesting. Now go to the market to buy some vegetables." So the swami went to the market and as he came to the centre he saw a large crowd of people running in all directions. He stopped someone and asked, "What is happening?" The man replied, "There is a mad elephant. Run!" The swami considered this for a moment and then said to himself, "Mad elephant, well I am also a mad swami. Let us see who wins. Perhaps my vibrations can alter the mood of this mad elephant." With this he sat down in the middle of the road and waited. He explained to himself very rationally that if you pour a glass of water into a bucket of water, the water from the glass will merge with the water from the bucket, and since he was Brahman and the mad elephant was also Brahman, what would happen if two Brahmans clashed with each other? Nothing. One Brahman would merge with the other. So the elephant, which was not in a philosophical or spiritual mood, picked up the swami with its trunk and threw him as far as it could. A couple of days later, when the swami returned from the hospital, Paramahamsaji said, "You forgot one thing. The man who told you to get out of the way was also Brahman, so you should have listened to him."

What this story conveys is that the idea of Aham Brahmasmi has to be converted into a force which emanates from the personality. In places where there is a high, vibrant spiritual energy, the attitude and behaviour of opposite forces are changed. A goat and a lion can drink from the same water hole, forgetting their animosity towards each other. That is the transformation of an idea. We all live within the limits or the dimensions of ideas, but are unable to convert those ideas into a living force. Conversion of an idea into a force is a process of actual dhyana, which has been defined as giving the experience of samyama. The word *samyama* means 'harmonious control', where everything moves according to the laws of nature and the divine, where there is no control of the human being, of the mind or of the desires. Everything is just the spontaneous, harmonious expression of a higher force.

In order to come to this stage, where harmony is experienced at all levels of our personality, different ideas have to evolve further from the main concept of Brahman. These ideas evolve in four dimensions: gross, subtle, causal and transcendental; or physical, mental, psychic and spiritual. These four areas or dimensions of human experience have to be integrated so that the physical energy and action is in harmony with the mental energy and movement, the mental expression is in harmony with the psychic energies and experiences the spiritual or transcendental state of being: "I am what I am". This kind of harmony is essential for meditation to be converted from a process into a living experience.

2. **Pranava dhyana**, which means 'meditation on the vibrational structure', is the next gradation of dhyana in this meditative process. This vibration is not what we experience in our day-to-day life, which is analyzed by the mind in terms of good or bad, positive or negative. The vibration referred to here is the *pranava*, or seed vibration, of the

individual personality. It is like listening to the sound created by the movement of the nucleus within an atom. That sound vibration which is heard within the nucleus of an atom is a very soft, subtle, unheard sound, which is not experienced by any one of us today. The rule is that wherever there is motion, there is bound to be a vibration. A hand moving through the air creates a vibration. Even the thought process creates vibrations which form patterns in the akasha. This is what modern science is also discovering. It is exactly this concept of vibration which yogis have tried to pursue in the course of their sadhana.

Pranava, the seed vibration, is represented by the mantra Aum. The three sounds of 'A', 'U' and 'M' represent the process of the manifestation of energy, of the gunas and of consciousness. So, the process of going deep into the realm of energy and consciousness, going deeper into the realm where the process of creation is taking place, and going into the deepest aspects of human personality to a time before birth, is this aspect of dhyana. You are a unique vibration. The realization of this unique vibration, which is represented within your personality in the form of the *anahada nada*, the unheard, unstruck sound, is the aim of pranava dhyana.

In order to reach this stage one has to work intensely with the different layers of waking, dreaming and sleeping states, and to develop equal awareness on all these different levels of consciousness. One should be as aware at the time of dreaming and sleeping as in the waking state, so that the consciousness is experienced as a continuous flow. Once this continuous flow of consciousness has been realized, then pranava dhyana is complete. Energy and consciousness merge into one and they are experienced as one idea, one body within the seed vibration of the pranava.

3. **Trimurti dhyana**, the next stage, is meditation on the three aspects of the personality: sattwa, rajas and tamas. *Trimurti* represents the three stages of life: creation, sustenance and transformation. It is the same trinity that is found in religious concepts such as Brahma, Vishnu and

Shiva; Father, Son and Holy Spirit; birth, life and death. As we go through this process of meditation, we pass through the total experiences of life from a point before birth, to birth, through life, to death, beyond death and back to the point before the next birth. It is definitely possible to go through this process, and it is not always necessary for an aspirant to go through this process in meditation. It can happen in the form of a dream or an experience, which later on changes the whole attitude towards life.

Of course, this type of experience is not permanent. It comes in the form of a dream, in a flash, or in an out of the body experience which is only momentary, whereas the effort made in dhyana is to make that experience permanent. When this becomes a continuous and constant experience, then it is difficult to identify with the normal lifestyle that one has led up to that point. So, there is an automatic break from the senses and their objects, from the world of name, form and idea. That is known as trimurti dhyana.

4. **Saguna dhyana**, which comes next, represents another state of meditation where the pure qualities of life, beyond the mind, are perceived. *Guna* means 'quality' and *sah* means 'with'. So, saguna dhyana is meditation with qualities, or developing the awareness of the pure qualities.

The qualities that we talk about in our life are adulterated qualities. The gunas that we refer to as sattwic, rajasic and tamasic are changed and adulterated qualities. Meditation on these adulterated qualities takes place in pratyahara and dharana. There we become aware of the tamasic, rajasic and sattwic natures, and their effect on our personal life, behaviour, expressions, interactions, etc. An effort to change the quality of our life is made in pratyahara and dharana. However, the pure qualities which exist in the unmanifest or transcendental dimension are observed in saguna dhyana.

The original form of the gunas is in the nature of *prakasha* or 'light', *kriya* or 'motion', and *stithi* or 'stability'. Light represents the self-effulgent nature of the three gunas. All three represent light and all three are self-effulgent. All the gunas have the quality of manifesting according to the attraction of prakriti. At the same time, they have the quality of remaining stable and not undergoing the process of change or transformation.

Realization of the three gunas independently as a force which is pure, self-effulgent light, which has the potential to transform everything and the potential to again become static, motionless and still is known as saguna dhyana, awareness of the transcendental qualities. This all happens in relation to Brahman. The level of seeing, the vision, the perception, is not mental. Therefore, meditation is never a mental process. It is always a process of self-expression, which is combined with knowledge or awareness.

5. **Nirguna dhyana** is meditation without gunas or qualities. In saguna dhyana there is still an awareness or knowledge of the three gunas existing as independent entities. In nirguna dhyana the gunas merge and fuse into one light, the eternal flame of spirit, which is known as *chaitanya jyoti*, in the process of developing the concept of Brahman and converting it into a living experience, four dimensions have to be passed through. In yogic terms, they are known as baikhari, upanshu, manasi and para.

Baikhari means that which can be expressed by the mind to another person. Upanshu means that which can be expressed by the mind to yourself. There is a difference between them. You can explain a defined concept of mathematics, physics, chemistry or biology to someone because all the parameters are known, but you cannot explain something which is undefined like taste. What is the taste of something sweet? What is the taste of water when you are really thirsty in the middle of the desert and get one sip of water? Can you explain the taste of a soft drink? It is something you can experience but not express. It is a different kind of experience and awareness.

So, baikhari means something you can express to another person. Upanshu means something you can express inside yourself. Manasi means something you see but cannot

199

express yourself, because logic and intellect are not functioning; there is just a vision or a glimpse without any rational awareness or connection. Para means something that you become. In order to become a real living experience, the concept of Brahman goes through these four stages of baikhari, upanshu, manasi and para.

6. **Savishesha dhyana** means meditation with special attributes. The attribute of Brahman is maya, which means the force of illusion, the creator or the source of the ego. It is in the presence of maya that we become aware of the ego reality. Without maya, the ego reality ceases to exist. So, as one goes deep into the meditative aspect, beyond the realm of the three gunas, sattwa, rajas and tamas, where the ego is actually manifesting in its full potential is where the aspect of maya is found. Maya is the veil or covering which prevents the vision of that pure light. It is this maya in the seed form which has been given the special identity of shakti, where shakti is recognized as a force having a separate identity from Brahman. That individual aspect of shakti which is recognized as being both the force of liberation and the force of bondage, which is recognized as having myriads of forms and being formless at the same time, is the savishesha aspect, the special attribute of Brahman.

In this aspect of shakti, the seeds of the tattwas are contained. We can call them the different limbs of shakti. Just as the body has different limbs which are all considered to be part of it, in the same way the five tattwas or subtle elements can be compared to the five fingers of shakti, through which it can create, take hold of something and drop it. The five tanmatras, which represent the essence or the attributes of the tattwas, are the other fingers of shakti. So, the definition of savishesha dhyana is awareness of the concept of shakti as a powerful force equal to that of Brahman.

7. **Nirvishesha dhyana** means meditation without special attributes. This nirvishesha aspect is the merger of Shiva and Shakti, Brahman and Maya, Purusha and Prakriti, which are the different terms denoting the same reality. Tantra

200

has defined this concept symbolically as *ardhanarishwara*, the image of Shiva in which the body is half-male and half-female. This form of Shiva represents the nirvishesha aspect of yoga, where the energies and attributes of both Shiva and Shakti are seen as one. This is what is meant by the vedantic concept of God as being one without a second. Both the father and mother figures, the positive and the negative attributes, the two opposite poles, the yin and yang, are contained in the same body, in the same circle. This ultimate realization of the last stage of dhyana is known as samyama.

Samyama here represents perfect control over all the experiences of consciousness. The word samyama is made from two roots, *sam* meaning 'perfect' or 'balanced', *yama* meaning 'control'. Samyama is perfect or balanced control over all the life experiences and processes; balanced realization of both the male and female aspects of the self. Samyama is also the absence of the experiences of cognition, cognizer and the senses. We are the cognizers and cognition takes place through the agency of the senses. When these three aspects or faculties, cognizer, cognition and the process of cognizing, fuse into one, this becomes the final dhyana. Just as in sleep all the different mental processes and sensory experiences fuse in the unconscious, in the same way, these three aspects fuse into one in samyama. That fusion is the final dhyana.

Fusion here is not an abstract term as in the fusion of the lower mind with the higher mind or the individual self with the supreme self. It is the fusion of the faculties which give rise to the experience, concept and process of distinction. It is this fusion or merger of the process of distinction which is the aim of dhyana and which leads to the state of samadhi.

SAMADHI

The *Yoga Sutras* describe samadhi as a state where just the object appears without the consciousness of one's own self. The keywords here are 'without the consciousness'. One's

201

own self means the individual person. So, the appearance of the object, without the consciousness of the individual, is samadhi. This object is not something physical. The word in Sanskrit is 'artha', which means the object or aim of meditation. When the aim of meditation is realized without involvement of the personal consciousness, that is known as the state of samadhi. Before understanding what samadhi is, however, we need to know about samapatti.

Crystal clear mind

Samapatti means 'complete absorption', which is the end result of dhyana. After the fusion of the three aspects of cognition, there is total absorption of the individual consciousness in samyama. This total absorption is the key which opens the doors of samadhi, because until and unless this absorption takes place there can be no experience of samadhi. Only when samapatti is attained will the vision of the self manifest naturally and spontaneously, without any process of the individual consciousness.

In the final stages of dhyana, the individual consciousness is perceived in the form of a clear crystal ball. When a crystal ball is placed on top of a coloured cloth, the colour is reflected inside it. If the crystal ball is placed on top of a flower, the image of the flower is reflected inside it. In the final state, the mind becomes like a crystal ball, and there is total samapatti, total absorption, to the extent that the external world no longer exists. Only the vision of the self is reflected inside. Now, this is where a danger awaits the spiritual aspirant, because no matter what state of experience is attained one is still living in a physical body, surrounded by different influences.

Just imagine that you have attained samadhi and your partner, who thinks you are crazy, questions the use of meditation and starts saying that you are wasting your time. These are the normal household problems. What happens at that time? A hammer falls on the crystal ball and it shatters. The negativity being experienced at that time will

202

be reflected in your mind totally. There is no way you can separate yourself from that negativity because it will feel as if it is coming from deep within yourself only. You have lost the distinction between outer and inner; you have fused yourself in the samapatti state where the mind has become pure and clear like a crystal. But any colour whether it is black or red or green will show up in that crystal ball.

This is where the main problem lies in meditation. One begins to reflect and experience within oneself the negativity or the other forces which are not self, but which exist all around within oneself. Therefore, those people who go deep into meditative states tend to become supersensitive, and a change of environment, a change of attitude, or even a word, can influence and disturb them greatly. This is because of their inner nature, their crystal clear mind.

Stages of samadhi
Certain yogic texts have described different forms of samadhi because even in samadhi there is progression. According to the tradition there are ten stages of samadhi, but three others have been included here which are equally important.

1. Nidra
2. Sahaja
3. Samprajnata
4. Asamprajnata
5. Savitarka
6. Nirvitarka
7. Savichara
8. Nirvichara
9. Ananda
10. Asmita
11. Sabija
12. Nirbija
13. Maha

Just as in sleep all the external and internal faculties merge into one stage of being, in the same way, there are different states of experience in samadhi.

1. *Nidra,* or deep sleep, is the first state of samadhi, which is experienced every night when we sleep. In reference to the deep sleep state St John of the Cross said, "I swear by God I die every night." In the state of deep sleep, there is an absence of time, space and object. Human beings are accustomed to living in the dimension of time, space and object. In the dimension where there is no experience of time, space and object, there is no human experience.

In the dreaming phase of sleep there is human experience, but in deep sleep there is nothing, no experience at all. The Yoga Upanishads state that in sleep all the external or manifest faculties of the self identify themselves with the higher self, and that state is similar to the samadhi experience. With this in view, nidra has been included as the first stage of samadhi.

2. *Sahaja samadhi,* the next stage after nidra, is experienced during meditation when the mind is switched off from the external world of name, form, idea, time, space and object. *Sahaja* means 'spontaneous' or 'easy'. Swami Vivekananda has described sahaja samadhi as being a state where one can be fully active in the world and totally absorbed in what one is doing. In this state of sahaja samadhi, one hour of sitting can extend into many hours, or a short sitting can transport the mind momentarily to a dimension beyond the body. This also happens during kirtan when people get up, dance about and fall down. Sometimes they cry and scream, but this is not primal screaming therapy, it is kirtan therapy. In kirtan that state is known as *bhava samadhi*, which occurs when absorption is experienced due to the linkage of an emotion.

This state can occur at any time. I remember once in the 1970s I was travelling in an open truck with Paramahamsaji and many devotees and they all began singing kirtan and dancing in the back of the moving truck. I was only a child then and I was really frightened that they would fall off the truck and be killed. The singing and dancing was totally uncontrolled and I felt even more frightened because

Paramahamsaji himself was involved, singing kirtan and dancing, while the truck was going down the road at forty m.p.h., which was quite a high speed on those roads. Somehow four or five of us got together and stood in the corners of the back of the truck, holding long poles. Each time someone came close to the edge, they were whacked back into the centre of the truck. After two hours there was a pile of bodies in the middle of the truck. The driver and the swamis who were sitting in the front of the truck were totally oblivious to what was happening in the back because of the noise of the engine.

In the ashram this state is also a common occurrence, especially during *akhanda* or uninterrupted kirtan. People fall down and remain in a state of reverie or ecstasy for several hours, and then drift off to sleep, waking the next morning in the garden, in the sadhana hall or a room. That is sahaja samadhi, which can happen spontaneously when there is some kind of link with the higher reality or with any of the attributes that we express in life. A feeling, an emotion or an idea can take one to that level provided there is intensity and total samapatti or absorption.

3. *Samprajnata samadhi* is the next state which follows sahaja. The word *prajna* means 'knowledge with awareness' and *sam* means 'with'. Therefore, samprajnata samadhi is that transcendental state where there is knowledge with awareness. In the *Yoga Sutras* of Patanjali, samprajnata is defined as follows:

वितर्क विचारानन्दास्मितानुगमात् सम्प्रज्ञातः ॥ १७ ॥

Vitarka vichaaraanandaasmitaanugamaat samprajnaatah
(*Samadhi Pada*:17)

This can be translated as: "Knowledge with awareness in association with reasoning, reflection, bliss and the sense of individuality is samprajnata."

This description starts from the most basic structure of the mind. Beyond the physical and pranic levels of awareness and experience, there comes a point of mental awakening. In relation to samadhi, this mental awakening must be understood in a broader sense. The experience of consciousness is a mental process, not a physical or pranic process. The growth that yoga envisages within the manifest consciousness is concerned with the supramental. So, awakening of the mental awareness and taking this awakening right to the edge of the manifest, where the boundary into the realm of the unmanifest or supramental awareness is crossed, is the aim of samadhi.

When we go through the process of pratyahara, dharana, dhyana and come to the state of samadhi, after attaining that mental purity where the mind has become crystal clear, at that time the perceptions in the form of object, motion, thought and instinct cease to alter the mental awareness. The recognition or the seeing of an object is a physical process. The motion of the mind from one idea to another is a distracted mental process. Thought is a process of mind which is moved by emotion, desire, ambition, like, dislike and so on. Instinct represents the deeper nature of the gross, manifest mind. For example, there is no instinct of self-preservation in the higher mind because it is beyond the area which tries to hold onto things.

So, in samprajnata samadhi the mind is taken beyond these four stages of perception into a state where there is total, continual, constant awareness. However, this awareness is linked with knowledge, not with the absence of knowledge. This knowledge has been defined here as reasoning, reflection, bliss and a sense of individuality. Reasoning is the finer faculty of the unmanifest buddhi. What form would reasoning take if it were not related to the body, the senses, the pranic field, the emotions, the feelings or even the gross intellect? That reasoning would be a subtle process of the finer mind, which would be all pervading and all knowing, while still remaining within the limits of the total human experience.

We are confined to the body as long as we live. It is our vehicle of expression. When we interact with the world outside, we use the faculties of the mind which are also limited to the world outside. But at the same time there is a higher awareness of omniscience which acts with the gross mind, the physical body and so with the environment, with the universe. This huge, infinite state of consciousness manifesting in this individual body and mind, and acting according to the limits of this particular body and mind, can be compared to a huge elephant sitting on an ant without squashing it!

In knowledge with awareness there is association of reasoning and reflection which is a reaction of reasoning. Reflection is thinking about and acting according to the laws that govern the physical, manifest nature. In order to illuminate this point let us define a miracle. It is generally believed that a miracle is what occurs when God performs the will of an individual. For example, if I say, "Let there be lightning," I do not have the power to create it. It is God that creates the lightning for me. This is the common view, but yoga looks at it the other way around.

Yoga says that the real miracle is an individual following the will of God. The individual follows his own self-will. We try to impose our will on God's will and ask God to act according to our wishes. I want to create lightning so I pray very hard to God, "Let there be lightning, let there be lightning." Now God has to act according to my wish. I pray, "Let the other person be happy." God has to act according to my wish. I pray, "Let me attain you." God has to come down from there according to my wish so that I can attain him. We are constantly trying to impose our will on God's will.

However, yoga says, "No, it is the other way around." The real miracle is for us to follow the will of God and not try to make God follow our will. This means that a reversal in self-awareness has to take place. That change is related to *asmita*, or the sense of individuality.

This final turnabout in self-awareness, which transforms the limited individual awareness into an expansive awareness

207

of the self, happens with the association of reasoning, reflection and idea. There is bliss also because in bliss there is contentment, satisfaction, fulfilment and joy. There is nothing lacking at this stage, and if there is anything lacking then one cannot attain samadhi, or even dhyana. What we lack is fulfilled or achieved during the stages of pratyahara and dharana. In dhyana and in samadhi the awareness is flowing; there is contentment, satisfaction and fulfilment.

This is a state of complete surrender, not of the limited self but of the whole being. The statement, "Let thy will be done", is confirmation that the higher self alone exists. "Make me an instrument of thy peace. Let me act according to your wishes. I do not have any choice or free will." It is the intimate relationship between two lovers. There is total identification, and it is acting through asmita. The crystal is being coloured according to reasoning, reflection and the state of bliss. If you are feeling ten percent bliss, then that ten percent will be reflected in it according to reflection and reasoning. If you are feeling forty percent bliss, then it will be reflected in the crystal.

4. *Asamprajnata samadhi* is the transitional state which follows samprajnata. As we move on from samprajnata, where there is knowledge in association with reasoning, reflection, bliss and the sense of individuality, to the next stage which is *savitarka*, the state of limbo or transition is asamprajnata. This stage of samadhi can be compared to the neutral gear of a car. When changing from one gear to another, it is necessary to go into neutral before moving into the next gear.

In samadhi the same can be experienced while going from stage to stage. When passing from samprajnata to savitarka, the neutral space when the changing of the gears takes place is asamprajnata. This neutral space is also found at nirvitarka, nirvichara, after ananda and after asmita. These stages represent the shifting of gears. They are the neutral spaces where the consciousness resides before moving to a different level of samadhi. So, in fact we can say that

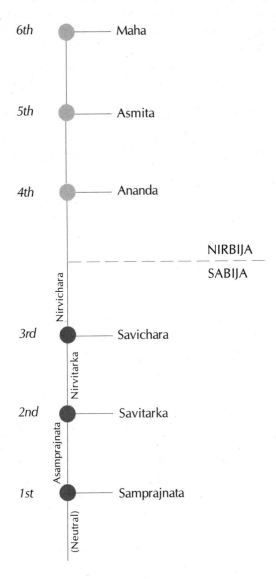

Diagram 4: Stages of Samadhi

samprajnata is the first stage of samadhi, savitarka the second, savichara the third, ananda the fourth, and asmita the fifth. Asamprajnata, nirvitarka and nirvichara are the neutral zones in between.

In the *Yoga Sutras*, asamprajnata samadhi has been defined as follows:

विरामप्रत्ययाभ्यासपूर्वः संस्कारशेषोऽन्यः ।। १८ ।।

Viraamapratyayaabhyaasapoorvah samskaarashesho'nyah
(Samadhi Pada: 18)

This can be translated as: "Stopping the content of the mind, whereby the mind remains in the form of traces in the other samadhi, asamprajnata."

In order to understand this let us take the example of deep sleep, where there is no external knowledge or experience. What happens in deep sleep when the bladder becomes full? You wake up because the urge to urinate is so intense that sleep is broken. So, even in the absence of consciousness there is still a trace of knowledge related to the body and mind. When an experience becomes very intense in the mind, a break takes place.

In samprajnata where there is association with reasoning, reflection, bliss and the sense of individuality, these four are colouring our crystal ball. Once you come to the point where you have to move into the next stage, you go into neutral, asamprajnata. However, before you put the gear into second or third, the link is there that you are going from first to second or from second to third. You cannot shift from first gear straight into fourth because the power will not be there. Nor can you shift from fourth down to first because the engine will blow up. Therefore, the link is there in the sequence from first to second, second to third, and third to fourth. It is this link that is known as the trace.

This link or trace has been defined as samskara, but here samskara is to be understood in a different context. The word samskara is derived from two roots, *sam* meaning 'with' and *akara* meaning 'form', 'link', 'continuity'. Thus samskara is the continuity or the flow from one stage into the next. Asamprajnata is identified by the traces of samskaras that are associated with one of the four aspects of knowledge experienced at samprajnata. The samskaras of reasoning, of reflection, of bliss and of individuality are the traces. These samskaras are in the form of the shadow image that is left, like the one percent of the root remaining after the weed is pulled out. There cannot be total elimination. This one percent is supposed to remain there because of the body, the senses and the mind, the agencies through which we act in this manifest world.

So, when we move from neutral gear into first, we are entering the field of reflection, reasoning, bliss and individuality. When the gear locks in first and we let go of the clutch, that fixed point is what is known as association of all four aspects together. That becomes the stage of samprajnata. When we again press in the clutch and start moving the gear back from the dimension or zone of first gear into neutral before moving into second, with this reversal into neutral we are coming into the level of the traces.

When we come to the level of the traces, there is a momentary blank or shoonya. So, when we reach a limbo in between the two stages, where there is no action or activity, that state is known as asamprajnata. However, this transition is only momentary. It is a split second transition. Evolved souls have been born who were not able to complete their sadhana in one life. One such example is Ramana Maharshi who, from an early age would go into spontaneous meditation and remain in that state for many hours or days without realizing it. That experience of shoonya is the asamprajnata state, where one has moved from one level but has not yet entered into the next level and is in the shoonya state.

Asamprajnata is defined as the process of reversal from one state and entrance into the next where the traces become active according to their intensity. According to the *Yoga Sutras* there are three degrees of intensity.

211

तीव्रसंवेगानामासन्नः ॥ २१ ॥

Teevrasamvegaanaamaasannah

मृदुमध्याधिमात्रत्वात् ततोऽपि विशेषः ॥ २२ ॥

Mridumadhyaadhimaatratvaat tato'pi visheshah
(*Samadhi Pada*: 21, 22)

This can be translated as: "Those who have an intense urge attain asamprajnata samadhi very soon." It means that they reach the state of shoonya. "With the intensity of urge arising through the mild, medium and strong conditions, the asamprajnata samadhi is attained."

The *Yoga Sutras* also state that:

भवाप्रत्ययो विदेहप्रकृतिलयानाम् ॥ १९ ॥

Bhavapratyayo videhaprakritilayaanaam
(*Samadhi Pada*: 19)

This can be translated as: "Those sadhakas and disembodied yogis who have again taken birth, have birth as the cause of asamprajnata samadhi." Examples of this are Ramana Maharshi and Paramahamsa Satyananda. When Paramahamsaji was young he used to faint and people thought he was possessed or having fits. However, it was not possession or fits but the state of shoonya. So, asamprajnata, nirvitarka and nirvichara are the transitional states between one stage and the next. These should not be considered as a separate samadhi, but as a stage when traces remain.

5. *Savitarka samadhi* is the next state. Savitarka is comprised of two roots – *sa* meaning 'with' and *vitarka* meaning 'reasoning'. So savitarka samadhi is absorption with reasoning. In the *Yoga Sutras* it is described as follows:

तत्र शब्दार्थज्ञानविकल्पैः संकीर्णा सवितर्का समापत्तिः ॥ ४२ ॥

Tatra shabdaarthajnaanavikalpaih sankeernaa savitarkaa samaapattih (*Samadhi Pada*: 42)

212

This can be translated as: "In that state of samadhi, on account of alternating consciousness between word, true knowledge and sense perception, the mixed state of mind is known as savitarka samapatti." If I draw a few lines on the blackboard and ask what they represent, you may say a flower. Why and how do you associate these lines with a flower? Why do you say flower and not rat or elephant? It is association of idea that makes you say the word flower. Association of idea equals word and the knowledge of the word has come from memory. You know that a line drawing does not look like a rose because there is no colour, shape or substance to it.

When all these components are put together, the image of a rose is created. When you imagine a rose in your mind, do you imagine it like a line drawing or do you imagine it in its full glory? The vision input has translated this line drawing back to knowledge and from knowledge it has gone to the level of association of ideas: the red colour, the shape of the rose, the smell, the weight, all these put together. From this association of ideas, the stimulation has again gone to knowledge and the word rose has come.

This is the process the mind goes through during recognition of the external experience. The same process applies with the transition of consciousness from neutral into second gear. An association takes place here, which is described in the *Yoga Sutras* as 'alternating consciousness between word, true knowledge and sense perception'. This word, true knowledge and sense perception belong to the total structure of reasoning, reflection, bliss and individuality. Reasoning and reflection are active mental processes. If these were not considered as active mental processes, then that area of mind would be blocked off and there would be only the experience of bliss. So, in savitarka the trace that remains and again becomes active is reasoning and reflection in the form of word, true knowledge and sensory perception.

Another name for samadhi is samapatti, or total absorption. When knowledge or an idea becomes fixed, active, manifests and gains intensity, there is total absorption of consciousness with what is being experienced. What is being experienced in savitarka is seen as knowledge. This knowledge is translated into a word on the manifest level. You have never seen bliss but you have the knowledge of bliss. You have never seen happiness but you have the experience of happiness. Would you define happiness as a tickling in the heart? Would you define bliss as a feeling of lightness in the body? No. How did these words bliss and happiness, which do not really mean anything, come into the picture? They are states rather than sensory experience. This example is being used to explain the state of savitarka. It is not this book that is seen by the senses; it is not the words that are read and understood by the senses; it is a state of perception.

Similarly, savitarka is also a state; the only difference is that while being in this state one is not active in the external world, but the process is the same. The experience is there, whether of happiness or bliss. That experience is being translated into a word which conveys the sense, feeling or idea of contentment, happiness, peace or bliss. While this state of experience is being translated into one of these ideas, there is a state of total and complete absorption. The whole being is experiencing that particular state, not just the mind.

Every atom and pore of the body is vibrating and pulsating with that experience. This is what tantra calls the cosmic orgasm, where the entire personality from the gross nature to the deepest subtle and psychic nature is completely filled with just one experience and nothing but that. Yogis have recognized savitarka as being a state which is experienced by the higher mind and translated into a word which is understood by the lower mind. So there is still a link, and because of this subtle link savitarka cannot be considered as the final samadhi. This subtlety is incredible.

Let us try an experiment. First place two fingers together so they are touching each other and you are aware of the sense of touch. Now go deep, as though you are looking through a very powerful microscope, and you will find that where you thought the fingers were touching each other, there is a gap. At this moment you are sitting on the floor or in a chair. But even though there is a sensation of sitting there, you are not actually there. You are sitting on space. There is a super microscopic gap between the body and the floor. If the body was joined to the floor, then you would become fixed and the skin would fuse with the floor.

Similarly, the chalk on the blackboard or the ink on paper is not fixed. If you draw what looks like a straight line on paper, when looking through a microscope you will find it is broken because all the molecules of ink and water are separate. It is not one big molecule stretching from one end of the paper to the other. There are tiny dots and drops, which are separate, but it appears to be a continuous line because they are so close together. This is what can be seen on a super-atomic level. Even the cells that are in the tissues are microns apart.

We are using this idea to clarify and to describe the states of samadhi. However, to prove the validity of these states in scientific terms will take another five or ten thousand years, because at present there is nothing that can dissect these fine layers. But if there is a process through which these fine layers can be dissected, then we will know that the so-called link which is seen does not exist, and that we all exist in space. Condensation of molecules and atoms in different degrees makes up different forms of matter. But the moment they are separate, there is just space. In the same way, here the link between the superconscious experience and the expressive mind within our body is so subtle that the whole thing is seen as one experience.

The body on the floor is being observed as one experience but, in reality, an experience which is happening on the transcendental dimension is being translated as a vision, an idea, a sensation, a feeling, a state, which is being recognized by the external mind. The link is very subtle and it is hard to separate these two things. This is what yoga has gone into by

215

defining the different states. In savitarka that impression is translated in the form of word, knowledge and experience. Vision is there, experience is being recognized as one thing but, at the same time, knowledge of that experience is also being recognized. There is not an absence of knowledge. At the same time, the word associated with that experience is also recognized. That is savitarka samadhi.

6. *Nirvitarka samadhi* is the next transition point, and it is similar to asamprajnata. Whereas in savitarka there was association of the consciousness with word, knowledge and sensory perception, here there is no association with any of these aspects. In the *Yoga Sutras* it is described as follows:

स्मृतिपरिशुद्धौ स्वरूपशून्येवार्थमात्रनिर्भासा निर्वितर्का ॥ ४३ ॥

Smritiparishuddhau svaroopashoonyevaarthamaatra nirbhaasaa nirvitarkaa (Samadhi Pada: 43)

This can be translated as: "After purification of memory, when the mind is as if devoid of self-awareness and true knowledge of the object is alone shining within, that is nirvitarka." In the nirvitarka state purification of memory takes place. Memory is the association of different ideas with words, events, stored information, impressions and so on. It is this form of memory which is encountered in normal day-to-day situations. Knowledge is intimately linked with memory, just as a few curved lines drawn on the board are recognized as a rose through the process of memory.

Association of ideas triggers off a memory in your mind which causes that image to be seen as a rose of your choice and colour. We are dealing with individual ideas, not with a collective idea. The initial idea is your own. However, when the words 'red rose' are uttered then the idea changes. The whole mind diverts and the image is seen as a red rose. Initially the memory created a rose with a colour of its own choice. So clarification of memory takes place when what we are looking at is seen in its real form without the superimposition of our own idea. It is seeing the picture in its true image.

Memory or smriti is also one of the vrittis. It is not just restricted to the sensations or experiences of the external and subtle levels. There is an extension of memory on the causal and transcendental level as well. Generally it is said that memory is remembrance, but awareness is a faculty of smriti. Even the knowledge that 'I exist', 'I survive', 'I thrive,' is considered to be an attribute of memory.

Memory is closely linked with awareness of ego or ego identity. Wherever there is ego identity, awareness of the ego, the lower mind, the senses and the body, then that external, manifest awareness is a form of memory. So, in the clarification of memory, it has to be understood that after the aspect of remembering there is the awareness that 'I exist', there is the knowledge that 'I experience', that 'I am seeing this and it is being translated into words, into an idea, into an experience'.

The vritti called smriti is different from past impressions. Smriti is awareness of one's self. However, when smriti becomes purified through the practices of sadhana, it becomes devoid of its own form. This is a state of self-awareness in which it appears as if everything has become void when actually it has not. Although you are not aware of the object, the object is there. The impressions of the object permeate the entire awareness. In this state the mind loses the subjective awareness, it loses the knowledge of the object, although the awareness and the object are still present.

You remember that you are concentrating on the object, then next there is only the object and you do not remember that you are concentrating on it. Again there comes a time when the object is also seen, but you do not remember that you are concentrating on it. The whole mind seems to be completely void, but it is not. This is because the awareness is completely permeated with the memory of the object, and thus the object cannot be known separately. This is known as purification of memory, which is the cause of the mind being devoid of itself.

217

It is important to remember here that if the memory is not purified, then the mind will slip into blankness, but if the memory is purified, then the object will permeate the whole consciousness and become one with the state of mind. The awareness and the object become one. The mind and the memory of the form become inseparable. Memory does not exist separately. At that time there is a momentary experience of the void, or shoonya, where the consciousness of memory, of the object, completely merges in the mind. At that point, the true knowledge of the object shines within. This is the difference between nirvitarka and laya.

In nirvitarka the true knowledge of the object is revealed. The object may vanish, but behind that you will see a bright light. In this state it is necessary to know the form or object of concentration, whether it is a rose or a shivalingam. The object should be with form, not abstract. Otherwise you may be misled because here the subjectivity of the mind is completely lost, the difference between outer and inner awareness is completely lost, due to the absence of memory.

The state of nirvitarka is different from normal consciousness due to the absence of memory. Therefore, you cannot remember this state because the normal consciousness does not function here. When you enter nirvitarka a different awareness takes over. So nirvitarka involves the purification of memory, or smriti, which gives rise to true knowledge of the object of concentration. You have gone into second gear and now you are coming out, carrying the traces, shifting into neutral and moving into third.

7. *Savichara samadhi* comes after nirvitarka, although it is actually the stage which follows savitarka. The word savichara is made up of the roots *sah* meaning 'with' and *vichara* meaning 'reflection'. In savitarka, one is aware of the object, its name, form and qualities. These three either alternate or, as in nirvitarka, the essential nature of the object is seen. So it is said that in savitarka the process of awareness is limited more to reasoning, whereas in savichara the process takes place through deep reflection.

This process of reflection has no association with knowledge, word or symbol. There is no thinking in language or in words. When thought is devoid of language, it is called vichara, reflection. In savichara there is only awareness in the form of vision, which is still filtered through to the lower mind. Here the mind alternates between time, space and object. There is no fusion. There is absolutely pure awareness of each separately. Either there is awareness of time and you forget about space and object, or there is awareness of space and you forget about time and object, or there is awareness of object and you forget about space and time.

The awareness of time, space and object is vichara. Here one aspect remains which is experienced by the lower mind in the form of vision. The consciousness is flowing without the basis of language. There is pure awareness which is independent of any other association or link. This is known as the reflective process, where the object of concentration is seen in the form of vision. In this experience there is total absorption and natural, spontaneous one-pointedness. This process is effortless because here no language or process of understanding is required.

It is like watching a waterfall cascading down from the top of a cliff to the bottom of a pool below. The water falls not in a continuous stream but in the form of many tiny drops. If you can concentrate on one drop as it falls from top to bottom, you will become one with the drop. When you become one with the drop you experience the downward motion, the movement of the drop from the top to the bottom of the waterfall. Your total perception is absorbed there. Although the body and mind continue to function, the absorption is involved in one aspect of the time, space, object continuum.

Either the consciousness is absorbed in the time aspect, in the time that it takes for the drop to fall from the top to the bottom, or in the space aspect, in the space through which the drop falls, or in the objective aspect, in which there is awareness of just the one drop without an awareness of anything else. So, if you are aware of space, there is no other awareness. If you are aware of object, there is no other object. There is total absorption in the one aspect. Despite the absorption, however, there is a movement, a motion, which leads to the next state, which is the transitional stage known as nirvichara.

8. *Nirvichara samadhi* means absorption without reflection. Here even that one-pointed absorption on a single aspect of the time, space, object continuum disappears. Behind that, however, something else remains, and that is known as the essential nature of thought or reflection. Again this is a stage of shoonya from which we move into a different dimension. We have moved from the dimension of reasoning to reflection. We then enter into the state of shoonya before moving into the next stage, ananda.

9. *Ananda samadhi* is blissful absorption. Here there is a state of absolute peace and bliss. Ananda or bliss is also the third aspect with which the consciousness is associated in samprajnata samadhi. But here bliss is not associated with the sensory experience or with any form of reasoning or reflection. It is experienced at a deeper level of conscious-ness, where there is total absorption in the feeling of bliss.

What is bliss? For Archimedes it was Eureka. That state was so intense that he ran naked from the bathroom to the king's court. If he had been in a more rational state of mind, he might have taken a towel with him and dried himself while running. If he had been in a normal state like us, he would have dressed first in order to be presentable. But that state of realization hit him so hard that he lost normal consciousness. That he was taking a bath, that he was naked, that he was going to the king – he forgot everything except the one idea, "I found it." That knowledge and joy is external ananda samadhi, where one becomes oblivious to every kind of circumstance or situation that may exist. One is only aware of the bliss in the state of total absorption. That state of bliss is the most critical point in any experience of samadhi.

Bliss is not just feeling happiness and joy. It is also fulfilment and attainment. The force and absorption of samapatti or samadhi is so great that the narrow path through which this divine experience manifests in the lower mind is suddenly expanded. In bliss the transformation of the lower mind takes place. Imagine an hour glass, the upper half of which is filled with sand which trickles down a tiny narrow passage to the lower half. That trickling down of the divine force is what has been happening up to savichara, making us more and more aware. However, when bliss comes in it does not trickle down; it becomes a force which transforms the total mentality, the lower tendencies of intellect, reasoning, and reflection.

This absorption is so intense that only the object, the vishaya, which is being experienced remains. There is no time and no space. When that objective experience, whether it is a symbol or any other thing, manifests and there is total identification and absorption in it, then there is no lower mind. It is a state of fulfilment, of achievement, a state of being. From becoming, we have become, we are 'That'. This is the experience of ananda.

This experience of bliss can manifest physically as well. There is a story about a Sufi saint at the time of Emperor Aurangzeb, who used to constantly sing *Anna Hal Hak*, which in Persian means, "I am God." This enraged the Muslim priests so much that they went to the emperor and demanded that this blasphemer be punished. So, at the order of the emperor, the skin of the Sufi saint was peeled from his body. As this was happening the sound of *Anna Hal Hak* or "I am God" was emitted from every pore of the Sufi saint's body. When the emperor heard this, he fell down at the saint's feet and apologized.

There is another story about Swami Nadabrahmananda, who is now ninety-seven years old. During his youth, he could retain his breath for three hours without any problems. During this time he would practise nada kumbhaka, whereby he could produce sound from any part of his body. An

221

investigation was performed at the Meninger Foundation in USA to validate this. He was placed in an airtight glass chamber with electrodes attached to his body to make sure he was not breathing. A monkey was placed in a second glass chamber and a burning candle in the third.

After three minutes the candle went out due to lack of oxygen. After ten minutes the monkey became unconscious due to the build up of carbon dioxide. But Swami Nadabrahmananda continued to sit inside the chamber, performing nada kumbhaka while playing the tabla continuously for two to three hours. A coin had been placed on his head and when he was asked to take his prana or nada to that area, the coin started to jump because the force of the rhythm was so great. From microphones placed along his spine, arms and thighs, the clear rhythm of the tabla was recorded coming out from these parts of his body.

If a vibration can be made audible in any part of the body, then it is not impossible for yogis to experience bliss in any part of the body. Do you feel the cold in any one specific part of the body? No, it is a total experience. In the same way, the bliss experience is a total experience. So, in ananda samadhi that experience of bliss becomes the turning point where the transformation of the lower mind and the merger with the higher mind takes place. The channel through which the higher experience passes into the lower mind expands and it becomes one continuous flow of bliss. This is the concept of *satchitananda*, the three attributes of God: *sat* meaning 'true', *chit* meaning 'eternal consciousness' and *ananda* meaning 'everlasting bliss'. This bliss is then automatically transferred into the next stage of samadhi, which is asmita.

10. *Asmita samadhi* is the stage in which the ego and the sense of individuality are completely finished. One becomes cosmic or universal at this point. This has been the vision of yoga right from the beginning, that one can become a cosmic being while still living in the body. Here the awareness is absolutely pure. There is no thought and no awareness of

time and space, just continual awareness with complete understanding or realization of that awareness. One becomes the master at this level, and then one is able to use the body, mind, elements, siddhis or other faculties, according to one's wishes.

This is what happens when this state is encountered by gurus at the time of their death. At the time of his death Sri Yukteshwar manifested two thousand five hundred kilometres away in a material body before Paramahamsa Yogananda. This is not a siddhi; it is the potency of that state, which even enables one to manifest different bodies. The potential is there to create a hundred different bodies; there is no limit.

Even in the case of Swami Sivananda, at the time of death his body began to levitate and people had to actually hold him to keep the body down, otherwise we do not know what might have happened. Perhaps he would have gone up with the body. There was such a powerful upward attraction that the body was pulling and lifting up the bed sheet. This is not a siddhi, it is a natural state in which the body becomes the consciousness, and it is possible for that consciousness to manifest with its full potential within the body.

Once a devotee asked Paramahamsaji, "What are your future plans?" He replied, "I am going to merge this body with the soul while I am still alive." This means that the possibility exists, and it is a reality which can be actualized. That is what happens in the ananda and asmita stages when there is total dissolution of the individual consciousness. At this time the lower consciousness is transformed and merged with the higher consciousness, so 'That' becomes 'This' and 'This' becomes 'That'.

11. *Sabija samadhi* means absorption with seed. All the stages that have been explained before are samadhi with seed. This seed can be defined as the object upon which the consciousness rests during the process of samadhi. Or it can be defined as the form of awareness, the seed or process

223

which makes one aware that, "This experience is happening to me, and I am perceiving it in this way." Right up to the last stage of asmita there is the awareness of the individual identity, which is the final thing to be dissolved. Even during dissolution there is still the awareness that, "I am the process of dissolving the individual identity."

So, sabija represents that last vestige of individual awareness, where there is the knowledge that, "I am being transformed, I am being changed into..." then blank. I become 'That'. In general terms one can say that as long as there is individual awareness, it is the sabija experience. From the normal state of life up to the asmita stage is sabija. Initially sabija can mean samskaras (impressions within the consciousness) or pratyaya (a fixed conditioning of mind, a fixed way of thinking, behaving, acting and living). So the total process of evolving the consciousness is a sabija process.

12. *Nirbija samadhi* means absorption without seed. This is the final state of total dissolution, the dissolving of the peripheral consciousness into the centre, where the motions of the periphery cease altogether and there is just one continuous flow of experience. According to the *Yoga Sutras*, once that flow is experienced, extending from the centre to the periphery and from the periphery to the centre, the cosmic experience takes place. This is described as follows:

निर्विचारवैशारद्येऽध्यात्मप्रसादः ॥ ४७ ॥

Nirvichaaravaishaaradye'dhyaatmaprasaadah

ऋतम्भरा तत्र प्रज्ञा ॥ ४८ ॥

Ritambharaa tatra prajnaa
(*Samadhi Pada*: 47,48)

This can be translated as: "After attaining absolute perfection in nirvichara samadhi, then the spiritual light or illumination is attained. The eternal and transient nature of the self is then known and the consciousness becomes one with the divine." That is the extent of samadhi, and beyond that another infinite process continues.

Progression of consciousness

We have gone through the stages of samadhi and tried to understand them through the relationship of the active peripheral consciousness with the inner consciousness. The word peripheral is used here because consciousness is seen in the form of a vortex. At the outside of the vortex is the whirlwind which lifts up all the dust and anything else which it encounters in its path or zone of activity. This whirlwind carries with it a force which represents the dynamic, active, nature or principle of consciousness. But behind or beyond this active principle of consciousness, within the self there is absolute stillness at the centre of the vortex.

Our area of experience is just the surrounding periphery. The force of movement of the mind, which lifts up dust, paper and other objects in its path, is the vritti aspect. As long as that has a form, a shape and a movement, it is known as the individual identity or the individual self. When this movement is stopped and one enters the zone of silence, stillness and passiveness, that is known as the awareness or knowledge of the superconscious mind.

Samadhi is progression from one state of higher consciousness into another. The four compartments of samadhi have been explained in the form of vitarka (reasoning), vichara (reflection), ananda (bliss) and asmita (sense of individuality). When we were dealing with dhyana, dharana and pratyahara, we dealt with the different compartments. Pratyahara is a means to dharana, dharana is a means to dhyana, and dhyana is a means to samadhi. In the various stages of samadhi every lower state is a means to a higher state. All these stages first break through the different patterns of consciousness and ultimately expand beyond the range of prakriti to encompass the cosmic or unlimited consciousness. This is the culmination of raja yoga.

225

12

Mantra Yoga

Mantra is the fifth yoga described in the Yoga Upanishads. The word mantra is generally translated as sound vibration. The literal meaning of *mantra* is 'the force that liberates the mind from bondage'. In Sanskrit the word mantra is derived from several roots: *mananaat* – 'bondage of mind', *trayate* – 'freed' or 'liberated', *iti* – 'through' or 'thus', and *mantraha* – 'the force of vibration'. What is the force that liberates the mind from bondage? According to yoga, the gross mind or mental nature has two attributes which hold it in bondage. The first is *mala*, which means 'impurities, and the second is *vikshepa*, which means 'dissipation'. So the manifest mind contains impurities and it is dissipated.

What are these impurities? They are the cause of our attraction to the tamasic and rajasic qualities of life, which limit the faculties of mind, causing it to act, experience and behave in a certain way. A tamasic or rajasic nature is expressed by the mind in a specific way. Attraction to the tamasic and rajasic aspects of life is mala. Vikshepa is the feeling of dissatisfaction with our present life. We want something more, something different, some form of amusement. Distraction of mind is vikshepa. The mind only jumps from one thing to another because it wants to amuse itself. If there were no desire for amusement, the mind would be absolutely quiet, still, tranquil and peaceful. If you think about this, you will understand how important it is in your life. This desire for amusement is vikshepa. The purpose of mantra is to free the mind from the pattern of amusement that it constantly seeks, to free the mind from attraction to the tamasic and rajasic qualities of life which satisfy the selfish ambitions and desires and keep the ego identity in the forefront.

Mantra is vibration. The ultimate mantra is anahada nada, unstruck sound or the sound of the vibrating nucleus within an atom. That is the anahada nada which, of course, means nothing also because it is the soundless sound. This is where yogic physics comes in. Wherever there is motion there is bound to be a vibration, which in turn creates a subtle sound. The atoms are constantly in motion and creating a set of vibrations. How do we become aware of that set of vibrations? Through a process of sensitizing the awareness and going deep into our psychic body. Please remember that the mind is one aspect of mantra yoga, the psychic body is another aspect, and sound vibration is the third aspect.

Mental aspect

Let us first deal with the mind, which in yogic terminology is a subtle force, not a physical force. In order to illustrate the functioning of the mind as a non-physical force, yoga gives the example of a single-celled amoeba. The amoeba does not have a brain or nerves, yet it responds to stimulation. If a grain of rice is placed in front of the amoeba, it will consume it. If a drop of acid is placed in front of it, the cell will go around it. What is it that allows the cell to accept the rice and avoid the acid?

Yoga views this faculty as a force which directs every kind of life force, energy and expression. It has been termed mahat, or the greater mind. Mahat is divided into four compartments: manas, buddhi, chitta and ahamkara. Mahat is viewed as the energy which pervades the entire structure of a human being, but which manifests and is expressed most dynamically in manas – the rational, thinking aspect; in buddhi – the discriminating, analyzing and understanding aspect; in chitta – the aspect of awareness that registers and stores; and in ahamkara – the ego awareness or individual identity. These four different areas interact with the world of the senses: name, form, idea, time, space and object. In brief, this is the yogic view of the mind.

Psychic aspect

The psychic body is a deeper aspect of the subtle body and the causal body, or the subconscious and the unconscious. The subconscious area is known as the subtle body and the unconscious as the causal body. The approximate borderline zone between the subconscious and unconscious is known as the psychic body. What does psychic body mean? The four states of consciousness: gross, subtle, causal and transcendental, are known as the two experiences of yoga. Gross and subtle represent the external experiences of mind. Causal and transcendental represent the inner experiences of mind or consciousness. The psychic body is the zone where both the inner and outer experiences are visualized and experienced.

The psychic body becomes the link between the external, physical and mental experiences and the deep, internal vibratory levels of our total personality. The whole theory of kundalini yoga, incorporating the chakras, the nadis and the awakening of kundalini, is based on the experiences of the psychic body. Therefore, the chakras are known as psychic centres. Mooladhara, swadhisthana, manipura and anahata are the four psychic centres which belong to the realm of outer experience, both gross and subtle. Vishuddhi, ajna, bindu and sahasrara belong to the inner dimension.

Mooladhara represents self-identity and security; swadhisthana – deep samskaras; manipura – external or manifesting dynamism; and anahata – emotions and feelings. These four chakras deal with the outer experience. Going beyond them to the aspect of transcendence, purity, expansiveness and openness is vishuddhi. The intuitive faculty, pulling something from the unknown and translating it in terms of the known, is ajna. In bindu there is awareness of the source, the point where the macrocosmic and microcosmic experiences merge into one. Finally, in sahasrara there is illumination. These four belong to the inner experience.

All these experiences take place in the psychic field, which is made up of different forms of vibration. These vibrations have been given a sound which can be understood by the lower mind – manas, buddhi, chitta and ahamkara. These sounds are fifty in number, and each sound or form of vibration is represented symbolically on the petals of the different chakras. Each chakra is activated by repetition of those particular sound vibrations. However, there has to be intensity of concentration and awareness with repetition, otherwise nothing will be achieved. Whether you repeat a one syllable mantra or a page length mantra, the effect of the practice will be null without intensity of mind, concentration and awareness.

The faculty developed here is concentration, awareness, intensity and visualization of the psychic body in the physical frame. Chakras do not actually exist in the physical body, but this is where they are visualized. They have been given locations on different parts of the body: mooladhara in the perineal region, swadhisthana in the sacral region, manipura in the lumbar region, anahata in the thoracic region, vishuddhi in the throat region, ajna in the mid brain, bindu at the top back of the head and sahasrara at the crown of the head. These are the areas in the physical body which correspond to the chakra points in the psychic body. The experience of the chakras and kundalini takes place in the psychic body which ultimately bypasses many of the deep, mental experiences. Kundalini yoga is therefore considered to be one of the quick methods of yoga through which one can bypass many stages. However, this requires a different approach to and understanding of the personality, and not everyone has this ability.

Sound vibration aspect

The third aspect is the mantra, the sound vibration which has been divided into fifty sounds. Different combinations of these sounds make up different forms of mantra. Take, for example, the mantra Om Namah Shivaya. "I salute Shiva" is an intellectual understanding or translation of this mantra. There are many people who misinterpret mantra, thinking it relates only to a particular god or goddess. At this point the mental trips begin: "Am I being converted? Am I expected to believe in something of which I have no knowledge or understanding? How can I believe in this naked Shiva who is adorned with snakes?" However, this kind of intellectual interpretation is not the purpose of mantra.

Repetition of the sounds of the mantra Om Namah Shivaya stimulates and awakens the faculties of the different chakras associated with those particular sounds. 'Na' could be a sound in any one of the chakras, as could 'ma', 'shi', 'va' or 'ya'. Sahasrara, which is the highest chakra, contains one thousand petals, each representing a different combination of the fifty sounds on the cosmic plane. In the same way, one consonant can be said in twelve different ways. For example, the letter 'K' can be pronounced Ka, Kaa, Ki, Kee, Ke, Kai, Ku, Koo, Ko, Kou, Kum or Kaha. So the one thousand petals represent the different combinations of the fifty sounds, and sahasrara contains that information. It is the DNA of the psychic body that stores all the information, which can only be reached after dissecting and isolating that DNA molecule.

So, these are the three aspects of mantra yoga: mind, psychic body and sound vibration. Next we will discuss the following points:

1. What are the different types of mantra?
2. How does mantra affect and alter the mental personality?
3. How does mantra awaken the psychic personality?

Types of mantra

Let us first understand the different types of mantras. Generally mantras are specific syllables or words which have been used by yogis, sadhus, researchers and thinkers to create a particular change in our system. Two main types of mantra are recognized traditionally. One is the universal mantra, the other is the individual mantra.

The universal mantras are well known and have been adopted by different traditions for use in their meditative and contemplative practices. Examples of long universal mantras are:

1. *Mahamrityunjaya mantra*: Om Trayambakam Yajamahe Sugandhim Pushti Vardhanam Urvarrukamiva Bandhanaat Mrityor Muksheeya Ma Amritaat.

2. *Gayatri mantra*: Om Bhur Bhuvah Svah Tat Savitur Vareneeyam Bhargo Devasya Dheemahi Dhee Yo Yonah Prachodayat.

Both of these mantras are composed of a string of different sounds linked together. In each mantra there is an emphasis on a particular type of sound. In the Mahamrityunjaya mantra the predominant sound is 'am', whereas in Gayatri it is 'ha'. This is how these combinations were made by the different yogic thinkers in order to create a particular change within the active, peripheral consciousness.

Examples of universal mantras of intermediate length are:

1. Om Namah Shivaya
2. Om Namo Bhagavate Vasudevaya
3. Om Namo Narayana

Some common short mantras are Soham and Om. These all come within the category of universal or common mantras which can be repeated by anyone and everyone who aspires for inner understanding of the mental, subtle and psychic personality.

The second group of mantras are the individual or personal mantras. These mantras are utilized for specific purposes according to need. These mantras can be either monosyllabic, known as bija mantras, or comprised of a combination of sound. Yoga recognizes both types of individual mantra. Different spiritual traditions have created their own sets of mantras, which awaken particular centres or give an understanding of a particular faculty of mind. For example, tantric mantras such as Hreem and Kleem are combinations of different consonants and vowels put together in order to create a dynamic change within the energy pattern of the personality. Vedic or vedantic mantras such as Aham Brahmasmi and Tattwamasi alter the normal state of consciousness and withdraw the senses by internalizing the mental faculties.

Anyone can adopt the universal mantras and practise them without direct guidance. Individual mantras are generally given to the aspirant by the teacher according to the personality type and the kind of change or stimulation needed to awaken the different compartments of the personality. This is the basic description of universal and individual mantras.

How mantra alters the mental pattern

Regardless of which tradition mantras belong to, the important factor is to see how they alter the mental patterns. Here yoga views the mental structure as being the predominant or active consciousness and dormant energy, whereas the psychic pattern of personality is active energy and dormant consciousness. Although the quantity of energy and consciousness may be equal, in one aspect consciousness is more active and in the other aspect energy is more active. So, in the mental pattern, consciousness is more active. The faculties of buddhi, manas, chitta and ahamkara are the different expressions of our active consciousness. Prana, chakras and kundalini are the different manifestations of active energy. This is the main difference between the mental and the psychic body.

Whatever the mantra may be, when we begin to repeat it with fixation of mind then one-pointed concentration takes place. This is the first step. At other times, when one is not concentrating, the mind jumps from one point to the next in search of stimulation and amusement. So the mental faculties and energies are dissipated. Buddhi, manas, chitta and ahamkara are dissipated. Mantra repetition helps to stop dissipation of these four mental compartments. Once the dissipation ceases, stillness descends in these areas. They become quiet, the activity stops. Dissipation is like opening the windows and feeling the flow of wind blowing the cloths and papers around. That is how our personality is all the time. Everything gets blown around in the rooms of buddhi, manas, chitta and ahamkara. When the windows are closed, stillness descends spontaneously. The same effect happens initially with mantra. Stillness of mind is the first indication of mantra concentration.

Secondly, through mantra yoga the mental processes are balanced or evened out, as the faculties and energies that exist within each compartment are equally distributed. What does this mean? Again let us take the example of the wind blowing through an open window. If you are in a direct line with the wind, you will feel its force. If you are sitting out of the direct line, you will not feel the wind but it will continue to be there. The only difference is that you are not affected by it because you are out of its direct line. However, when the window is closed, you can walk through the whole room and find the same stillness everywhere. No matter in which direction you turn, north, east, south or west, the same stillness will be felt. There will be no wind blowing in any part of the room. This is what is meant by equal distribution of energies and faculties within each compartment of the mind. In the second stage of mantra there is equalizing of the mental activities in each compartment, so that the mind becomes more homogeneous.

The third step in the process of mantra repetition is the elimination of mental tensions. When we are confronted with a particular experience, idea or objective awareness, there is tension on one side and relaxation on the other, like a standing wave effect. This is what normally happens when we experience the influx of ideas, impressions or situations in any of the four mental compartments. Sometimes an

233

emotion, desire or ambition gains momentum and intensity, creating tension or disturbance. When such distractions and disturbances occur, tension builds up in one aspect of consciousness. It can be due to a thought only. People go into depression because of a thought or a feeling. People have anxiety attacks because some environmental situation is changing. Because of that tension there is the feeling that "I cannot cope with it." So, elimination of tension or the peak activity of consciousness takes place in the third stage of mantra yoga. This standing wave effect becomes a smooth horizontal wave.

In this process, if there is a weakness in certain aspects of consciousness, which results in an inability to cope with situations, or if there is a lack of self-esteem or self-confidence, even these weaknesses within the personality will be balanced out by the practice of mantra. As the activities of consciousness become smoother or more linear, we gain self-confidence, we improve our attitude towards life and we feel an inner strength coming up from deep within. If there is an inability to sleep, by the practice of mantra we can sleep normally, as the low ebb of consciousness rises and the high peak comes down. In the same way, memory, concentration, expression and interaction all improve. Improvement of the conscious faculties that are used to express our personality is the third aspect of mantra.

The fourth aspect of mantra is sensitizing the mind to such an extent that it becomes like a radar which is able to detect the more subtle vibrations of people, places and everyday situations. This mental sensitivity created by inner harmony, equilibrium and balance will pick up any wave in the environment which is not attuned to your feeling. If someone is angry and walks into the room, you will feel that rush of energy. If you are also angry, then you will not feel it because your shields will be up. If somebody is in a different mood or state of mind, you will pick that up because you have extended your receptive powers outside. Sensitizing of consciousness is the fourth aspect of mantra yoga. With this sensitivity of mind or consciousness, we internalize the faculties of consciousness in order to go into the psychic body, where the energy is awakened with the help of mantra.

This is how mantra yoga helps to alter and rebalance the mental personality. Next we will deal with the effects of the practice at the psychic level.

How mantra awakens the psychic personality

After the conscious faculties have been balanced and harmonized, the concentration, awareness, intensity and sensitivity that have been developed through the initial practices, while passing through the mental body, become the means of entry into the psychic body. The first awareness in the psychic body is of prana, and the use of mantra further develops this awareness. We are all expressing our prana in one way or another, dynamically or passively, externally or internally, but we are not aware of that pranic expression.

This unconscious pranic expression can cause imbalances which filter down to the level of the mental body and become the cause of pranic blocks. These blocks are experienced in the forms of lack of physical energy, mental tiredness or lethargy and an unwillingness to do anything, even to think. This unwillingness is not a process of consciousness, it is a part of the pranic activity filtering down to the mental body and resulting in symptoms of lethargy and so on. So, pranic blockage is the first aspect of psychic imbalance which mantra helps to correct.

The initial experience of mantra will be mental relaxation. This relaxation will not be a lethargic relaxation but a dynamic relaxation. In this state of dynamic relaxation, the pranic structure is rebalanced. After rebalancing of the pranic structure, visual, mental impressions of the psychic body in the form of chakras, yantras and symbols are created by means of concentration. We do not awaken our chakras, they awaken themselves due to the combination of visual impressions, the vibratory influence of mantra and the intensity of concentration on the mental, visual image.

235

Take ajna chakra, for example. Meditation begins with a mantra, and when the consciousness becomes sensitized, ajna chakra is visualized. The moment we begin to visualize the ajna chakra yantra, the awareness of the total perception and faculty of consciousness is directed to that level in the psychic body. The visual impression is an aid, just as we use binoculars to bring distant objects closer for us to see. In the same way, visual impression is used as an aid to help us become aware of a psychic experience. Just by seeing something, nothing will happen. It is the constant hammering with the vibration of the mantra that makes you feel the stimulation within the chakra. You will begin to feel heat, some funny sensation, and experience the movement of the vortex there. The head will begin to float in some other dimension. So, mantra and intensity of concentration work together in the psychic body.

With the relaxation of prana comes the stimulation or awakening of the nadis, or the chakras, or of a particular psychic faculty related to a chakra. The faculties of each chakra will begin to manifest all the more if the specific bija mantras are used. For example, if you use the bija mantra *Yam* while concentrating on anahata chakra, you will definitely feel something there. If you use the bija mantra *Om* with concentration in ajna chakra, something will be felt there. However, if you use the bija mantra *Lam* of mooladhara chakra and try to awaken vishuddhi chakra, then nothing will happen. You can try but there will be no sensation whatsoever. Even concentration will not be possible because these two are totally unrelated. It is like pointing in one direction and trying to see what is in the other direction.

In the psychic body, sound vibrations play a very vital role. The sound vibration depends on how it is repeated, chanted and used. For example, there is a meditation practice with the chanting of Om in several different ways consecutively. The first time the Om is short and sharp, the second time it is short and smooth, the third time it is of medium duration and whispering, the fourth time it is of longer duration and loud. Each time a different result or experience is produced. That is a very important aspect of mantra.

The yogic tradition states that it is possible to awaken the chakras and kundalini solely through the use of mantra, without undergoing basic training in hatha yoga or raja yoga. It further states that it is even possible to attain samadhi straight away through the use of mantras only. However, it takes time to reach that level of intensity and very few people have it from the start. In order to build up that intensity and concentration, one has to go through different stages and preparation. Therefore, we cannot involve ourselves in the mantras immediately. Those who have tried to do this without the necessary preparation have gone mad. If there is too much mantra practice, the mind goes off.

Mantras stimulate energies that can be difficult to channel. Sometimes mooladhara becomes so active that it is impossible to control the feeling of insecurity. One goes into depression. It is difficult to control the sexual drive. There is absolutely no control over such expressions of energy unless there is a very powerful guru sitting close by who does not believe in love and compassion but in using the stick when necessary. So do not try for results through mantra immediately.

According to the tradition, the highest universal mantra which can be used to awaken and to enter into the realm of the psychic body is the ajapa mantra Soham with the breath. Three major Upanishads discuss the ajapa japa technique as being the final step before illumination. Experiences of the psychic body vary from person to person, according to their level of psychic and mental evolution, and according to which chakras are more active within the personality. This is the concept of mantra altering the psychic framework.

How mantra is practised
The process of using mantras is known as *japa yoga*, or the yoga of mantra repetition. Japa yoga is a part of mantra yoga science. Four different stages of mantra repetition have

237

been classified: (i) baikhari, (ii) upanshu or madhyama, (iii) manasi or pashyanti, and (iv) para.

1. *Baikhari*, or verbal repetition, is the initial stage of japa yoga. When the mantra is pronounced verbally, there should be clarity of speech and intonation, concentration and awareness. Correct pronunciation is considered to be important. If there is intensity, concentration and clarity in the practice, the mantra will work more effectively and it will alter the mental frame, the mental attitude, the mental behaviour. This also applies to kirtan. Sometimes we make changes in the kirtans according to the pronunciation we are accustomed to, so we should try to pay attention to this.

Baikhari has five methods, categorized as follows:
1. Continuous verbal repetition aloud
2. Verbal repetition with breath
3. Verbal repetition with mala
4. Verbal repetition combined with physical activities
5. Kirtan, chanting and singing of mantras in different tunes or ragas.

In the first method there is continuous verbal repetition in a steady tone without any fluctuation. When the same mantra is sung, with different rises and falls in intonation, it becomes kirtan. The second method is verbal repetition with the breath. Of course, we cannot repeat the mantra while breathing in but we can repeat it while breathing out. So, the inhalation is normal and the mantra is chanted aloud while breathing out. The third method is verbal repetition with a mala. This is similar to continuous verbal repetition, but the awareness is fixed upon the movement of each bead which keeps the mind alert and the attention on the mantra. Fourthly, verbal repetition can be combined with physical activities such as walking, sitting quietly, working in the garden or kitchen and travelling, provided one is not involved in the process of driving or flying a plane.

2. *Upanshu* or *madhyama* is the next stage of japa yoga. *Upanshu* means 'whispered sound'. In baikhari japa the

mantra repetition can be practised either alone or in a group which is repeating the same mantra. In these two situations the mantra can be repeated aloud. However, if there are people present who may not understand what you are doing, or who are in a different frame of mind, then you can whisper the mantra. Whispering also helps to keep the awareness on the mantra when the mind becomes introverted, but there is still a lot of mental activity.

Upanshu japa has four methods:
1. Continuous whispering repetition
2. Whispering repetition with breath
3. Whispering repetition with mala
4. Whispering repetition combined with physical activity.

There is no chanting or kirtan in this stage.

3. *Manasi* or *pashyanti* is the stage of mental japa. *Manasi* means 'mental' and *pashyanti* means 'seen by the mind's eye'. In manasi japa, we have the following five methods:
1. Continual mental repetition on its own
2. Mental repetition with the breath
3. Mental repetition with the mala
4. Mental repetition with concentration on a symbol
5. Mental repetition with chidakasha writing
6. Mental repetition with physical activity.

These are the methods of manasi japa. Mental repetition with concentration on a symbol, yantra or an image of the deity or guru is clear. Mental repetition with chidakasha writing, seeing the mantra written in chidakasha, is rarely used. Here the yantra or symbol is not seen but the written letters or syllables of the mantra are visualized in English, Sanskrit or any other language. In this process, for example, you may write 'Om Namah Shivaya' in chidakasha and as the mantra is repeated mentally the vision is moved through the letters that are being repeated. The mind follows the pronunciation by observing the letters that are written.

4. *Para*, or transcendental repetition, is the last stage of japa yoga. Para has one form only, which is ajapa, or effortless and continuous mantra repetition. It often happens that

239

when we stop chanting a mantra consciously, the repetition continues involuntarily in the mind and remains with us. This often happens with kirtan or a piece of music. It continues within the mind, without any conscious effort or voluntary control on the part of the aspirant. It becomes like a mental obsession. That is the para aspect which we experience according to the sensitivity and involvement of our mind with the mantra. These are the four stages of japa yoga.

Rules for mantra sadhana

Japa yoga further states that generally mantra repetition should become a meditative process. Therefore, a proper asana must be selected and a proper time must be fixed, either in the morning, afternoon or evening. Try to maintain the same time for your mantra practice. If the time you have fixed is six o'clock, then you should make every effort to keep to that time every day. If a couple of days are missed it does not matter, but there should be an effort to maintain regularity of timing.

If you miss your regular time for mantra practice, you can compensate for it at another time. The idea behind setting a regular time is that in twenty-four hours of unconscious activity, whether sleeping or waking, there has to be a fixed time when the mind can become attuned to the inner self. That fixed time is your personal time and there should not be any kind of distraction or disturbance during it. In twenty-four hours of activity, there should be ten minutes, fifteen minutes, half an hour or one hour every day devoted to your process of generating self-awareness. If the time is fixed, then it becomes a process of mental education.

If you are used to eating at ten o'clock, then you will automatically feel hungry at that time. If you are used to going to sleep at eight o'clock, then at that time you will start to relax, feel drowsy and want to go to bed. When that urge manifests you will not need to think about it. In the same way, mantra sadhana should not be taken lightly because the aim is to create an urge to practise which comes up spontaneously at a set time, without your conscious effort.

A proper asana or posture should be selected and maintained for the duration of the practice so that there is no movement to distract the concentration. Do not start japa immediately. Allow the body and mind to become stable and quiet. Once you are comfortable and the body and mind are settled in a state of tranquillity and stability, then begin the practice of manasic japa. If you are using a symbol, concentrate on it and visualize it first. When the symbol is seen, then begin the mantra. Do not try to bring the symbol in half way through the mantra practice. If you are using a mala, begin the mantra practice with the mala.

It is also important to keep to a fixed number of malas each day until there is an inner urge to increase the number. However, you should not start with ten malas and after a week reduce the number. Begin with one mala, and when there is involvement, increase to two malas, then three malas, and in the course of time go up to ten malas.

Initially, we do not have control over the alertness of the mind. We can become still but we cannot maintain the same degree of alertness throughout the practice. With the intensifying of concentration, if there is the feeling of sleepiness or drowsiness, then change the mantra from manasic to upanshu, the whispering mantra. As whispering is a physical activity, the mind is again made aware of a physical process and alertness returns. If, after some time, again due to the habituation of the mind, uncontrolled internalization takes place where drowsiness or sleep is experienced, then change to baikhari, saying the mantra aloud.

Dissipation is different to drowsiness. When the mind becomes dissipated, you know that it has gone out of your control. You are not unconscious at that time, however, and you should be able to return to the mental state and continue the practice. At this time you do not need to change to upanshu or baikhari. This is done only when

241

you go into the unconscious mind, where the mantra awareness is lost due to deep internalization over which there is no control. You can control mental dissipation after a few moments, but you cannot control the unconscious even after a few minutes, it will become even more intense. So, in the meditative process of mantra, we begin with manasic japa and, depending on the mental state, move on to upanshu and then to baikhari japa.

Mental purging is also an important aspect of japa yoga. Initially with the practice of mantra there can be an outburst of mental stuff. It is a process of cleansing or purification that mantra creates before coming to a point of balance. The superficial aspects of thoughts, emotions or desires, which are not needed within the mind, and which need to be expressed because they have gained in intensity, or samskaras which have come up from the depths of the consciousness in the form of a desire or an emotion, will be swept away by the mantra. As they are being swept away, one will see a cloud of desire or fear manifesting. It may be an intense craving for food, or a desire for sleep. So, mantra takes one through a process of purification before it rebalances.

This purification and rebalancing process is not speeded up by more rounds or more intensive practice. The normal course of sadhana should be followed whether you practise mantra for one hour, three hours or five minutes. It is not the repetition that is important, but the awareness of the rhythm, the vibration and the process. It is not possible to remain firmly one-pointed on the mantra for a long time. There is bound to be dissipation of mind, the mind will run hither and thither. It follows a natural course.

Psychic sound, psychic breath, psychic symbol
There are three important aspects of mantra meditation:
1. Unbroken, continuous awareness of the psychic sound, or mantra.
2. Linking that psychic sound with the psychic breath.

242

3. Combining the psychic sound and the psychic breath with the visualization of the psychic symbol.

Awareness of the psychic sound or mantra is clear. However, we need to understand what is meant by linking the psychic sound with the psychic breath. Awareness of the psychic breath begins with awareness of the physical breath. We breathe in and out through our nostrils, but we can also experience the breath in different parts of the body and in different ways. For example, in ajapa japa the breath is seen in the passage between the navel and the throat. Later, it is seen between the navel and ajna. In other stages, it is seen in the spinal cord. So, the movement of breath which is being experienced or imagined or visualized in different parts of the body is the psychic breath.

The third aspect, combining the psychic sound with the psychic breath and the visualization of the psychic symbol, is actually a more advanced process. In the beginning it is not possible for most people to visualize the symbol. Therefore, you should imagine the symbol. Gradually, as the intensity of concentration increases, the symbol begins to take shape, first in the form of a shadow image, then in the form of an outline, then in the form of a mono-coloured image, then in the form of a two-coloured image and then in the form of a multi-coloured image. When the multi-coloured image is seen spontaneously, it is actual visualization. Initially, begin with imagination and repetition of the mantra.

These three aspects are necessary. If the mantra is being repeated by itself without being linked to the breath and without awareness of the psychic symbol, then often, due to intense internalization and concentration, control over the body is lost. For example, many times the mala falls from the hand and you are not asleep, but the consciousness has moved from the body into another dimension. When the mala drops you become aware that your fingers have stopped moving and the mala is on the floor. This is due to loss of voluntary control or voluntary consciousness of the body.

Paramahamsaji has explained that even in this absence of consciousness there is a state where the faculties of mind can become tired by this kind of mental dissipation. He gave the example of a bird flying over the ocean searching for a place to land when it needs to rest. When the bird sees a plank floating on top of the waves, it alights and rests there for a while. After resting, the bird continues flying, but as it flies it always remembers the location of the plank to which it can return and rest when it feels tired. Just as a bird flying over the ocean keeps in mind the location of the resting place, in deep meditation, in the process of deep internalization, there has to be a base to which we can return, rest and regenerate our awareness, alertness and vitality before moving back into the subtle mental dimensions.

The symbol and the breath act like the plank. They form the base to which the mind is repeatedly brought back to rest, to become aware, to avoid any type of subtle dissipation that might be happening in the deeper layers of our consciousness. After resting on this base and consolidating our awareness, we again resume our mantra journey with freshness and clarity of mind. Therefore, these three aspects of psychic breath, psychic symbol and psychic sound (awareness of the sound while the mantra is being repeated) are very important.

13

Laya Yoga

The next yoga that has been discussed in the Yoga Upanishads is laya yoga. In theory, laya yoga is similar to both kriya and kundalini yoga. In kriya and kundalini yoga the practices aim at awakening the chakras and nadis, and they deal more with the experiences of the psychic body. The techniques of laya yoga are more meditative in nature. They deal with the various expressions of consciousness, combining and harmonizing those expressions with the manifestation of energy.

Upanishadic kriya yoga

The theory of how the energy evolves from mooladhara to sahasrara, plus the awakening of kundalini, is similarly dealt with in laya yoga. It could be termed the upanishadic kriya yoga. *Laya* means 'dissolution'. What does one dissolve here? Energy is not dissolved, rather it is awakened, and dissolution of mind is achieved in kundalini yoga as one progresses through the chakras. Laya yoga is not just having a vision or experience on a pranic or mental level, it is dissolving oneself completely in the cosmic self. This dissolution is seen in the transformation of the normal patterns of consciousness. The nature which was bound to manifestation becomes transcendent. The experience of laya yoga is so profound that it is like death and rebirth; there is total dissolution of the limited, mapped nature and rebirth to a new dimension.

Let us compare the laya yoga of the Upanishads with the kriya or the kundalini yoga of the tantras. Kriya and kundalini yoga both work with the energy structure. The energy is gradually raised from mooladhara to sahasrara, and this raising of energy is the kundalini experience. However, this awakening must take place in two different areas: the area of energy and the area of consciousness.

In kundalini yoga there is a tendency to sidestep the experiences related to mind and consciousness. The conscious experiences are not negated, but there is more emphasis on directing the flow of ida, pingala and sushumna energies, on sensitizing and developing the experience of the chakras in the form of energy whirlpools. On the other hand, in laya yoga, side by side with the awakening of energy, one must observe the changes taking place in the field of consciousness. These changes manifest in the form of an altered thinking process, an altered analytical process, altered patterns of awareness, and so forth.

In kundalini yoga there is an effort to concentrate on the energy pattern, rather than on the awareness of the changes taking place at the conscious level, with the idea that transformation of energy will balance out and harmonize the changes that take place in the planes of consciousness. In laya yoga the drive towards externalization which seemed inherent in the senses, mind and emotions has been overcome; even the remaining samskaras lead towards the inner realms of samadhi.

Lokas or levels of consciousness

In laya yoga, consciousness is observed more intensely and energy simply becomes the tool or medium through which changes within the consciousness take place. So kundalini yoga deals mainly with the seven major chakras: mooladhara, swadhisthana, manipura, anahata, vishuddhi, ajna and sahasrara, as well as with all the other minor chakras, whereas laya yoga deals with the lokas: bhu loka, bhuvah loka, svah loka, mahah loka, janah loka, tapah loka and satya

246

loka. We can say that these lokas correspond to the chakras and they are also seven in number: bhu – mooladhara, bhuvah – swadhisthana, svah – manipura, mahah – anahata, janah – vishuddhi, tapah – ajna, and satya – sahasrara. However, the seven lokas represent the various finer states of expression of consciousness which is experienced with the arousal of energy and kundalini.

Ritam and satyam – changing and unchanging reality

The two aspects of consciousness, known as ritam and satyam, deal with the apparent or changing reality and the true or unchanging reality. Consciousness works on two levels, that of the changing and that of the unchanging reality.

What changes take place in the apparent reality? For example, the caterpillar that transforms itself into a butterfly expresses the changing reality. The form of a caterpillar is as real as the transformation into a butterfly. We cannot say that a caterpillar is an illusion just because we have seen a butterfly, nor can we say that the butterfly is an illusion because we previously saw a caterpillar. Both are real within the changing phenomenal reality. Even our life process is part of the changing reality. We are the same person, yet different each day, each year. When we were children our body was different. Just because we are grown up, we cannot negate our childhood, which was our reality when we were small. Such shifts occur within the changing reality.

The unchanging reality refers to the essence of life, the life force, the consciousness, which in its deeper, subtler aspect is the same as that which we experienced when we were young, and that which we will experience when we grow old. So the essence of life is the unchanging reality.

When this unchanging reality is confronted with different situations that alter the expression of consciousness during different times and conditions, that is known as the changing reality. So *ritam* means 'the changing principle'; *satyam* means 'the unchanging principle'. The patterns of consciousness, thought, expression, observation, analysis and witnessing, which change with the awakening of the different chakras, are the ritam aspect which is experienced in the six lokas up to tapah. The seventh is satya, where the absolute reality, the ultimate consciousness, sahasrara, in the form of Shiva, is experienced. This is the concept of laya yoga.

The practical aspect of laya yoga

Another aspect of laya yoga is the practice. The introductory practices are very similar to the practices of kriya or kundalini yoga. The difference is that in each state a meditative practice is added which specifically goes through the process of making us aware of the changes that are taking place at the level of consciousness, rather than at the level of energy. In each stage of awakening, or in each state of experience of the lokas, certain things are observed and the experience of consciousness is dissected into different items.

The first thing that is observed is the total experience we are having on the physical, rational, pranic and emotional levels, and how that experience is affecting our behaviour, thought, performance, interaction and so on. After this complete picture is taken, we begin to separate the emotional experience, for example, and see how that experience is affecting the consciousness and how that effect is changing our mental and external performance. Suppose we awaken the faculty of mooladhara. We know that once mooladhara is active both the positive and negative experiences will manifest. The negative experiences will manifest in the form of increased sensitivity and insecurity, increased intensity of the sexual urge and increased desire for some kind of satisfying relationship in which we feel secure.

We call these experiences negative, but actually they are related to our external life. How do we fulfil that craving which is experienced inside with the awakening of mooladhara? Often the only way we can handle it is by running wild in our external life. However, when we begin to practise laya yoga, the complementary attributes or qualities for these different states are awakened. If insecurity is manifesting intensely, then through the process of observation, the complementary factor will be developed so that the vacuum is not felt. If there is an intense desire, then through the process of observation, another quality will be developed. How to direct the mind away from the trap of intense desire is taught through this meditative process.

With swadhisthana chakra awakening, there is a much stronger manifestation of the samskaras which, in external terms, relate to the four main instincts of life: (i) sexual urge, (ii) fear, (iii) desire for food, and (iv) desire for sleep. These four instincts have their seats in mooladhara, swadhisthana, manipura and anahata chakras respectively.

How can one control or eliminate those samskaras? Firstly they are exploded or made more manifest by the different sadhanas of hatha, kriya and kundalini yoga. Secondly, their effects are channelled and the released energy is used positively, and here the sadhanas of karma yoga and bhakti yoga become essential. Thirdly, the more meditative approach of laya yoga can be employed by undergoing a process of contemplation, reflection and reasoning. In this way each chakra is dealt with on a level other than that of energy.

Introductory kriya yoga gives a series of meditations that develop awareness of the changes in consciousness which accompany the awakening of the chakras. In the first stage this deals with the instincts, interactions and external life, and thus relates directly to the lower four chakras. As these vrittis are pacified or thinned out, one can see the more subtle influences associated with the tattwas which are related to each chakra. With this clearer state of consciousness the mind and senses can look inwards more deeply. These faculties which were previously employed in gathering information and experience from the external world begin to use their powers to explore the inner nature, and this is where real laya yoga begins. Through such sadhana, however, we can only go as far as anahata. Beyond anahata a different kind of experience takes place which has nothing to do with the mind or body, nor with the situations and experiences which we have been accustomed to.

The black hole and the white hole

In laya yoga, mooladhara, as the basis of mundane experience, and vishuddhi, as the basis of a new dimension of experience, are emphasized. Mooladhara chakra is the black hole into which the divine faculties, the humane qualities and the transcendental awareness of life descend. Once that higher awareness is sucked into mooladhara, we become ordinary beings, seeking sensual pleasure and living life as we have lived it for generations and generations. Mooladhara is the black hole of our life. Since we are so caught up in the powerful attraction of this black hole, there is no escape for us. It is here that the wheel of life or the law of karma is experienced.

The other end of the spectrum is the white hole, which is vishuddhi. The symbolic representation of vishuddhi is the white circle, which represents the ether element or space, from where all creation takes place. So, we can say that just as externally there is the theory of the 'big bang' and the expanding universe, within us there is this theory of the white hole and the 'big bang'. The white hole is vishuddhi, with its tattwa of akasha, space, the first of the elements belonging to the physical world. Creation is continuously and constantly expanding at the different levels of anahata, manipura, swadhisthana and mooladhara. These are the four waves of the 'big bang'.

The upside down tree

Vishuddhi is not really associated with any of the life experiences we have known. Rather we can say that vishuddhi is the seed of life, the causal body, from which the different bodies take birth. It is the seed from which the upside down tree of the *Bhagavad Gita*, with its trunk, branches, leaves and fruit are seen.

250

This has been described in a very beautiful, poetic form in the fifteenth chapter of the *Gita*. The tree, which has its roots reaching upwards and its branches growing downwards, represents our growth or evolution in life. The root of this tree is akasha tattwa, the first tattwa to come into being. From akasha tattwa the other tattwas have emerged. Anahata represents the trunk. Manipura represents the branches, vitality going in all directions, nurturing and supporting the entire life. Swadhisthana is represented by the millions of leaves. These leaves symbolize the *karmashaya*, in which karmas are stored in the deeper levels of consciousness, and we do not know what each leaf means. Mooladhara represents the forbidden fruit that we eat every day and every moment.

In the pure vedantic approach to yoga, mooladhara and vishuddhi are the important chakras. Birth and creation are represented by vishuddhi; death and stagnation are represented by mooladhara. The effort here in the vedantic approach to yoga is to try to go to the source, vishuddhi, where everything is pure, new, just coming out from the other side of the black hole. So, in laya yoga there are specific meditations which dive into understanding the causes of attraction and bondage to the phenomenal world. The realizations release one from the force of the mooladhara dimension and propel one into the pure space of vishuddhi

Mooladhara is a fantastic psychic centre because it is the only chakra which has unlimited potential. It is the chakra which can bind a person with ropes of karma and samskara so strongly that they are impossible to break. Yet it is also a chakra which, if handled correctly, can propel you deep within. With understanding, one can dissolve identification with the changing patterns of consciousness and the restrictions of manifest existence, dissolve oneself completely and again take birth from vishuddhi.

Total dissolution

The first path of being bound by the samskaras and karmas is the natural path of life. That is what is known as being caught up in the wheel of life, janma chakra. There is a beautiful poetic description of this in the *Bhaja Govindam*, by Shankaracharya. "Punarapi jananam punarapi maranam, punarapi jananee jatare shayanam," which means, "Again we take birth, again we die, and again we lie in the womb of our mother." That is the natural course of life. The reverse of that is the extreme path, which is laya yoga, manipulating the mooladhara consciousness to such a degree that the force of mooladhara propels us to come out of that cycle of birth and death.

The intermediate path in this spectrum is kundalini yoga. It is not possible for everyone to have the mentality, willpower or drive to go through the full experience of mooladhara and bypass all the other levels. Since we do not have that drive, let us start climbing back up along the tree. Leaving the fruit and leaves we come to the branches. From the branches we come to the trunk and start climbing up to the roots. That is kundalini yoga. At each step there is a leaf, a twig, a tiny branch, a bigger branch, the trunk; every step of the way there is some kind of support. The moment you lose this support, there is laya; total shoonya, void, freefall.

Previously it was only the more evolved rishis and munis and the determined sadhakas who tried the method of laya yoga, jumping over the cliff into the void. According to yoga there are three types of personalities: (i) *pashubhava*, the instinctive personality, (ii) *veerabhava*, the warrior personality, which is the human dimension, and (iii) *divyabhava*, the divine personality. Human beings are considered to be warriors because they are always struggling. Every step of the way, we struggle for money, success, name and fame, and only warriors can struggle. So pashubhava and veerabhava, the instinctive and the human personalities, practise the other branches of yoga. Only those with divyabhava, the divine or transcendental personality, have the will, conviction, force and power to practise laya yoga.

Laya yoga is where dissolution takes place, not only of mind or prana but of the total life force manifesting in the phenomenal world. Identification with the changing reality of ritam ceases and one again takes birth in the unchanging cosmic reality of satyam. This is the laya yoga that has been described in the vedic yoga tradition. Gradually, in the course of time, we have to develop that strength, that power. One aspect of this effort is through our own regularity, determination and steadiness in sadhana, practice, and vairagya, non-attachment to known or desired experience. Once these basic qualities are established, a new perspective develops spontaneously. Para vairagya, or supreme non-attachment, results from the new realizations of the nature of consciousness. It fuels our disidentification from the experiences of the manifest nature and our leap into the stillness and effulgence of pure consciousness.

This is an introduction only to laya yoga. It will take many years to develop this yoga into a form which can be practised and understood properly by everyone.

14

Esoteric Yoga

STATES OF CONSCIOUSNESS

The esoteric aspect of yoga is not something that can be understood intellectually, nor is it scientific in the sense that we know science to be. It is not a theory that can be measured by any known scientific measurements, instruments or minds. The esoteric aspect of yoga deals with the energy of atma, but not in the sense that we know it. This atma or energy is considered to be the source of light which is manifest in every visible and invisible aspect of creation. It is both seen and unseen. Just because we cannot see the sun when there are clouds, or because it is night, does not mean that the sun does not exist. It exists in some other place, some other space or time, illuminating different objects. The existence of the sun is a permanent reality, at least in our lifetime. Just as the clouds cover the sun, the knowledge of atma is covered by the veil of tamas. To attain to constant knowledge of the luminous atma is the esoteric aspect of yoga. Once it is known, then it is said that one attains immortality. This immortality is spiritual as well as physical in nature.

Surya tradition

There is a science in yoga known as surya vijnana. Tantra also has a branch called surya tantra. Surya tantra is the way to realize and know the vitality and energy hidden in the sun and to see that vitality and energy. These two traditions

254

deal with the same thought, that the sun is the lens through which part of the radiance of atma is seen.

This is not a primitive form of sun worship. When tantrics and yogis evolved this theory and the systems of practice to realize the potential of the sun, they did not consider the physical sun as being the gateway or the lens through which the radiance of the spirit comes. They used the sun as an example, as a symbol, of the source of light, vitality and energy. The sun that they describe is not luminous because of its chemically known components like nitrogen, hydrogen and other gases. According to their concept, the eternal sun is illumined by the tattwas, the elements.

This ancient yogic philosophy or esoteric system teaches that the atma is the radiant centre of all beings. The sun is the second manifestation of the ever radiant, luminous atma. The sun represents the pure form of the tattwas at the time of their creation. The tattwas are the elements which control all the known and unknown experiences of spirit. There are two kinds of tattwas. The first kind is *deva tattwa*, the divine element, and the second kind is *mrityu tattwa*, the decayable element. Because of the reaction created when these two meet, a third kind of tattwa comes into being. This is the *prana tattwa*, the pranic element.

When these tattwas begin to combine and permute with each other, the different subtle and physical tattwas come into being. These subtle, physical tattwas are thirty-six in number. They are constantly being created, and according to the density achieved in their process of permutation and combination, they take on different life forms. The human life form is one of these, and all the life forms of the original atma and the tattwas can be experienced in this human form.

Just as the atma represents the most transcendental aspect of experience, the human life form represents the most dynamic aspect of human experience. These life forms are experienced within the body in the form of chakras and upa, or minor, chakras. We have only discussed seven chakras, mooladhara to sahasrara. The upa-chakras are considered to be minor psychic centres or vortices of energy, such as bindu, lalana and nasikagra. Apart from these there are thirty-two more chakras situated along the spinal vertebrae. The surya tradition teaches that there are thirty-three vertebrae in the full spinal column and each vertebra gives the experience of a set number of life forms. A *devi* is the aspect of energy which controls or is manifest in that life form. A *devata* is the aspect of consciousness that is manifest in that life form.

Awakening surya shakti

Just as this concept of the sun is recognized in the esoteric sense as the lens through which the luminosity of spirit is seen, in the same way, the eyes are also seen as the lens through which the form and nature of atma is seen in the human body. The eyes have the ability to see. They can observe, but they alone cannot decide, judge, act or move. Their main function is just to see. This observation is understood to increase the awareness of the luminosity of the self. For example, the more twigs that are thrown onto a fire, the higher and brighter the flames become. In the same way, the nature of the faculty of sight is to increase the knowledge and awareness of the luminosity of the self. The surya tradition teaches that by focusing the sight on a flame which is radiating light, it is possible to change the whole visual structure and concept, so that matter is not perceived as matter but as energy. Once matter is perceived as energy, then the sun of the tattwas is known and the transcendental form of atma is experienced.

To increase the faculty of sight, this tradition has evolved certain techniques which are related to the third eye. The third eye is a concept to describe a process that happens in the realm of consciousness. In this process, the vision which sees matter, name and form is changed into extrasensorial vision which sees the energy beyond matter, name and form. In order to achieve this stage, one has to control the sensorial faculty of vision or sight. Through the control of this sensorial faculty, it is possible to awaken the extrasensorial faculty of vision.

To learn to control this faculty, different practices were evolved. Trataka is one such practice and different yogas describe trataka using different objects. The surya tradition emphasizes trataka on something luminous, like the sun or a flame. There are gradations of practice. Trataka on a candle flame, the awakening of manipura chakra and the awakening of the third eye are some of the different techniques which are used to bring about a change in the sensorial and extrasensorial faculties. The main emphasis is on maintaining awareness and control of the mind while the technique is practised. Mudras, bandhas, mantras and many other methods are used to awaken the surya shakti. These methods cannot be described here, they are not generally spoken of and they need correct guidance.

This is just a brief summary of the esoteric aspect of yoga. With this idea in mind, the practices of kundalini yoga, kriya yoga, hatha yoga and raja yoga were developed. Therefore, in all these yogas there is the similarity that the pranic channels and chakras must be opened up. This is a central theme of yogic literature, where the practices aim for awareness of surya in the form of pingala nadi, in the form of kundalini, in the form of chakras, in the form of asana and pranayama and in the form of Gayatri.

The theme of the Mandukya Upanishad

There are two lokas or planes. The first plane is known as divya loka and the second is known as kala loka. *Divya* literally means 'divine', and *loka* means 'plane', so *divya loka* is the plane of divine or transcendental experiences, beyond time and space. The word *kala* is translated as time. *Kala loka* is the plane which comes under the influence of time and its secondary aspect, space.

The tantras further state that divya loka is a plane where qualities manifest which are not bound by any of the laws of nature. These qualities are beyond the laws of nature yet entirely pervade nature. These qualities are the three gunas: sattwa, rajas and tamas. In its pure form, each guna is different from any concept we may have of it at present, for our concepts are based on the mundane level of existence and material or physical experiences.

With our mundane rationality, we call tamas, inertia; rajas, activity; and sattwa, the pure, unadulterated quality. However, these three gunas are not only physical in nature; they are also transcendental. In the transcendental aspect, the gunas have a different meaning. *Sattwa* represents the state of luminosity, effulgence. *Rajas* represents the state of creativity, manifestation or creation. *Tamas* is total stillness, motionlessness. So, luminosity, creativity and stillness are the three qualities which manifest in divya loka.

The three gunas correspond to the type of experiences that each life form can have. The states of experience within each life form are also determined by the gunas. They are known as the waking or conscious state, jagriti; the dreaming or subconscious state, where one is neither awake nor asleep, swapna; and deep sleep, known as nidra or sushupti. In nidra, one is not aware of the world and the senses, or name, form and idea. The external consciousness merges with the inner aspect of consciousness, and this is the state generally known as the unconscious or deep sleep. At this level of understanding we can say that jagriti corresponds to sattwa, swapna to rajas and nidra to tamas.

There are three drashtas, or witnesses, who experience these different states of consciousness on the gross plane, the subtle plane and the causal plane. The seer of the consciousness which is manifest and is in the state of jagriti is called *vaishwanara*. The seer who observes the state of swapna and who is aware of the subtle dimensions of consciousness is known as *tejas*. The seer who observes the state of nidra and who is aware of the causal dimensions of consciousness is known as *prajna*.

Even the syllables of the Aum mantra are particularly related to the three states of nidra, swapna and jagrit. If you say, "Aaaa," it feels as if the sound is contained within the physical structure. If you say, "Uuuu," it feels as if you are blowing the sound out, like a trumpet, projecting the sound outwards. If you say, "Mmmm," it feels as if the sound vibration is contained within itself. These three sounds make up the mantra Aum. So we have the 'A' sound, which represents the physical nature of the jagriti state, the 'U' sound, which represents the outgoing, expanding, creating, looking ahead nature of the swapna state, and the 'M' sound, representing the causal body of the sushupti state. This is the particular theme of the *Mandukya Upanishad*, which describes the three states as being represented by the three letters of Aum.

Pranava or Aum

It was mentioned previously that sattwa, rajas and tamas, which manifest in divya loka, each have a definite vibration which identifies it as being separate from the other gunas. These three qualities also give birth to a vibration which is made up of the combination of those three different vibrations or pulsations. This pulsation or vibration is known as the pranava or the mantra Aum.

In the original form, Aum represents the state of each atma: where there is total luminosity, sattwa guna; dynamic creativity, rajoguna; and perfect motionlessness, stillness, concentration and one-pointedness, tamoguna. The vibration which belongs to sattwa corresponds to the vocal sound of 'A'. The vibration of rajas corresponds to the sound of 'U', and the vibration of tamas corresponds to the sound of 'M'. The combination of these three sound vibrations is known as Aum, or the pranava, and it represents the luminosity of each atma. This atma is the pranava, on the vibratory level. Therefore, the surya tradition defines sattwa plus rajas plus tamas as being equal to atma.

Many of the yogic texts which are deeply influenced by surya tantra do not talk about the soul or consciousness as being a separate field of experience, other than vibration or

259

nada. The ultimate aim of nada yoga, and more especially mantra yoga, is to awaken the unheard or the unstruck sound, the anahada nada. The anahada nada is experienced or heard in the highest states of meditation, when the gross mind has been fully transcended. To build up the awareness of the nada or sound vibrations in the human personality, there are many practices such as mantra yoga, swara yoga and nada yoga.

ATMA – THE TRANSCENDENTAL STATE

Since we are descending from the transcendental state towards the earth, from the state of luminosity to the state where the bondage of maya is experienced, we will first take up the seer of the transcendental state, which is atma. Aum, which is represented by the atma, is considered to be the turiya aspect of consciousness. The turiya state is where the limits of the conscious, subconscious and unconscious states have been crossed, and where one is no longer bound by these states. At present, we are bound by the experiences of these three states. We cannot do without sleep, and in the physical sense this is the bondage of the state of nidra or tamas. We dream and we react in the dreams, emotionally as well as intellectually. When we are awake we also react to those dreams, searching for their meaning. In the physical sense this is the bondage of rajas or swapna. In the waking state we react to different people, to the environment, to circumstances, and in the physical sense this is the bondage of the jagriti state.

When turiya is attained, there is no more reaction and no need to undergo the experiences of jagriti, swapna or nidra on the physical plane, the subtle plane, the causal plane, or on any other dimension. There, one experiences the continuity of atma or pranava, Aum. This concept is not given in scientific terms but in the esoteric sense, as it has been described in surya tantra and elaborated on in the *Mandukya Upanishad*.

260

PRAJNA – THE CAUSAL STATE

After experiencing the transcendental turiya state, which is being in atma, one steps down into the causal state called nidra or sushupti, witnessed by prajna. This is the state where the seed enters the prepared earth, where there is inertia, motionlessness, one-pointedness. It is the concentrated form of consciousness, where the seed of life is sown. This seed of life contains the physical attributes of the different tattwas. We have mentioned that there are thirty-six tattwas. First is the divine element, deva tattwa, second is the decaying element, mrityu tattwa, and with the combination and permutations of these two a third is generated, which is the prana tattwa. Then there are the tattwas represented by the chakras in each vertebra.

The causal state of nidra or sushupti contains the seed of life. This seed is made up of the combinations of the thirty-six tattwas. These thirty-six tattwas are not only the physical elements which we perceive in the form of earth, water, fire, air and ether, and which are the five basic elements necessary for the creation of a physical, perceivable life form. Those five elements belong to the physical or manifest dimension. There are many other tattwas belonging to the thirty-six, which exist in the causal, subtle as well as the physical dimension.

All thirty-six tattwas combine in seed form in the causal plane, and the first awareness which dawns there is the awareness of prajna. *Prajna* means the 'all knowing', 'what is known'. The *Mandukya Upanishad* describes a very beautiful process of prajna. Prajna is the causal state in which the seed of the tattwas, the elements, is being germinated. It represents the third matra or syllable of the mantra Aum, which is the sound 'M'. In this seed state of the tattwas, there is no activity, no motion which is expanding outwards. The whole energy of the different tattwas is under the influence of tamas, perfect stillness or quietness. The seer or drashta of tamas is known as prajna, the all-knowing consciousness.

It can also be said that prajna is the Ishwara of the causal state. Here Ishwara means the non-decaying, non-changing principle, aspect or quality. This Ishwara is also called the drashta, the seer or observer of the condition or the environment, which is being experienced in the causal state, in the state of tamas, the state of perfect stillness. In the causal state there is absolutely no desire. There is no function whatsoever, so how can there be desire? The *Mandukya Upanishad* describes this condition or state beautifully in the fifth sloka:

यत्र सुप्तो न कञ्चन कामं कामयते न कञ्चन स्वप्नं पश्यति
तत्सुषुप्तम्। सुषुप्तस्थान एकीभूत: प्रज्ञानघन एवानन्दमयो ह्यानन्द
भुक्चेतोमुख: प्राज्ञस्तृतीय: पाद: ॥ ५ ॥

Yatra supto na kanchana kaamam kaamayate na kanchana svapnam pashyati tatsushuptam. Sushuptasthaana ekeebhootah prajnaanaghana evaananamayo hyaanandabhuk chetomukhah praajnastriteeyah paadah. (5)

"The third aspect is deep, dreamless sleep, lying beyond desire. Prajna is the lord of this territory. He abides in deep sleep, in which all things have vanished, and he enjoys bliss. Prajna lies at the gateway to the dreaming and waking states."

In prajna, deep sleep or the causal state, there is absolutely no activity, no subtle movement of thoughts or desires or of the tattwas. So, deep, dreamless sleep is the self-contained aspect of consciousness. This territory is beyond the desire aspect, which we have to deal with in the second stage of swapna and in the third stage of jagriti. Desire is the beginning of an action, a karma.

Here the word karma means movement or action, not latent impression as it is usually understood. Karma is related to the dimension of dream and wakefulness. In the state of nidra, where each faculty is centred on its own state of being, there is no action, nor is there any seed which creates action in the form of desire. This further emphasizes the point that it is absolute stillness. Prajna is the lord of this territory.

Prajna, the all-knowing, self-contained consciousness, abides in deep sleep, in which all things have vanished. Here, when it is said that things have vanished, it refers to duality ceasing, including the concept of you and me, the body and the experiences of the body. It also means that all the experiences related to jagriti and swapna, all the experiences related to name, form and idea, disappear. When everything disappears, one experiences the advaita aspect, unity with the individual soul. This unity with the individual soul is experienced in the state of tamas, one-pointedness and stillness.

TEJAS – THE SUBTLE STATE

After prajna comes the next stage, which is tejas, the rajo guna; it is swapna, the subtle dimension. It is in the subtle dimension that the tattwas become active and begin to interact with the other forces more dynamically. They give birth to a form of energy which is not material but more in the plane of akasha, the ether element, vayu, the air element and agni, the fire element. The tattwas which were originally lying in the seed form in the causal state begin to interact with each other dynamically and create these three forms of life. These three forms of life are the original elements which form the *pancha bhootas*, or five elements. They belong to the subtle dimension of ether, air and fire. They are considered subtle because they have no definite shape. They have no solid material forms, only gaseous forms, air forms and space forms.

From these three forms arise different mental experiences, such as thoughts, feelings, desires, motivation, and all the subtle qualities which make up the body of the total mind. The total mind knows no distinction between conscious, subconscious and unconscious. It is just a state where these three elemental energy forms or life forms manifest as thoughts, desires, motivation and action. First, an idea develops and later it is recognized as a desire. Idea is the first recognized form of thought and desire is the second one. Then, due to that desire, there is motivation, the building up of effort to fulfil that desire, which is the third aspect of thought. Implementation, working to fulfil that motivation, that desire or thought, is the next aspect of thought.

This process, from thought to implementation, is carried out by the interaction of the tattwas on the subtle plane. The seer or drashta, of this subtle plane is known as tejas. *Tejas* also means 'golden light', 'golden flame'. In yogic terminology it is known as *hiranyagarbha*, the 'golden womb or 'golden egg'. The word *garbha* means 'womb', and *hiranya* means 'golden'. Yogis have felt that this aspect of the subtle dimension is the womb of creation. Like the mother's womb, where formation of the body takes place, in the cosmic womb formation of life events, karmas and samskaras takes place. Gold is the colour attributed to this subtle state because gold is the purest and brightest metal, and the whole structure of hiranyagarbha, or tejas, is pure in nature, covered with self-luminosity.

At the same time, a different function is happening in the process of creation or manifestation. Here the atma, which was experienced in the causal state as prajna, the all-knowing, adopts an identity. This identity is of the individual unit, or as we know it, 'I am'. This 'I' and the concept of 'I am', the awareness of 'me' as an independent, individual unit, is experienced in the hiranyagarbha state, the tejas state. Here in the subtle dimension, creativity is manifesting in the form of thoughts and the transformation of these different thoughts into implementation. So, in tejas thought is the main force which gives birth to the original elements, which are the three gaseous elements. The two elements which are born of these are water and matter. They are needed to further express the potential of the tattwas, which when combined become the total experience of atma.

Tejas, the self-luminous being which is radiating light, is the Ishwara of the subtle dimension or the subtle body. From thought, the thinking process, which is the main function of tejas, there comes action and creativity. Up to this point, we have been discussing the manifestation of the divya tattwas, not the mrityu tattwas. The divya tattwas manifest from above, downward, and the mrityu tattwas move from below, upward. Thought, which is experienced as the first function of atma, is just a single idea, 'I am'. From this idea comes a desire to experience 'I am' in the final form of energy manifestation.

The thought 'I am' becomes the desire 'Let me be many'. This does not refer to population growth, or the birth of Eve from the rib of Adam; it is the urge to experience the different activities of the subtle mind individually. Thought, emotion, action, motivation and desire are experienced individually; there is a distinction between the different mental experiences. 'Let me be many' means let me become aware of these different functions.

So diversification of mind has taken place. Mind has been blown up into different pieces in the process of creation or manifestation. This mind is experienced later on either as intellect, which analyzes all the individual, independent experiences, or as awareness, which observes and recognizes the different emotions such as anger, fear, frustration, anxiety, pain, pleasure, etc. This aspect is known as chitta, the observer aspect. Another aspect of mind simply remains aware of the thought patterns as they are created from the subtle dimension, as they undergo this transformation and are implemented. This happens through the faculty of manas. The deep-rooted awareness of 'I am' and the reminder 'I am' is known as the ego principle, ahamkara. All these functions take birth in the subtle dimension.

Upanishadic description of tejas
The fourth mantra of the *Mandukya Upanishad* gives the following description of tejas:

265

स्वप्नस्थानोऽन्तः प्रज्ञः सप्ताङ्गएकोनविंशतिमुखः
प्रविविक्तैजसो द्वितीयः पादः ॥ ४ ॥

*Svapnasthaanoantah prajnah saptaanga ekonavinshati-
mukhah praviviktabhuktaijaso dviteeyah paadah.* (4)

"The dreaming state is the second aspect over which Tejas
rules. Seven limbs and nineteen mouths belong to him and
the objects he enjoys are invisible."

Tejas is described here as having seven limbs and nineteen
mouths, a very peculiar being. The objects that tejas enjoys
are invisible. Visibility and invisibility, in this context, relate
to the world of matter and the dimension of energy or ether,
space. All the activities which happen in space are considered
to be invisible because there is no definite form or shape
which is recognized by the mind. What is the form or shape
of a thought, idea, desire, or motivation? It has no concrete
form. Form and shape manifest according to their implementation on the physical level, on the level of matter.

So, in the subtle dimension it is said that the objects
that are enjoyed are invisible in nature. There is no definite,
concrete or defined form of an idea, belief, desire, ambition
or motivation, but at the same time, these have been
identified as objects, as independent expressions of the
various tattwas. Here, an 'object' means an independent
manifestation. It does not mean something made out of
matter, but something which is identified as an idea,
thought, emotion or desire. So, whatever is identified in
the subtle dimension is considered to be an object of
experience for tejas.

The seven limbs of tejas

Tejas, the Ishwara or drashta of the subtle dimension, has
seven limbs. These are known as the lokas or planes of
existence: bhu, bhuvah, svah, mahah, janah, tapah, and
satya. These seven dimensions of consciousness are
experienced as one evolves in the subtle dimensions, away

266

from the world of matter and the physical level of experiences. These seven lokas represent the subtle qualities or the altered states of the subtle dimension.

Bhu loka is the basic dimension of the subtle body and the first level of experience, just as the mooladhara experiences are the first basic ones in the physical dimension. From here, the awareness becomes more refined as we progress from one dimension to the next, until we reach *satya loka*, the seventh dimension, which is the borderline, where the realm of tejas and prajna meet.

The nineteen mouths of tejas

The nineteen mouths are the five jnanendriyas, five karmendriyas, five tanmatras and four aspects of the greater mind: manas, buddhi, chitta and ahamkara. The five tanmatras are the essences of the elements, the quality which each element portrays corresponding to the sense of smell, touch, sight, taste and hearing. In kundalini yoga the tanmatras are mentioned in the descriptions of the different chakras. For example, the tanmatra of mooladhara is described as the sense of smell. This sense of smell is not just an attribute of the nose. In physical terms it can become an attribute of the nose, but in subtle terms it represents the essence or the quality of the earth element. The five tanmatras become the mouths through which tejas feeds itself with information related to the subtle and gross dimensions.

The jnanendriyas, sensory organs which provide knowledge and information that is stored in the field of consciousness, are five in number. Through the eyes we receive information about the environment and the visible and invisible worlds. Through the ears we receive information about the sounds and vibrations that surround us, both audible and inaudible. The tongue provides information about taste. The skin provides information about texture. The nose provides information about the smell of various elements and their elemental and chemical compositions. The information received through the jnanendriyas feeds the subtle seer, tejas, and enriches the level of understanding of the invisible and visible dimensions.

The karmendriyas are definitely physical in nature: the legs, arms, mouth, excretory and reproductive organs. Although they are physical in nature, there is a link between them and the subtle dimension. Each activity of the karmendriyas creates a change in the pattern of mental and emotional experiences which are related to security and a sense of satisfaction, to fulfilment of an ambition or a desire and so forth. All this information is received by tejas.

The dream state

So the four aspects of mind, the five tanmatras, the five jnanendriyas and the five karmendriyas are the nineteen mouths described in the tradition through which the seer of this subtle state feeds itself. Other traditions elaborate on this further. When the senses are cut off from the external world, as in the dream state, tejas creates its own empire, its own world, and it acts in the world which it has created. The information used to create this subtle world, with its subtle images and ideas, is received from the external world. The empire, the drama, the enactment of tejas is experienced in the form of dream.

In the *Prashnopanishad*, it is said that the mind itself creates its own visions, even when sensory detachment with the outside world has taken place. At the time of sleep, where does the mind receive inputs to create its own drama, its own play? From the interactions of the subtle dimension with the external gross dimension. So what is most relevant here is the faculty to re-enact and invent a drama, to act out a play; this is a faculty of tejas.

In scientific terms we can see dreams to be of different types. Some dreams come from sources which have no connection with our external life or world and relate to what we call the future or the past. Some dreams are based on actual events that have happened during the day or during our life. Some dreams are just fantasy.

268

We can define dreams in different ways. We see a dream of an event that is going to take place in the future. Where does it come from? We may not know that this event is going to happen in the future. We see an accident happen in a dream and later read about it in the papers. So we feel we are psychic and can foresee events. There has been no sensory input of this information to our subtle world, so where does the information come from? When events are picked up from the empire of prajna and are seen as a dream by tejas, then that is known as knowledge of future events or knowledge of past happenings, of past lives. This is one kind of dream.

Another kind of dream is based on something that has happened in our life and impressed us very much. We see something that has happened to us during the day or in the course of the past few weeks or months. The impression of something that has touched our heart or influenced our mind can be seen or re-enacted in the form of a dream. So, memories also create dreams, but memories are the inputs which tejas has already stored in its field. The realm of tejas, the subtle field, is very vast. It is related with the external world of matter and also with the empire of prajna. It creates its own visual drama.

When the subtle dimension of tejas is enacting its own play or drama, then that dream sometimes becomes fantasy. We see ourselves flying and doing miraculous things that are not physically possible. How do we see ourselves doing impossible things, like jumping or flying high over mountains or buildings? This is the self fantasy of the subtle tejas dimension. These are the three areas of experience one can have in the subtle dimension.

VAISHWANARA – THE WAKING STATE

This is the description of the fourth and final state of consciousness as it moves downward. We have discussed consciousness as atma in the transcendental aspect, prajna

269

in the causal aspect and tejas in the subtle aspect. Now, we come to the aspect of vaishwanara or the waking state, where one is aware of the external world and enjoys the external experiences of the jagrit dimension.

First, we will discuss the subtle aspect. In the state of tejas there is the experience of three subtle elements, ether, air and fire. In further manifestations two more elements, water and earth, are born, which are known as the physical or material elements. In physical terms, earth is the denser form and water is less dense. These elements consist of material substance which we can hold in our hand, which the senses recognize as being liquid or solid. So the liquid and solid manifestation of the tattwas happens in vaishwanara.

The Upanishads have referred to vaishwanara as the first manifestation because they move from gross to transcendental. However, we have adopted the other approach, moving from transcendental to gross. That is how the tantras and the other darshanas have viewed the individual body. In the fifteenth chapter of the *Bhagavad Gita*, there is a description of an inverted tree, which was mentioned previously. This reversed tree has its roots in the heavens; the trunk, branches, leaves, flowers and fruits manifest downward, not upward. This is an apt description of the yogic and tantric systems of thought. They have also said that the world is maya, illusion, because everything happens in reverse. Trees here grow upward, while the trees that grow in the divine dimension grow from above, downward.

Vaishwanara is the seer, that state of consciousness which presides over the waking experiences. Vaishwanara is made up of two words, *vaishwa*, meaning 'manifest universe', and *nara* meaning 'subject to the decaying principle'. So *vaishwanara* is the aspect which observes the changing universe. The manifest universe is constantly in the process of change, decay, evolution, growth. The seer which presides over this process of change is vaishwanara.

270

The natural process of evolution which we experience in our day to day life is experienced by vaishwanara, and not by the atma. Therefore, it is said in the surya tantra that atman, or the sun, which is the dimension of luminosity, is unchanging. What changes and transforms within us are the three aspects of consciousness. They evolve, progress and revert back to their original source just as a seed becomes a plant, which in turn produces a seed and reverts back to its original seed form, having the same potential.

Experiences of vaishwanara

Vaishwanara, the dimension of vaishwa, is confined to the sensorial experiences. This confinement creates a different vision or perception of life, in which we are unable to experience realities which do not exist within the limited framework of our concept, idea or thinking process. What fits in the other category is dismissed as just a belief. For example, nobody has seen God, but there is a belief that something does exist, though God is an idea which has not manifested in the form of an action on the external realm.

The idea of God goes through the mental process from formation of an idea, to motivation, to implementation, but since its implementation on the physical plane does not correspond to any kind of sensorial experience it becomes an abstract idea. Abstract ideas are ideas unimplemented through the agency of the senses. They belong to a different category of experience which is termed belief. Belief becomes a non-sensorial aspect of life and everything else becomes the sensorial aspect of life. What we touch, what we see, what we hear, what we smell, everything within the range of these faculties belongs to vaishwanara.

As human beings we think that we are the only type of intelligence with the capacity to experience the divine nature, but we are thinking in terms of the vaishwanara aspect. We feel that we can attain that divine experience, whereas those people who are established in yoga say that there is nothing to attain; you are what you are. Then we begin to think,

271

"Well, if I am what I am, what am I doing here?" We are just trying to learn to accept ourselves as we are. These are not simple words. There is a very deep rationality behind them. Firstly, it has been the experience of many of us that we do not know ourselves. Secondly, we do not accept ourselves as we are. Thirdly, our body, mind and emotions create an environment around us to which we become enslaved. The list is endless. It shows that we are tied down to the experiences of vaishwanara, and it seems there is really no escape. All the efforts we make are subject to the physical and mental environment which we create around us. For some people everything is going smoothly, but for others life is very difficult because they cannot adjust to the situations, events and environment.

Why do some people adjust easily and some people find it difficult? Everyone is experiencing the same environment, the same situations, so why is it easy for some and difficult for others? We can say that it is the programming of the mental computer. Yoga says that it is the body and mind which create the environment in order to experience the outside world. In family situations we create an environment, and when there is a disruption of harmony in that environment, there is tension and fighting. When we cannot cope with that situation, we begin to bottle up and then there is suppression. All this is due to the environment which is self-created by the body and mind. There are certain methods to awaken a different kind of experience. Developing the ability to adjust to the prevailing environment is one method, cultivating naturalness and spontaneity is another.

Coordinating the external faculty with the inner faculty in the mind is a continuous action which is being performed by the ego. For example, if we look in the mirror, what do we see? If we see ourselves, it means that we are observing our own ego only. If we were free of ego, we would say, "I see the mirror." Although we know that we are seeing a reflection in the mirror, we do not acknowledge the existence of the

272

mirror. What do we see? We see ourselves. That is the function of ego. No one will say, "I see the mirror," but everyone will say, "I see myself." This is also reversed seeing because what is actually on the right is seen to be on the left. This kind of vision is known as maya or illusion and it relates to the inverted tree from the fifteenth chapter of the *Bhagavad Gita*.

So in a simple situation like this we see our own ego reflected. With this kind of mentality, how far will we go? We may try to go up, but we will always come back down. This is exactly the play of Vaishwanara. It can create situations where we think that we are going very far. If we apply our mind to it, however, we see that we will again come back to square one. Therefore, most of the traditions say that in order to enter the kingdom of heaven, one should be like a child. The child's mind is not submerged in the state of rational thinking and intellect. The childlike mind is always full of laughter. It is always natural and spontaneous, flowing in the stream of life, without thinking about what is going to happen next. It is always joyful and singing, innocent and in tune with everything. This is the basic training that is given in yoga.

Upanishadic description of Vaishwanara
The description of vaishwanara in the *Mandukya Upanishad* is similar to that of tejas.

जागरितस्थानो बहिष्प्रज्ञः सप्ताङ्ग एकोनविंशतिमुखः
स्थूलभुग्वैश्वानरः प्रथमः पादः ॥ ३ ॥

*Jaagaritasthaano   bahishprajnah   saptaanga
ekonavinshatimukah   stoolabhugvaishvaanarah
prathamah paadah.* (3)

"The first aspect is the waking state, the awareness of external things which is the terrain of vaishwanara. Seven limbs and nineteen mouths are possessed by him. His enjoyment lies in the visible objects of the world."

273

The nineteen mouths of vaishwanara

The nineteen mouths of the jagrit dimension and its drashta vaishwanara are all the senses or the indriyas. Vaishwanara is the master of these. He feeds on all the information received by them from the manifest world and decides on a natural course of action in order to contribute, live and evolve in this material world.

Although we live in the world by coordinating the sensorial experiences with the rational mind, negative mental patterns build up unless this sensorial input is properly controlled and regulated. To break these rational, intellectual patterns is very difficult. If we think about how much we have to eat and sleep, then food and sleep become obsessions. Comfort and pleasure, name and prestige also become obsessions. When external things become obsessions they rule our lives. In this regard, we should remember the maxim: "Eat to live, not live to eat."

Yoga says everyone lives to eat, to satisfy themselves, to indulge through the senses; that is eating with the nineteen mouths of vaishwanara. There are very few people who eat to live, you can count them on your fingers. They are the realized beings, the saints. They live simply, accepting whatever is fed to them through the senses in order to survive in this world. Otherwise they would not be here, they would revert back to their original state

The seven limbs of vaishwanara

The seven dimensions experienced by vaishwanara are the seven chakras and each chakra has a different meaning in the spiritual sense and in the material sense. Although vaishwanara contains all of these, in spiritual terms it is the mooladhara experience.

In the material and physical sense, on the gross level, mooladhara is the basic instinctive aspect, the centre that deals with sexuality, security and insecurity, inhibitions, fears, complexes and so forth. However, in the spiritual sense, it provides the means of transcendence of the

274

vaishwanara state. Only when we are able to get out of the room in which we have confined ourselves will we be able to experience the scenery outside its walls. So, going beyond the mooladhara state means coming out of vaishwanara, that state of manifest and waking consciousness which ties our faculties down to the material plane.

Mooladhara is closely linked with swadhisthana, which represents the unconscious in the physical sense. In spiritual terms being aware of, or awakening, swadhisthana represents the entry into the tejas state – witnessing the subtle, the deep, the unknown dimensions about which we have no experience right now.

Manipura, on the physical level, represents vitality, energy, strength, stamina and dynamism which is often limited by selfish expression or orientation. On the spiritual level, widening and deepening the concept of self gives entry into prajna, the self-luminous state.

Anahata is commonly called the heart centre, representing emotions and feelings. The pure expression of the unlimited self is at present veiled in sleep. Once anahata is awakened, it is the place where the atma, associated with turiya, is experienced. Anahata is considered to be the seat of the soul, according to tradition. The soul is not located in the brain, it is in the heart, and not the physical heart but the deeper heart.

Vishuddhi is connected with communication and hearing in the physical sense, and in spiritual terms with purity and transcendence, awareness of the unadulterated, transcendental tattwas. Ajna, in physical terms is connected with vision. It is the intuitive faculty, the entry into the divine dimension in spiritual terms. In vishuddhi and ajna there are progressive stages of this dimension of turiya. Sahasrara is the final merger.

These are the seven dimensions which are the realm of vaishwanara. What we experience now in physical terms as sexual complexes, fears and inhibitions, dynamism and vitality, purity and divinity, are the physical manifestations

275

of these chakras, of which vaishwanara, the consciousness of mooladhara, is the enjoyer.

Yogic perspective on everyday life

We have completed our description of the different states of consciousness according to upanishadic and tantric thought. However, one question still remains. What role does an individual play, and what is the aim and direction one has to take? Until we understand this, everything else remains just a theory. This is something we really have to think about and understand. Only then will we see how our life is linked with spiritual life. Once we can see this link, the process becomes natural and spontaneous.

There are certain points that we have to consider, especially when we talk about the direction of human life, of the human personality and of humanity. To realize the potential within we have to remember that our awareness now is sensorial, and this is the full extent of the awareness so long as we occupy the body and use the mind only as a tool to interact in the world. This sensorial awareness is very much physical. All the information related to the world around us comes through the senses – the eyes, ears, nose, tongue and skin.

These five faculties give experiences which are linked with an emotion or thought and create knowledge about the information which the senses have received. If the sensory receptors of the skin become aware of heat, immediately that heat sensation will be converted into a thought, "I am hot," or "I am sweating." In this way our self-awareness begins to link us with the external world and the extent of perception becomes totally sensorial. Therefore, it becomes difficult to accept that there is a non-sensorial dimension as well.

When we encounter difficult physical conditions, such as illness, disease, tension or lack of some vital necessity like water, food or sleep, it becomes a strong sensorial need and our whole life revolves around it. The eyes are trained to look for water, the nose to smell food and the senses adapt

276

to our physical needs. During the big blackout in New York many years ago, when there was darkness for a couple of hours, people did not know what was happening. Some committed suicide because their senses and mentality had adjusted to certain external conditions and when those conditions suddenly changed, they could not cope.

Many people who come to the ashram experience difficulty initially when sitting on the floor. They have stiff backs, stiff joints and their knees point upwards, but gradually their posture improves and they adapt. In this way, our body generally adjusts to the external, physical environment in which we live. Some illnesses, diseases and discomforts of the body are related to changes in the physical conditions, but some are not.

Sometimes we wonder why people do not get over their diarrhoea during their stay in the ashram. We can attribute it to different things such as climate, food or culture shock, but that is our external analysis of a reaction that is taking place within. If we are unable to see a link between an external event and what we are experiencing internally, we analyze the cause as something mental or psychic. We are experiencing something inside, but we are unable to express it so it becomes a blockage or a suppression which creates other states of discomfort, such as diarrhoea, fear, depression or neurosis. These altered states can in turn become the cause of something deeper.

In all these levels of illness and disease, we are seeing something which starts due to external change and begins to affect the entire structure of jagriti, the conscious state, and swapna, the subconscious state. So far, all our attempts to find relief from the unconscious, subconscious, mental and physical areas of tension and discomfort have been physical in nature. We also try to eliminate a disease without wanting to change the environment or our adaptability to the environment because we never think on that level.

If we have negative thoughts about someone in a group, we think that only that person is bad; we will not think about everyone in the group or about the environment. That is a limited thought. Anger is directed towards something, fear is because of something, sleep is a requirement because of something. We are trying to manipulate superficial aspects of what we are experiencing without realizing that the disturbed state reflects a lack of external and internal subtle harmony.

If there is a headache, for example, we rely on a pill. While the pill can block out the sensory knowledge of the headache, it does not identify and remedy or eliminate the cause of the headache. Maybe a stiff neck was the cause of tension and maybe just an adjustment of the neck joints would have cleared the headache, maybe underlying insecurity was causing those neck muscles to tense in the first place; however, we were not aware at that level until now. Only recently have people thought in a holistic way and come up with different systems of healing. Generally our perception is confined to what is being experienced in the body or to the immediate environment in which we are living, in terms of family, friends and society, so we do not consider our spiritual life seriously.

We need to get a yogic perspective on life. Once the thought of spirituality comes into our head, we feel that we should make an effort to understand this non-sensorial dimension. We attempt to understand it through relaxation, centring ourselves, improving our environment and lifestyle, learning yoga in depth to awaken the kundalini. This idea becomes the force that somehow propels us from the confined limits of physical and mental perception to a broader state of experience.

Managing ego, self-preservation and desire
There are difficulties, however. The first difficulty is in imbibing and implementing the new ideas with which we come in contact. The ego, which is the most predominant faculty directing our actions, ideas, thoughts and the process of implementation on both the physical and subtle planes, is

guided by the instinct of self-preservation. If the person sitting beside us suddenly has a heart attack, of course, we will try to help him. At the same time, however, the thought, "Thank God, it did not happen to me!" will arise in the deeper layers of our mind. This thought arises due to the ego identity which is intimately connected with the survival instinct.

This self-preservation instinct is genetic in everyone. In order to survive there are certain requirements which have to be fulfilled. The first and foremost requirements are of the body: food and water to quench the physical hunger and thirst, clothing and shelter to protect us from extreme climatic changes. Second are the social needs: status, the search for money, social enjoyment, friendship and happiness become the social actions or needs. There are also subtle and emotional needs: looking for affection, love and companionship, looking for ways to satisfy the needs of the subtle mind. Then there are psychic needs, the need to learn a process according to our personality and inclination by which we can develop our inner potential; the need for a guide in order to progress and evolve in life. These needs all relate to the instinct of self-preservation, which can also be termed the survival of the fittest.

The survival instinct becomes the force through which we fulfil our personal ambitions and desires and adopt the most suitable method for our individual growth. Most people take up a career in life, but it is very difficult to find a single person who thinks, "If I take up this career, thousands will benefit." People generally think, "This career suits me fine. I feel comfortable in this situation." If we find ourselves in a difficult job which is not to our liking, even though it is helping millions, we will leave it.

So this survival instinct and 'I' are very much interconnected in our day to day affairs and life. Even when we begin the spiritual journey, this 'I' is always predominant. We always think, "What can I expect?" because we cannot do without expectation. Even in spiritual practice there is always

279

a very subtle expectation. People often say, "I have not had any experience in my meditation, although I have been practising for so many years. Maybe I am wasting my time." There is an expectation or a desire to see the results of something, which goes on right until the end. Therefore, in advanced stages of sadhana one has to give up even the desire to be realized.

In creation, desire was the first link forged between divinity and humanity; it is also the last link which has to be broken in the process of evolution. However, if we simply wait for this last desire to drop away, we may be waiting indefinitely. Desires or aspirations have to be controlled. The self-preservation instinct gives birth to desire. The interaction between the external world and the senses creates the cycle of idea, desire, motivation and implementation. In the subtle dimension of tejas, the mind can also create an idea and convert that into a desire to be implemented. This triangle of ego, self-preservation and desire on the level of vaishwanara and tejas is the cycle through which we pass in our lifetime, and on an external level we call it evolution.

Evolution, according to our present understanding, can be termed organized conditioning, where we organize the conditions that we are experiencing in a form where we think we are gaining, evolving. So, organized conditioning of ego is the process of evolution, but if there is no awareness of this process as it happens, if we are not aware of the link between one event and another, this lack of awareness is avidya. On the one hand, we need to cultivate the attitude of a detached witness of our own ego, needs and ambitions. On the other hand, we need to use these aspects of change in an enlightened way to develop positive qualities, and have a relaxed and constructive attitude towards them.

The five afflictions

The *Yoga Sutras* have described the *pancha kleshas*, or five afflictions, as avidya, asmita, raga, dwesha and abhinivesha. These five afflictions are the cause of bondage on the level of vaishwanara. The moment these five kleshas are transcended, the vaishwanara identity or awareness begins to merge into the tejas dimension. Avidya is ignorance or the absence of conscious awareness. Asmita is the feeling of 'I' in terms of 'I am the enjoyer', 'I am the performer', 'I am the doer'. 'I' being identified with an action is asmita. Raga is attraction towards a sensorial object or pleasure. Dwesha is repulsion, or seeking for something new; for example, after achieving something and playing with it for some time we become bored. Abhinivesha is the fear of death.

These five kleshas which bind us to vaishwanara, the physical plane (and to tejas, our subconscious conditioning) and keep the consciousness grounded can then be explained as follows:

1. *Avidya* is better translated here as lack of awareness, rather than ignorance. It is due to over-identification with the senses, which does not allow us to see anything beyond their realm. We know that radio waves exist and that they are in the environment around us, but we cannot see them. In order to experience them we need to have a proper instrument, which again feeds a sense. So actually it is still through a transmuted sensorial experience that the unseen waves can be known. Despite all this, if there is still non-acceptance of the existence of radio waves, then it would be termed ignorance, not being able to expand the sensorial perception and the lack of awareness of how to do it.

2. *Asmita* is the feeling of 'I', identification with 'I' in every action as if I am the performer, I am the enjoyer, I am the doer. The needs of the self-preservation instinct have to be fulfilled. To fulfil them our total effort is to make sure there is no deviation, so that we ultimately attain what we aspire for. If you know you have to go to work between certain times, that the boss is waiting and you must punch your time card, then no matter how you are feeling you will go to work. You will punch the time card and do your work until you become so depleted of energy that you fall sick and are confined to bed to rest. Even then you will try to get

281

well quickly so that you can go back to the job because it fulfils your particular need for money with which to buy the necessities of life. So, with work there is identification of 'I'.

When there is success, there is identification with success. When there is failure, there is identification with failure. In every circumstance a very strong feeling of 'I am the performer', 'I am the enjoyer', 'I am the doer', develops. To get out of this identification with the actions is a very difficult process. There is only one way to get free of it – surrender. This rope of 'I am doing' is so powerful that, in order to be free of it, there has to be an equally strong opposite idea. This opposite idea is surrender. Very few people can come to this final point of surrender but for them it becomes a very powerful tool to cut the last bonds of karma.

3. *Raga* is attraction towards a sensory perception or field. This attraction can be experienced in many different ways. For children there is the attraction to new toys. They play with a toy, grow tired of it and then want something new and better. For some people the attraction is computers. They are always updating the computer memory, the hard drive, the software and the processor. These are all just toys for grownups used in a different way. Instead of playing with rag dolls, we play with living dolls. Instead of playing with toy cars, we play with real cars. Instead of playing the game 'house', we play a game in our own house. The play does not change but a different version of playing is adopted at every level. This adopting of play to satisfy ourselves is raga. The whole faculty of the mind and senses is directed towards an object we are attracted to, and if there is no attraction there is no force on this planet that will take us towards it.

Therefore, positive thinking has great importance in yoga. Yoga always stresses being positive, creative and constructive. Do not identify with any ideas which are negative or detrimental in nature towards anyone or anything, not even in dreams. This also includes negativity towards oneself because if there is no negative thought about the self, then

282

there will be no guilt either. Positive thought will create positive desire, positive motivation and positive action whereas negative thought will create negative desire, negative motivation and negative action, and then there will be problems. We face these kinds of problems in our life. So, in order to transform the state of raga there has to be a positive input, a positive idea created.

4. *Dwesha* is repulsion. When we are fed up and tired of something, the mind and senses seek new stimulation. Then what we have is taken for granted; it is never really understood or fully known. For example, some people have a habit of collecting books. They like books very much and spend their time in bookshops, going through different editions. When they find a book they like and might read, they buy it. This is an ongoing process until one day they sit down in front of their library, look at all the books and begin to wonder, "There are so many books and I don't think I have read one fully. Do I have a psychological problem?"

After thinking about this, it strikes us that this type of acquisition can be considered as the play of both raga and dwesha. Raga is definitely there, the attraction to books. That attraction is so powerful that one buys new books every time one enters a bookshop. But on having the book in one's possession, dwesha comes into force. This dwesha is not hatred, as it is often translated, but a feeling of taking things for granted: "Now I have it, so I can read it any time." This taking things for granted becomes the cause for *parigraha,* accumulation. Its opposite is one of the niyamas, aparigraha, or non-possessiveness. After realizing this, one can begin giving the books away. After giving them away, one can borrow them back and read them because they are not yours and not taken for granted anymore. This is a manifestation of dwesha.

5. *Abhinivesha* is the fear of dying. All our efforts in life are to survive. At the time of sickness, the underlying fear of death is the force that makes us try to heal ourselves quickly.

The fear of death generates the opposite force, the will to live. The self-preservation instinct battles with the fear of death, which is also related to one of the four pravrittis: (i) desire for sex, (ii) desire for self-preservation, which generates fear, (iii) desire for food, and (iv) desire for sleep. Death goes against the principles of self-preservation and in this way the fear of death becomes an exaggerated form of self-preservation, thus also becoming an affliction.

For each of the kleshas, there is an opposite quality. The opposite of avidya is expansion of the field of perception. The opposite of asmita is surrender. The opposite of raga is positive thinking. The opposite of dwesha is aparigraha, non-possessiveness. The opposite of abhinivesha is the acceptance of any circumstance. This sensory perception is not just the physical senses but the nineteen mouths of vaishwanara, ten physical, four mental and five pranic, which cover the dimensions of annamaya, manomaya and pranamaya koshas.

Elimination of the kleshas

It is said that avidya, the first of the kleshas, is the source from which the other four kleshas or afflictions take birth. Avidya was defined as confined perception or non-awareness. So these kleshas are definitely sensorial by nature. Apart from the klesha experiences, based in the sensorial field of human life, there is also the belief experience. That information which does not fit into the physical or subtle sensory field of perception is classified under the category of belief, speculation or abstract ideas.

Sensorial experiences are seen in three forms: (i) the latent form, the seed, (ii) the active form, a fully laden tree, and (iii) the burned out form, the dead tree, which does not have the capacity to produce any more flowers or fruits. In the same way, sensorial experiences are seen to have three forms when combined with the kleshas. Every kind of sensory experience, whether a thought, an idea or a physical action, and whether due to an external need or to ill health, passes through these three stages.

The Yoga Sutras, Yoga Upanishads and other yogic texts have described avidya as mistaking the non-eternal for the eternal. In this context, this misconception relates to understanding the sensorial experiences as the totality of human perception without acknowledging the non-sensorial aspect.

Developing viveka

Avidya is a negative quality, so there has to be a positive quality also. This positive quality is viveka. Viveka is right knowledge and avidya is misconception, confined cognition. So, if we are able to overcome avidya with the help of viveka, it becomes illumination. In order to get rid of the darkness, you do not have to fight it. All you have to do is light a lamp; the lamp does all the work. As soon as the wick of the lamp is burning, the light will spread. In the same way, avidya or ignorance is removed by lighting the lamp of viveka.

This is a very important concept that we should understand. It simply means there is no fighting with ignorance. Generally we tend to fight. There is a very deep desire or motivation to be on top. It is very hard to accept that our perception and knowledge is limited according to our level of evolution. This non-acceptance of ourselves as we are and the feeding of this subtle motivation to be on top keeps taking birth within us. Striving to fulfil our desires on the external level is just a continuation of avidya. Our struggle to fulfil a desire, to implement an idea, even if it is only to come to a balanced state of health again after an illness or disease, is always accompanied by this process of wanting to achieve or to change something.

There should be no struggling with avidya, no struggling with the normal state of life and evolution. Evolution will take its own course, but we have to be open-minded in order to allow it to do so; there should be no barrier. In vedantic terms avidya is known as maya, a limiting or defining force. If maya or avidya is the negative force, then there has to be a positive force as well. The positive force becomes Brahman, the expanding, effulgent consciousness. Viveka becomes the process of attaining that experience of Brahman. Avidya becomes the tool for experiencing maya. These are the vedantic concepts of the yogic terms.

Process of dhyana – klesha and karma

Another method for overcoming the kleshas is through dhyana. Here, dhyana is not one-pointed meditation as it is sometimes translated, but something different altogether. In this context, dhyana is a state of awareness where the all-watchful faculty of the self, the observer, is activated. This state of dhyana is achieved after we have gone through and experimented with the processes of pratyahara and dharana.

Withdrawal of the senses from the external objects, from name, form and idea, and training them to experience the subtle realities, to become aware of the subtle dimensions, is the state of pratyahara. It is like turning the car around and going back along the same road to the source. The process of returning is the process of diverting the senses from their attraction to external sensory objects and turning them towards experiences of the inner dimension of tejas.

Dharana is concentration of mind, which is retained to make the mental faculties one-pointed without any dissipation. One-pointedness is pin-pointing the awareness to the experiences which tejas is having, so that there is no pull from the external sensorial dimension of vaishwanara.

In dhyana there is continuity, deepening and expansion of the state that was experienced in dharana. Awareness is not confined to just one experience that we are undergoing but expanded to all levels of the subtle dimension, where idea, desire, motivation and implementation can be seen simultaneously. The awareness of one of these aspects is normally more powerful than the other three. If we are aware of an idea, the experience of desire, motivation and implementation is in the background. If we become aware of an action, idea, desire and motivation tend to retire to the background. In dhyana, all four aspects are experienced at the same time, and therefore there is a reduction in the hold of the kleshas.

We know that the kleshas are in three forms. In dharana and pratyahara, we are aware of the burned out and the active kleshas. In dharana, the burned out kleshas are in the foreground and the active ones are in the background. In pratyahara, when we are withdrawing the mind from sensory perception, the active form is predominant and the burned out form is in the background. In the state of dhyana, the seed or latent form of the kleshas is observed. It is possible to eliminate kleshas when they are seen in the seed form. This elimination of the kleshas on the subtle level is what is generally termed as overcoming the karmas.

There is so much talk today about exhausting one's karmas that the word karma appears in the Webster's and Oxford dictionaries. They define karma as 'impressions being carried forward', 'the law of cause and effect', or 'the seed of desire'. Actually, the karmic process is the maturing of the kleshas from the latent to the active and then to the burned out form. The process of karma is linked with kleshas; it can be observed as the kleshas change from the latent form to the burned out form.

Practices of yoga: viveka and dhyana

So viveka and dhyana are the two methods that have been prescribed for overcoming the bondage of the kleshas. Dhyana is the process of raja yoga, the seventh limb of Patanjali's *Yoga Sutras*. Viveka is the process of jnana yoga, the search, the enquiry, the journey, to know 'Who am I?' Yogic literature also suggests that apart from having theoretical concepts of the kleshas, avidya, karma, maya and viveka, it is always better to follow a practical system as well.

Saying that dhyana is the process of raja yoga implies that an individual should follow the instructions of raja yoga. Saying that viveka is the process of jnana yoga implies that an individual should be instructed in the system of

287

jnana yoga. This practical performance of the yogas becomes the means to divert one's attention from the external, physical plane towards awareness of the internal, subtle plane, and teaches how to use the faculties of both dimensions. Then we are able to control and direct the faculties and forces of both the physical and the subtle dimensions, the levels of vaishwanara and tejas.

From here the practices of yoga actually begin. These include hatha yoga, raja yoga, bhakti yoga, jnana yoga, mantra yoga, laya yoga, nada yoga and so on. There are many yogas and they should be used according to the inclination and needs of the aspirant along the path.

Yogic aspiration

What are the inclinations of an aspirant? Keeping in view all the points we have been discussing, there are physical, mental, psychic and spiritual aspirations. When we come to the yogic path there is physical aspiration to gain some kind of physical benefit. We may have a back or stomach problem or a headache and start yoga believing that asanas will help us to overcome the problem we are facing. Anything to do with the physical body in relation to the preventative, curative and regenerative aspect of yoga can be called physical aspiration.

Then there are mental aspirations. People want to develop their willpower and concentration, or to learn how to manage stress and tension. There are also those who seek yogic counselling due to family problems, or who have emotional and other deep-rooted mental conflicts and want to learn ways to overcome them. In this way we can group mental and emotional aspirations.

Some people have heard about the chakras, or wish to learn how they can turn the key inside their spinal cord, open Pandora's box and awaken kundalini and gain siddhis. For other people psychic experiences are a spontaneous yet unexplained aspect of their lives. Such people need to understand how to balance their psychic personalities and

288

harness their talents and energies creatively. These are the psychic aspirations. Finally, there are the spiritual aspirants who have the desire to know the underlying truth behind the appearance. When these four types of people come to yoga they will adopt different methods suitable to their aspirations.

Practical Aspect

Introduction

The Yoga Upanishads describe the process of the different yogas as having a definite purpose – the awakening of kundalini. Therefore, the practical aspect dealt with in this part of the text includes a study of kundalini yoga techniques which are at times significantly different from the hatha yoga techniques that are normally used in the Bihar Yoga tradition. We should be very clear from the beginning that the kundalini yoga techniques given in the Upanishads are not suitable for general practice. Upanishadic teaching literally means that teaching received while sitting at the feet of the guru.

The Yoga Upanishads all say that asana, pranayama, mudra, bandha and kriya are to be practised in such a way that their effect is not limited to the physical body and its experiences. They have created a practical system which specifically develops a type of mental awareness, concentration and balance conducive to the awakening of kundalini shakti. They are very effective in this attempt as long as the practitioner is thoroughly prepared and has obtained the guidance of a realized guru or master.

15

Asana

The asanas described in the Yoga Upanishads have as their aim the awakening of kundalini. Therefore, the selection of asanas given in the upanishadic texts is very limited. Although the practice of both major and simple asanas is described, the thrust is to go deep into the psychic experience through the medium of the body. So the practices are not just physical movements. A distinct effort is made in each posture to try and experience what is happening at the subtle levels of the body.

In raja yoga, four different physical states have to be experienced before an asana can be perfected. The first is awareness of the normal physical posture to which the body is accustomed. The second is creation of flexibility in the body. The third is adjustment of the internal systems with the posture so that there is no pain or tension. The fourth is concentration of the mind in the asana, which leads to perfect stillness and relaxation.

Of the vast variety of asanas that have been described, thirteen are considered important: vajrasana, gomukhasana, veerasana, simhasana, sukhasana, swastikasana, siddhasana, padmasana, kukkutasana, mayurasana, chakrasana, koorm-asana and poorna dhanurasana. These are the major asanas, basic as well as advanced, described in the upanishadic texts as postures that influence the physiological condition and help to induce deep meditative states. Their aim is the awakening of kundalini. They also open and awaken the chakras and nadis, with the purpose of developing one-pointed concentration of mind. With this aim in mind, the rishis selected practices which could provide physical stability and open up the psychic body, enabling the prana to flow more evenly to all the different organs and areas, creating stimulation and increased sensation at the chakra level and preparing the entire system for the rising of kundalini.

VAJRASANA (THUNDERBOLT POSE)

Technique

Kneel on the floor with the feet stretched backwards. The knees should be together, heels apart, with the big toes crossed. Initially, if the ankles are stiff and there is strain or pain in the feet try placing the five toes on top of each other.

Lower the buttocks inside the feet, so that the heels are out to the sides. Place the hands on the knees, palms downward. Close the eyes and concentrate on the breath. If there is pain in the thighs, the knees can be separated slightly while maintaining the posture.

Duration: Sit in vajrasana for as long as you feel comfortable. Vajrasana is recommended straight after meals to improve the digestive process. At this time combine the

295

posture with abdominal breathing and practise for five or ten minutes.

Practice note: Vajrasana is a very important meditative posture because the body automatically becomes upright and straight in the position without any effort. If the body is bent forward there will be discomfort. Vajrasana can be used as a meditation posture by people suffering from sciatica, back pain and sacral infections. It is the prayer pose of Muslims and the meditation pose of Buddhists.

Physiological effects

Vajrasana is a posture specifically for the digestive and reproductive systems. Pressure is exerted on vajra nadi and the energy is channelled into the digestive area in the form of nerve, blood and tissue activation. The energy of manipura chakra is thereby increased, improving digestion. Vajrasana also increases the parasympathetic energy in the lower body and allows relaxation to occur more easily. Furthermore, it is good for the treatment of ulcers, digestive complaints and back problems.

In the Yoga Upanishads it is said that vajrasana affects vajra nadi, which is associated with the sciatic nerve. Vajra nadi corresponds to the sciatic nerve up to the hip joints and along the spine. It is one of the ten major nadis that run along the spinal passage into the brain. One of the functions of vajra nadi relates to the sexual energy, which is stimulated when the insides of the feet are pressed against the buttocks. The Yoga Upanishads mention that the sexual impulses can be controlled through vajra nadi. The vajra, or thunderbolt, is the weapon or force of Indra, king of the gods. It is also mentioned in Greek mythology as being the thunderbolt of Zeus. The kingly aspect is represented by the mind, which is the king of the senses.

Vajra is the stimulating factor for the sensory inputs and outputs. Vajrasana is therefore a physical aid for the practice of pratyahara. Voluntary control of vajra nadi induces automatic pratyahara. After sitting in vajrasana for five minutes, there is greater calmness in the mind, better concentration and awareness of sensory experience.

GOMUKHASANA (COW'S FACE POSE)

Technique

In the Yoga Upanishads the basic position only is described:

Sit with the legs stretched forward.

Bend the left leg and place the left heel beside the right buttock, so that the left knee is pointing forward.

Then fold the right leg over the top of the left leg and place the right foot on the other side, so that the right heel is touching the left buttock and the right knee is on top of the left knee.

Both knees should be pointing forward.

Place both hands on top of the right knee.

In the hatha yoga version the arm position is also specified:

Raise the right arm over the head and bend it backward so that the fingers are pointing down and the elbow is pointing upwards. Bring the left arm behind the back and clasp the fingers of both hands together.

297

The raised right elbow should be behind the head. Straighten the torso, hold the head back and close the eyes. Initially the hands may be supported by the back.

As you come into the final posture, move the arms away from the back a centimetre at a time, so there is a space between the back and the hands.

Remain in the pose as long as is comfortable, then change sides.

Variations: The position of the arms has two variations. In variation 1, when the right knee is uppermost, the right arm is raised. When the left knee is uppermost, the left arm is raised. This creates a lateral stretch on the side of the leg which is on top and greater constriction on the other side of the body. In variation 2, the arm on the side of the lower leg is raised, in order to have an equal stretch on both sides of the body.

Note: The hatha yoga version of gomukhasana described here differs from the upanishadic variation in which the upper portion of the technique has been eliminated. It is impossible to remain in this meditative posture with the hands behind the back for half an hour or an hour. Therefore, the upanishadic version simply maintains the leg posture with the hands on top of the knees, keeping the spine straight. The practice of gomukhasana is conducive to structural stability and balance.

Concentration: Concentration is fixed on ajna chakra at the psychic level or on the respiration at the physical level.

Physiological effects

From an anatomical point of view, the legs and hips are not rotated externally as they are in the normal meditative postures, but the knees are brought to the centre instead of out to the sides. This affects the pelvic structure and stretches the outer side of the thigh, rather than the inside. This position also squeezes the pelvic organs and tones both the male and female reproductive organs.

The base position locks the hips and pelvis, which creates a firm base for stretching the sides of the trunk and opening up the chest. Thus it is beneficial in the treatment of asthma and other respiratory diseases. It also opens up the pectoral muscles at the front of the chest, unlocking a lot of the tension that one acquires from the stooped posture of day to day sedentary living. A lot of tension accumulates in the shoulders, so this is a very powerful stretch to break the shoulder tension, while opening up and improving the lung function.

VEERASANA (WARRIOR'S OR HERO'S POSE)

Technique

Sit in vajrasana. Raise the right knee and place the right foot flat on the floor beside the left knee.

Place the left hand on the left knee and the right elbow on top of the right knee, with the palm of the right hand supporting the chin.

Keep the body motionless and in a straight line.

Close the eyes and relax.

Repeat with the left leg placed beside the right knee.

Breathing: Slow, deep breathing.

Concentration: Concentrate on bhrumadhya or ajna chakra.

Physiological effects

This practice of half vajrasana opens the nadis and displaces blood from one side of the body to the other. It is very good for the reproductive and abdominal organs and helps clear the mind for mental work. Veerasana, the warrior or hero's pose, is the posture of being on the move, ever ready, and at the same time it is a posture in which deep relaxation can be obtained in a short time.

In this posture there is support for the head, which is why one feels mentally calm and relaxed. The thinking process becomes very clear and precise. If practised by those who think too much, have disturbed thoughts or are unable to control their thoughts, it will regulate the thought process and cause excess thinking to subside. Therefore, it has also been termed the thinker's pose or the philosopher's pose.

SIMHASANA (LION POSE)

This is the posture of simhasana, the lion pose. It is not simhagarjanasana, the roaring lion pose, but simhasana, the lion which is sitting quietly, waiting for something to happen. Generally simhasana is associated with the roaring lion, but the Upanishads give the roaring lion posture as a variation. Simhasana is the position in which the mind has to be fixed in order to go deep into meditative states.

300

Technique

Sit in vajrasana with the knees about 45cm apart and the feet flat, toes touching.

Place the palms of the hands on the floor between the knees, with the fingers pointing towards the body.

Lean forward on the arms, keeping the elbows straight. Arch the back, expand the chest and tilt the head back, not so that the neck is strained but in a gentle way, and look straight up.

Practise shambhavi mudra, fixing the gaze at the eyebrow centre.

Physiological effects

In this posture there is a very definite extension of the spinal cord and the body is absolutely fixed. There is total physical stability. The whole weight of the body is not on any one specific part. There is more pressure in the frontal region of the body, not in the back or in the buttocks. The arms act like levers, providing support for the body.

This pose differs from vajrasana in that it is not closed but open. The knees are spread apart and the hands placed between the knees. It has some of the effects of vajrasana by putting the pelvis into a position which frees the abdomen, allows the body to tilt forwards and takes a lot of weight off the abdomen and diaphragm, improving respiration. It also has an effect on the digestion and on respiration. However, by arching the back, the energy being generated in the abdomen is directed towards the head. So there is a backward bending effect on the spinal cord as well as the freeing of a lot of tension from the chest and diaphragm.

Shambhavi mudra is the key technique in this pose. It acts on the cerebral cortex and concentrates the prana. The concentration of the eyes and the optic nerves helps to provide greater concentration, stopping sensory distraction. Once we are able to control the sensory distractions, it is much easier to induce the state of pratyahara, the dissociation of the mind from sensory experiences.

Bhadrasana is a similar practice. The posture is the same, except that the hands are placed on top of the knees and the gaze is directed to the nose tip instead of the eyebrow centre. The spine is maintained upright and the head is straight. This posture is used mainly for sitting for extended periods in meditation or in other techniques.

In both simhasana and bhadrasana, the optic system, which occupies a large part of the brain at the back of the head, is affected. The normal function of the eyes is to look around gathering information from the environment. When one gazes at a certain point, a large part of the brain is stilled and this has very important ramifications for our psycho-physiology, our sense of identity, as well as our sense of connection to the world. It is one of the most direct ways of influencing the central nervous system.

In shambhavi and nasikagra, you look up towards the eyebrow centre and down towards the nose tip respectively, not out to the sides, because this is the best way to lock the eyes. By focusing the gaze on a central point, whether at the eyebrow centre, which represents the top of the spinal cord, or at the nose tip, which represents mooladhara chakra, you are switching on the central nervous system and influencing the core structures around the limbic/hypothalamic system. Just by closing the eyes, alpha waves are generated in the optic system at the back of the head. By crossing the eyes in a meditative attitude, alpha waves spread from the back of the head to the frontal lobes, producing a profound meditative or relaxed state very quickly. These techniques are very powerful and should only be practised by more advanced practitioners who are able to cope with the effects as they occur.

SUKHASANA (EASY POSE)

BSY ©

Variation 1: The simplest form of sukhasana is sitting cross-legged with a belt or a cloth tied around the knees and lower back. This is the ideal meditation pose for those who have difficulty sitting in any of the other meditation postures.

Hold the spine upright and balance the body on the buttocks.

Concentrating on physical balance, observe if there is more pressure on the left or right side of the body and try to balance it out.

A light, spacy feeling, similar to padmasana, may be experienced.

While maintaining the posture, place the hands on the knees or bring the palms together in front of the heart in namaskara position.

Variation 2: When the hips are more flexible, sit down and cross the legs so that the right foot is under the left thigh and the left foot is under the right thigh.

The knees should be close to the ground. The thighs, knees, ankles, feet and toes are loose, relaxed and free.

Place the hands on the knees in chin or jnana mudra. Keep the head, neck and back straight but without strain. Relax the whole body.

Practice note: Sukhasana is a relaxing posture which can be used after extended periods of sitting in siddhasana or padmasana. Although it is said to be the simplest meditative posture, it is actually one of the most difficult postures to perform properly. The knees should be close to the ground or on the ground so that backache does not develop.

In India, where it is normal to sit in a squatting position from an early age, flexibility of the knees and hips is developed when young. In western countries, where it is normal to sit in a chair from an early age, mobility of the hips and knees is not developed, and so the legs become stiff when sitting in cross-legged positions.

While sitting cross-legged, the legs can easily go to sleep if they are even a millimetre out of alignment. Without proprioceptive awareness, or a sense of position, which is developed from a young age in cultures where squatting is the norm, we tend to contract the muscles around the joints, so that the legs go out of alignment and go to sleep.

SWASTIKASANA (AUSPICIOUS POSE)

Technique
Sit with the legs outstretched.

Bend the left knee and place the sole of the left foot against the inside of the right thigh so there is no contact between the heel and the perineum.

Bend the right knee and place the right foot on top of the left thigh.

Insert the right toes between the left thigh and calf muscle so there is no contact between the heel and the perineum.

Reach down between the right thigh and calf muscle, and pull up the left toes.

Place the hands on the knees in chin or jnana mudra.

Contra-indications: Swastikasana should not be performed by people with sciatica or sacral infections.

BSY ©

Physiological effects

Swastikasana is a simplified form of siddhasana. It is one of the simplest meditative postures in which the legs and the body are locked in one position. This posture has the effect of squeezing blood from the legs into the pelvis and spine. It is a healthy position to sit in, particularly if one has tired legs, varicose veins, muscle aches or oedema (fluid in the legs). It helps to redirect the energy upwards. The spiritual benefits are the same as for siddhasana but at a lower level, because there is no contraction of the perineal muscles.

From a neurological viewpoint, the legs in the embryo resemble little buds or leaves which come out of the hips, acting as extensions of the mooladhara pelvic region. The soles of the feet are very sensitive and by bringing them into contact with the thighs and calf muscles, the proprioceptive sense and neurological control over the lower body is increased.

SIDDHASANA (ACCOMPLISHED POSE FOR MEN)

BSY ©

Technique

Sit with the legs straight in front of the body.

Bend the right leg and place the sole of the foot flat against the inner left thigh with the heel pressing the perineum (the area midway between the genitals and anus).

Bend the left leg. Push the toes and the outer edge of the left foot into the space between the right calf and thigh muscles. If necessary, this space may be enlarged slightly by using the hands or temporarily adjusting the position of the right leg.

Place the left ankle directly over the right so that the ankle bones are touching and the heels are one above the other. Press the pubis with the left heel directly above the genitals. The genitals will therefore lie between the two heels.

If this last position is too difficult, simply place the left heel as near as possible to the pubis.

Grasp the right toes and pull them up into the space between the left calf and thigh.

Again adjust the body so that it is comfortable.

Sit on top of the right heel. This is an important aspect of siddhasana. Adjust the body until it is comfortable and the pressure of the heel is firmly applied.

The legs should now be locked, with the knees touching the ground and the left heel directly above the right heel.

Make the spine erect and feel as though the body is fixed on the floor.

Place the hands on the knees in jnana or chin mudra.

Close the eyes and relax the whole body.

Practice note: Siddhasana is the practice described for male aspirants and can be performed with either leg uppermost. The same practice for females is called siddha yoni asana (accomplished pose for women). The only difference between the two is the position of the lower heel, which in siddha yoni asana is placed inside the yoni or female organ. The benefits are the same.

In the beginning it is easier to assume and maintain this posture if the buttocks are elevated by a small cushion. While sitting in siddhasana, adjust the pressure of the lower and upper heels. Try to equalize the pressure from both heels. The further the lower heel is pulled in, the more difficult it becomes to insert the toes between the thighs and the calf muscles. When you try to insert the upper toes between the thighs and calf muscles, an intense, hard pressure is created in the lower swadhisthana region. If the legs are moved slightly so that the lower heel is not actually pressing into the perineum, then a reduction in pressure will be felt and you will be able to sit in the posture for a longer time than in actual siddhasana. To reach a point where you can sit comfortably in siddhasana for half an hour to one hour, you have to progress gradually from the outer periphery of the perineum to the centre.

Contra-indications: Siddhasana should not be practised by persons with sciatica or sacral infections.

Physiological effects

Siddhasana moves the focus of concentration from the sides to the centre of the body. The sense of touch has a profound, stimulating effect on the central nervous system. When you touch yourself, you awaken different nerves and sensations. For example, in swastikasana the sense of touch has a soothing, relaxing effect, whereas in siddhasana the central nervous system is stimulated in a profound way. The pleasure centres of the brain are stimulated yet, at the same time, they are regulated and controlled. By stimulating mooladhara and swadhisthana, the base of the brain is directly affected as well as all the functions of the hypothalamus, pineal and pituitary areas, where the basic instinctual drives of sleep, hunger, reproduction and so forth are controlled.

Physiologically, this is one of the most powerful postures because it balances out the functioning of the reproductive system. Most people are either hypertense in this area and hold in repressed energy in the form of a defence mechanism, or they lack tone. Siddhasana helps to rebalance in either direction. It can reduce the testosterone level and increase or decrease blood pressure. It provides a constant, gentle stimulation to the brain, gradually bringing awareness and prana to this area.

Yogis use this posture for a specific reason. Here the two sexually related psycho-muscular locks are performed simultaneously: moola bandha, by exerting external pressure on the perineum, and vajroli mudra, by exerting external pressure on the urinary organ. In this way the sexual impulses are redirected from the lower chakras of mooladhara and swadhisthana through the spine to the brain. Physically siddhasana is practised for maintenance of brahmacharya. Spiritually it is practised to reverse the energy flows of apana and of mooladhara and swadhisthana chakras, from the gross to the transcendental level.

In padmasana there is no stimulation of the sexual centres. Concentration is on the alignment of the body and there is the feeling of floating in space. In siddhasana there is intense awareness of the pressure at mooladhara chakra and the movement of energy from mooladhara along the spinal passage towards the brain. If one sits in siddhasana for extended periods, there will be a noticeable tingling sensation in the mooladhara region for ten or fifteen minutes. This could be caused by a reduction in the blood supply or by a resettling of the pranic flow in the lower chakras.

PADMASANA (LOTUS POSE)

BSY ©

Technique

In order to perform padmasana, flexibility of the knees is required, which can be gained by practising premeditative asanas.

Sit with the legs stretched forward. Bend the right knee and place the right foot on top of the left thigh.

The sole of the right foot should be turned upward so that the heel is close to the pubic bone.

Bend the left leg and place it on top of the right thigh. Make sure that the left sole is turned upward and the left heel is close to the pubic bone.

Both knees should ideally touch the floor in the final position. Keep the spine upright. Place the hands on the knees in either jnana mudra or chin mudra.

Practice note: Padmasana is not just a posture of the legs. The position of the spine is very important. When practising padmasana, the spine must be straight and upright as though it is fixed to the ground. If the spine is not straight from the bottom up, then any attempt to straighten it will create tension in the lower waist and back region, which is not the purpose.

If there is tension, stretch fully to move the strain from the lower back into the upper region. Then the posture will feel very comfortable.

309

One should also be aware of the shoulders. In a normal, relaxed state there is a tendency for the shoulders to bend forward slightly. Slowly and gently bring the shoulders back until they are perfectly relaxed and at ease.

Observe the total posture of the body again. Make the necessary adjustments either by bending forward or backward, until you come to a point where the spinal cord is no longer felt.

The pressure should be evenly distributed, without causing any spinal tension. This perfect alignment indicates the correct posture of padmasana.

Contra-indications: Padmasana should not to be performed by persons with sciatica, sacral infections, or weak or injured knees. It should not be attempted until flexibility of the knees is acquired through practice of the pre-meditative asanas.

Psychophysiological effects

By locking the feet on top of the thighs, the knees are pushed down, tilting the pelvis. This straightens the spine and re-establishes the lumbar curve so that the upper body is aligned and can rest comfortably, thereby creating the perfect seat or asana for meditation. If the knees are higher than the pelvis, it causes a flexing of the lower back and slouching, which can lead to backache and respiratory difficulties in the posture.

Secondly, when sitting in this position there is pressure on the lower spine, which has a relaxing effect on the nervous system. The breath automatically slows down, muscular tension is decreased and blood pressure reduced.

When mastered, this posture holds the body completely steady for long periods of time. As the body and mind are interconnected, steadiness of body brings steadiness of mind. This steadiness is the first step towards productive meditation. There is deeper concentration of the mind. The mind is not pulled from one tense area of the body to another or from one stressful experience to another. This allows the concentration to go deeper into the experience of akasha, space. This is the mental benefit of padmasana.

There is also a psychic benefit. Padmasana directs the flow of prana up sushumna from mooladhara to sahasrara, thus increasing the meditative experience. Along with the awareness of space, one begins to experience the symbol, or yantra, and concentration on the chakras is developed. In this way padmasana becomes a tool for the awakening of kundalini shakti.

KUKKUTASANA (COCKEREL POSE)

Technique

Sit in padmasana.

Insert the arms between the calves and the thighs, near the knees.

Place the palms of the hands on the ground with the fingers pointing forward.

Balancing on the hands, raise the body off the ground, keeping the head straight and the eyes fixed on a point in front. Remain in the pose for as long as is comfortable, then return to the starting position.

Concentration: 1. *Breath*: In this practice the concentration is on the breath. Initially there is a tendency to hold the breath while pushing down and straightening the arms in order to support the body weight. However, once the

311

final position is reached, there has to be an effort to maintain the stability of the body and concentration on the inhalation and exhalation. The breathing process is to be observed in the nasal passages.

2. *Bandha*: As one moves into the final posture, there is an automatic contraction of the perineum. This is an aspect one should try to develop more and more in kukkutasana. With contraction of the perineum, the medhra or nadi complex, situated midway between mooladhara and swadhisthana chakras, is stimulated. Yogis have mentioned that the medhra is where the seventy-two thousand nadis, or conductors of prana, emanate and spread throughout the system. Initially one can also practise moola bandha while going into kukkutasana.

3. *Mudra*: In the final position of kukkutasana, moola bandha is performed along with awareness of the breath in the nostrils. The nasikagra centre is responsible for the switch of mooladhara. Concentration on the breath has the function of stimulating the nasikagra centre. With concentration on nasikagra, along with contraction of the medhra, this pose becomes a very powerful tool for awakening both mooladhara and swadhisthana chakras, and for removing any kind of pranic blockage which may exist there prior to the awakening of kundalini.

Contraindications: This is a strenuous asana, not suitable for people with heart conditions, high blood pressure, prolapse, hernia or back pain.

Physiological effects

Kukkutasana improves balance, strength and flexibility in the pelvis, shoulders and arms. One has to use the strength of the body to get into and maintain the posture. It has a very powerful effect on the nervous system, creating a sense of balance, calmness and stability. It is a very powerful balancing posture and also helps in developing mastery, balance and stability within other systems like the circulatory and the digestive systems. All the asanas from the padmasana group open up the pelvic region and have a beneficial effect on the pelvic and reproductive organs.

It is also interesting to note that kukkutasana strengthens the earth element in mooladhara chakra, creating a sense of stability. The paradox here is that as mooladhara is raised off the ground, the earth element is strengthened. This is due to the awakening of mooladhara.

MAYURASANA (PEACOCK POSE)

Technique

Kneel on the floor. Place the feet together and separate the knees.

Lean forward and place the palms on the floor between the knees with the fingers pointing towards the feet. Adjust the hand position according to comfort and flexibility.

Bring the elbows and forearms together.

Lean further forward and rest the abdomen on the elbows and the chest on the upper arms.

Stretch the legs backward so they are straight and together. Tense the muscles of the body and slowly raise the trunk and legs, until they are horizontal to the floor. Hold the head upward.

The entire body is now balanced on the palms of the hands. Maintain the final position for a short period of time, then slowly and carefully return to the starting position. The asana may be repeated when the breathing rate has returned to normal.

313

Practice note: Practise according to physical capability. Initially, try to keep the body in one straight line. Gradually, as you progress in the practice, keep the chest in the same posture while lifting the legs higher and higher. Eventually a curve is created by the backward extension of the spine and the actual position of mayurasana is experienced. Beginners should place a cushion or a folded blanket under the head in order to avoid injury if the body falls.

Breathing: Inhale in the starting position. Exhale while raising the trunk and legs off the ground. Retain the breath outside in the final pose. Inhale while lowering the body. Breathe normally in the final pose when holding for a longer time.

Duration: Practise for as long as the breath can be retained. Repeat up to three times, allowing the respiration to return to normal after completing each round. Avoid muscular strain.

Concentration: Concentrate on manipura chakra and on maintaining balance in the final pose.

Sequence: Perform this posture at the end of the asana sequence. Do not perform it before inverted poses.

Contra-indications: Mayurasana should be avoided by persons with high blood pressure, hernia, gastric ulcer and acidity, and weak wrists.

Physiological effects

Mayurasana develops the strength of the whole body and the integration of the nervous system, but it is basically a balancing pose. The trick is to find the centre of balance, bringing the elbows to a point just below the navel so that you do not actually need to use the strength of the arms very much, although, of course, strength is required, especially in the wrists and shoulders.

After raising the body into the final position, however, it is more a question of balance than strength. When this point of balance is found, the body is gently tensed but in perfect alignment. When the body is aligned in this posture, strength develops without strain. There is tension without strain, and this tension has a beneficial effect on the entire system.

From other points of view, mayurasana is also considered to be an inverted posture. Blood is pushed down towards the brain, creating a temporary increase in blood pressure. Upon returning to the starting position, the blood pressure will normalize, or even go a little lower than before. This posture strengthens the cardiovascular system. As a balancing pose, it has a powerful effect on the central nervous system. However, its major physical effect is on the abdominal organs because it puts a tremendous amount of pressure on the abdominal cavity. It squeezes the liver, spleen, kidneys and digestive organs, and strengthens the solar plexus.

In the Upanishads mayurasana is considered to be a major posture for various reasons. The practice brings about elimination of toxins due to the awakening and stimulation of manipura and agni mandala, within the zone of samana vayu. Therefore, when the practice is performed for purification or for spiritual benefits, the following dietary measures are recommended: avoid spices, meat, milk products, oily foods and stimulants. Take a fruit diet or a sattwic diet in order to speed up the removal of toxins.

CHAKRASANA (WHEEL POSE)

Technique

Lie on the back with the knees bent and the heels touching the buttocks.

The feet and knees should be about 30 cm apart.

Place the palms on the floor beside the head with the fingers pointing towards the shoulders.

This is the starting position.

Slowly raise the body and arch the back, allowing the crown of the head to support the weight of the upper body.

Move the hands in further towards the body for more support if necessary.

315

Straighten the arms and legs as much as possible without straining and lift the head and trunk from the floor.
Arch the back as high as is comfortable in the final position. Straighten the knees further by moving the trunk towards the head.
Let the head hang between the straight arms.
Lift the heels and balance on the balls of the feet and the hands for a few seconds, then lower the heels.
Hold the final position for as long as is comfortable.
Slowly lower the body so the head rests on the floor and then lower the rest of the body.
This is one round.

Breathing: Inhale in the starting position. Retain the breath inside while raising the body. Retain the breath inside or breathe normally in the raised position. Exhale while lowering the body.

Duration: Hold for as long as is comfortable. Do not strain.

Concentration: On manipura chakra, or on relaxing the spine in the final position, and on the chest and abdomen.

Sequence: Chakrasana should be practised only after mastery of preliminary and intermediate backward bending asanas. It may be followed with forward bending asanas such as halasana and sarvangasana which apply a tight forward lock on the neck.

Contra-indications: Chakrasana should not be performed by people with back pain or any kind of back problems, high blood pressure, coronary ailments, stomach ulcers, toxic

316

intestines, partial deafness, dilated eye capillaries, or by anyone who has recently fractured bones or undergone abdominal operations. It should not be attempted until preliminary backward bending postures are mastered.

Physiological effects

This position is the most powerful extension of the spine possible. It is also an inverted position. The whole nervous system is in a position it would normally never have to deal with. So in this way we are actually stretching the nervous system, and that is the whole purpose of chakrasana because it is not something we would do normally. Our body is constructed so that we can bend forward easily, stretching the spine in one direction only. When extension or bending in the other direction takes place, each and every nerve, ligament and nadi is stretched. That stretch opens up the nadis that form a plexus at the different chakra areas. Therefore, in the Yoga Upanishads chakrasana is used for opening or awakening the chakras.

When one breathes in this posture, certain habitual tensions are removed from the three major diaphragms of the body: the respiratory diaphragm, the perineum, and a third diaphragm under the brain. Furthermore, this posture integrates the upper and lower parts of the body, so that the legs and arms work in a way that they do not normally do. Connecting the upper and lower parts of the body in this way allows one to feel the body as a more complete unit.

So, chakrasana is an integrating practice which has a powerful effect on the respiratory, digestive and uro-genital systems. It is very effective in the treatment of many diseases related to these areas. Although most people are generally quite healthy by the time they are able to do this pose, as a preventative it is beneficial for almost everything.

Many people find it difficult to raise the body into this position. However, that is not due to weakness in the arms, rather it happens because the nervous system is not ready to go into that pose. We lose our sense of position in space, which

317

in physiological terms is called proprioception. We can know where our arm is in space; however to know where our body is in this position is difficult and therefore we lose our strength. It is not that the strength is not there. So, any position that arches the back, for example, kandharasana, grivasana or setu asana, is good for developing proprioceptive awareness. Arm strengthening practices may also help to raise the body.

KOORMASANA (TORTOISE POSE)

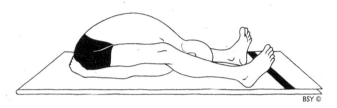

Technique
Sit down with the legs spread as wide apart as possible. Lean forward and insert the hands under the knees with the palms downward. Bring the forehead to the floor.
Slide the arms under the knees and clasp the hands behind the back.
In the final position the back is just like a tortoise shell. The legs and arms are like the four limbs of the tortoise coming out of the shell.
Remain in the posture for as long as is comfortable. Then release the hands and slowly sit up.

Breathing: Inhale in the starting position. Exhale while bending forward. Breathe normally in the final pose. Inhale while releasing the pose and sitting up.

Duration: For spiritual purposes, try to remain in the posture for long periods. For physical or mental effects, 5 minutes is enough.

Concentration: Concentration on swadhisthana or manipura chakras at the psychic level, or, at the physical level, on relaxing the spine, back muscles and abdomen and on the breath in the final position.

Sequence: Precede or follow with a backward bending posture.

Contra-indications: Koormasana should not be practised by people with slipped disc, sciatica, spondylitis, hernia or chronic arthritis. It should only be attempted if the spine is sufficiently flexible.

Physiological effects

Koormasana is an advanced forward bending posture requiring greater flexibility of both the hips and shoulders. The purpose here is not to bend the spine but rather to develop flexibility in the pelvis. The back should be kept straight while bending forward, working the pelvis until finally one is able to place the chest on the floor.

The hatha yoga texts state that this posture awakens sushumna. It places a profound stretch along the coverings of the spinal canal called the meninges, which ascend into the brain. So, in this posture one is almost able to stretch inside the brain through these spinal coverings. Stretching the spine has profound effects on all the internal functions. Forward bending massages and compresses all the internal organs from the pelvic organs to the digestive organs and diaphragm, then the lungs.

In this posture the relationship between oneself and the earth is enhanced. Opening oneself up to the earth and coming into contact with the earth has a tremendous effect on the whole neurological and psychophysiological functioning. Different asanas have different effects, depending upon the direction in which one is sitting in relation to gravity, whether the spine is upright, forward, flexed, extended or inverted. By placing the front of the body onto the earth, a sense of inner psychological change is created, a sense of indwelling and security. This posture also increases proprioceptive awareness and gives an understanding of the difference between the back and the front of the body.

In the final position, there is a complete extension of every ligament and nerve along the back of the body. The arms are stretched, the legs are pressing the tops of the

319

shoulders, the head is pushed down to the floor and the whole spine is stretched out in all directions. It is not just one movement of the spine, as in other postures which bend forward or backwards. Here the whole spine seems to extend in all directions. The perineum and forehead are pressed against the floor in this posture, directly stimulating mooladhara and ajna chakras, which helps to awaken sushumna nadi within the spine.

Yogis use this practice to stimulate the nerve plexuses along the spine as it creates a change in the blood circulation and removes what is known in yoga as 'nadi knots'. These are knots within the nadis, adhesions within the veins, arteries and ligaments that cause stiffness, tightness and blockages. After performing this posture, the body will feel light when it goes into shavasana. There will be a sensation of expansion as if one is floating. The whole back will feel flat. So, the removal of blocks and the opening up of the three major psychic knots of yoga: rudra, vishnu and brahma granthis, or the three major diaphragms, takes place in this posture.

POORNA DHANURASANA (FULL BOW POSE)

BSY ©

Technique

Lie on the stomach and bend the knees. Stretch the right arm over the right shoulder, so the elbow is pointing upward. Clasp the right foot with the right hand, making sure that the thumb is on the sole and the other four fingers are on the top of the foot, or clasp the big toe.

320

Then reach back in the same way with the left arm and clasp the left foot. Raise the head, chest and thighs.

Pull the feet as close to the head as possible in the final posture, so that the body resembles a fully stretched bow. Maintain the final pose for a comfortable duration, and then return to the starting position.

Wait until the breath and heartbeat return to normal before attempting to repeat the posture.

Practice note: Poorna dhanurasana is prescribed in the yogic texts as the reverse posture for koormasana. It is a difficult variation of dhanurasana and it should not be attempted until the back is very supple.

Breathing: Inhale deeply in the starting position.
Retain the breath while coming into the final position.
In the final position, retain the breath inside or practise slow, deep breathing.
Exhale while returning to the starting position.

Concentration: Concentrate on manipura chakra at the psychic level, or on the abdomen or back at the physical level.

Contra-indications: This asana is for advanced practitioners and should only be practised if the back is very supple. People with cardiovascular problems, high blood pressure, hernia, colitis, peptic or duodenal ulcers should not attempt it.

Physiological effects

One of the main effects of this posture is to press the whole body weight down onto the digestive system, around the diaphragm, opening up that area. It has a powerful effect on the liver and abdominal organs. The whole front of the body is stretched to the extreme, having effects all the way down from the head and neck, through the chest and abdomen, into the pelvis. The main effect, however, takes place around the diaphragm. This is a powerful practice for the awakening of manipura chakra at the psychic level. Physically it revitalizes the solar plexus and activates the sympathetic nervous system, which temporarily raises the blood pressure and increases the circulation of blood and prana throughout the system.

16

Pranayama

Before going into the practical exposition of pranayama, the use of the breath in the pranayama techniques must be clarified. The breath is a medium through which to gain awareness of pranic movement, or pranic expansion and relaxation. Since it is difficult to go deep enough to experience the movement of prana, it is necessary to use the breath initially in order to internalize the sensory faculties. The practice of pranayama actually begins when pranic awareness has evolved in the mind.

Three aspects of pranayama

1. *Awareness of prana*: There are different stages of practice to go through in order to develop an awareness of prana. This first stage is becoming aware of the link between the breath and the prana on the gross plane, the breath that is breathed in and out through the nostrils. The second stage is becoming aware of the vitality that is absorbed by the body from the air that is breathed. The third stage involves becoming aware of the pranic force that activates, not only the gross or physical functions of the body, but also the subtle experiences of the senses and mind. The fourth stage goes deeper into the energy structure of the body, where one becomes aware of the essence of energy, or the pulsation of prana.

   2. *Prana nigraha*: The second aspect is prana nigraha, which concerns the manipulation or control of the breath,

along with the physical and mental reactions that are related to the breath and the prana. A very good example of this is the practice of pranayama combined with bandhas and other techniques. Here the feeling of losing control over the normal breathing faculty leads to agitations that are both physical and mental in nature. So techniques such as nadi shodhana, kapalbhati, bhastrika, etc. are not actually pranayama techniques, but prana nigraha techniques. They control the flow of air into the body, and adjust the systems of the body with the controlled flow of air, so that there is no discomfort experienced on the physical, mental or psychic levels.

3. *Expansion of prana*: Once control is gained over the breathing process together with the various subtle functions related to the breath, the expansion of prana begins, which is the final stage of pranayama. The expansion of prana or the actual technique of pranayama deals with three main pranas. In the first stage, the flow of prana vayu, the energy that is moving upwards between the diaphragm and the throat, is reversed and made to flow down towards the solar plexus. In the second stage the flow of apana vayu is reversed and made to flow up towards the solar plexus. In the third stage prana and apana are fused with the samana energy at the solar plexus.

These are the three stages of pranayama explained by Patanjali in the *Yoga Sutras*. To reverse the downward flow of apana, inhale and pull the apana force upwards. Exhale and push the apana force back down again. To reverse the upward flow of prana, inhale and pull the prana force downward. Exhale and push the prana force upward again. To merge both apana and prana with samana, inhale and reverse the flow of apana and prana simultaneously and bring them together at the navel. Hold the breath and merge these two forces in the agni mandala. Exhale and simultaneously push the apana force back downward and the prana force back upward.

323

Prana and the brain

There are two main aspects of prana. One is known as prana shakti, which is the vital force, comprised of the five prana vayus, or minor pranas. The second is known as chit shakti or manas shakti, which is the mental or conscious force, having its seat in the brain. Prana vayu is the means by which the nerve signals travel in the body. Without prana, there is no movement. The brain has ten compartments, but in our present stage of evolution we are only able to utilize one of these. So there are nine other compartments in the brain that we are attempting to awaken and integrate into our conscious personality.

In order to awaken the nine-tenths of our brain that is sleeping, we must spread the prana into the different dark areas of the brain because the part that is illumined or conscious is but a small fragment. In our daily life, we use the frontal lobe especially. Underlying this, however, is all the unconscious activity that we cannot feel, which we do not ever know is going on below the level of our conscious awareness. It is this relationship between the conscious and unconscious parts of ourselves that we deal with in pranayama, how to take the conscious part of the personality and bring it into contact with the unconscious part of the brain, especially the structure called the reticular activating system.

At the base of the brain is the structure called the reticular activating system (RAS), which can be considered as the mooladhara of the brain. It is from the RAS that energy rises upwards and awakens functions in other parts of the brain. Above this is the medulla oblongata which contains the respiratory centres and then the limbic systems and the hypothalamus gland, which control fear, rage, blood pressure, hunger, satiety, weight control, pleasure, sexuality and other functions, including the pituitary gland and autonomic nervous system.

The structures that control respiration exist in the base of the brain and it is this part of the brain that we are able to influence by working with prana nigraha techniques. Of all the unconscious automatic and autonomic nervous system processes in the body, the only one that can be consciously controlled is breathing.

So the breath is said to be a doorway to controlling all the other internal processes of the body such as the heart, digestion, blood pressure, excretion and absorption. By developing a relationship with the conscious part of the breath, through prana nigraha, we are able to influence the deeper and most subconscious aspects of the consciousness.

Method of teaching

Regarding the different variations or methods of pranayama techniques, one should always remember that these practices have never been taught in public like asana. Pranayama has always been guided according to the individual's physical and mental condition, by observing the student's physical and mental states. There is no fixed rule regarding the practices of pranayama. In relation to speed of practice, one has to consider the capacity of each individual and to know what he wants to achieve.

Except for the most basic practices such as deep breathing, alternate nostril breathing or ratio breathing, which can be done by anyone, advanced pranayama has never been taught in general classes. Those pranayamas which stimulate the nadis and pranas, and alter the state of the nervous system and other systems, are never given a hard and fast rule. It depends on the observation of the teacher, who must know the science of pranayama, and it is a very deep study.

Hatha yoga and kundalini yoga techniques

In the kundalini yoga techniques, inhalation is often through pingala nadi and exhalation through ida nadi or vice versa, while in the hatha yoga versions both nostrils are used. In the hatha yoga techniques there is an emphasis on the generation of heat or prana, which aids the other techniques of hatha yoga to achieve purification. This build-up of pranic energy also removes blockages from the nadis.

Kundalini yoga uses the approach of balancing the swara, left and right nostril or ida and pingala breath flows, more than hatha yoga. The common logic and theory behind kundalini yoga is that nobody can practise it until they have perfected hatha yoga and certain parts of raja yoga, at least up to asana and pranayama. Therefore, the yoga tradition always speaks of the hatha yoga practices as essential for achieving physical purification, harmony and balance. The next stage is to practise asana and pranayama in order to harmonize the flow of the swaras. Then, in the third stage kundalini yoga begins. So the system of kundalini yoga is never taught to the aspirant in beginners classes.

When you rub two sticks together hard enough and for long enough, you produce fire. Similarly, by stimulating the pranas in a particular way, you produce certain effects like fevers, boils, diarrhoea, etc. on the physical level, so you can imagine the effects that incorrect practice can have on the subtle levels of your being. Therefore, a teacher is essential. One cannot learn pranayama from a book.

In pranayama practice it is necessary to progress gradually. You should not push too hard or too much. The effects are not realized in the short term; you have to see these practices as long term techniques that you have to bring into your life every day. Practise pranayama with awareness, relax and gain beneficial results in the long term. Once you start to experience pranayama as a part of your life, you will have much more respect for the practice.

PRE–PRANAYAMA PRACTICES

For pranayama to become effective, it is necessary to understand how to breathe properly. There are many different interpretations about correct procedures for breathing, but the pre-pranayama practices can all be classified into three main groups – lying down, standing up and sitting. With these techniques we learn how to breathe properly, using the natural breathing capacity to arrive at a point of comfort and relaxation. Initially these pre-pranayama practices need to be perfected before attempting the practices of pranayama, because in pranayama there has to be specific awareness of the breath, of correct breathing, and of which area of the lungs or which muscles we are trying to use.

1. Yogic breathing
The first group of breathing techniques is known as yogic breathing. It can be performed in any position and at any time of the day. However, the best position is shavasana.

Technique
Stage 1: Thoracic breathing
Lie down in shavasana and become aware of the normal breathing process. Here one needs to isolate the different muscles being utilized for breathing.

Inhale while expanding the chest or rib cage, so that the ribs move outward and upward.

Exhale and the ribs will move inward and downward. Make sure that the abdomen does not move.

Continue this practice for five minutes.
Stage 2: Abdominal breathing
Begin the practice of abdominal or diaphragmatic breathing. Keep one hand on the navel and the other hand on the chest.

Breathe deeply and feel the abdomen and the navel moving up and down with the breath.

Try not to move the chest or the shoulders.

As you inhale deeply, the lower lobes of the lungs inflate, pushing the diaphragm downward and the abdomen outward.

The lower the diaphragm moves, the more air is being inhaled into the lungs.

As you exhale, the lower lobes of the lungs deflate, so the diaphragm moves upward and the abdomen contracts.

This ensures maximum expulsion of air from the lungs. Continue this practice for five minutes. Feel the navel rising and falling with each ingoing and outgoing breath.

Stage 3: Complete breathing

By combining thoracic and abdominal breathing, it is possible to inhale the optimum amount of air into the lungs and also to exhale the maximum amount of waste air. Therefore, this type of breathing is known as complete yogic breathing.

Inhale deeply and expand first the abdominal region and then the chest, in one slow, smooth motion, until the maximum amount of air has been drawn into the lungs. Then exhale by relaxing the chest first and then the abdomen, so that the maximum amount of air is expelled from the lungs.

The whole movement should be continuous, without jerks, from abdomen to chest and from chest to abdomen, like a wave.

Continue the practice for five minutes.

Feel the stomach rising and then the chest rising as you inhale, the chest falling and then the abdomen falling as you exhale.

This practice generates a deeper awareness of the muscular movement that takes place during the respiratory process.

Physiological effects

The main muscle of respiration is the diaphragm, which rests between the thoracic cavity and the abdominal cavity. The ribs have two main muscles, the outer rib muscle or external intercostal, and the inner rib muscle or internal intercostal. The abdomen has three main muscles. There are many possible combinations and permutations of muscle movement between the diaphragm, abdomen and chest. Basically you can either keep the abdomen tight and move the chest, or keep the chest tight and move the abdomen, or relax and move both areas.

The main muscle that we work with is the diaphragm. We cannot really feel the diaphragm, rather we feel the effects of the diaphragm moving. This is because the diaphragm does not actually have proprioceptive or sensory nerves. However, we can sense the diaphragm internally by yogic means.

When the diaphragm moves down, two things can happen. One, the abdominal contents are pushed down. If the abdominal wall is relaxed, it will move out. The chest will not move much until this abdominal area is full and then the chest will rise. If the abdominal area is tight, pressing down on the abdominal contents makes the chest rise.

When lying in shavasana, the floor holds the rib cage steady. So, it is much easier to practise abdominal breathing than thoracic breathing. In shavasana an uncoupling takes place and the abdomen will automatically move up and down. This is the best way to learn abdominal breathing. As the spinal cord and the back muscles are relaxed and in contact with the floor, this awareness can then be easily extended into the chest and into the thoracic muscles.

2. Standing pre-pranayama practices

In the second group, the breathing techniques are performed in the standing position. These practices increase ventilation and remove the stale air that accumulates in the lower lobes of the lungs.

Technique I

Stand erect with the feet together. Keep the arms straight and place the hands on the thighs.

Inhale deeply from the abdomen. Simultaneously raise the arms above the head in one slow, smooth motion.

Count from one to ten. If the count of ten is difficult, then reduce it to seven or five, according to your breathing capacity.

Raising the arms opens the chest up vertically, inducing the maximum amount of air into the lungs.

Exhale while lowering the arms and contracting the abdomen. This will expel the maximum amount of air from the lungs. Again count from one to ten. Repeat the practice ten times.

Technique 2

Stand erect with the feet together and the arms at the sides.

Inhale and raise the arms sideways. Bring the palms of the hands together over and behind the head.

Exhale and slowly lower the arms sideways. Count to ten while inhaling and exhaling.

Repeat the practice ten times.

This method opens up the chest and lungs horizontally.

Technique 3: Bandha hasta utthanasana

Stand erect with the feet together. Cross the wrists in front of the stomach, keeping the arms straight.

Inhale deeply and raise the arms over and behind the head, keeping the wrists crossed.

Exhale and slowly spread the arms sideways so that they form a straight line at shoulder level. Inhale while raising the arms over the head and re-cross the wrists.

Exhale and slowly lower the arms, so that they are again in front of the stomach.

Repeat the practice ten times.

Technique 4: Utthita lolasana

Stand erect with the feet two feet, or a metre, apart and the arms at the sides.

Inhale deeply and raise the arms over the head. Bending forward from the waist, make the sound Ha-Ha-Ha-Ha, swinging the arms between the legs up to ten times until the lungs are completely emptied.

Then inhale slowly, returning to the upright position with the arms over the head.

Exhale and lower the arms. Repeat the practice ten times.

Physiological effects

These are the four pre-pranayama practices performed from the standing position. They generate awareness in different areas of the lungs. Generally the full capacity of the lungs is never used. In fact it is quite possible that the first breath we took when we came into this world, and which filled up all the air sacs, is still contained somewhere in one of those air sacs that are not being used. When we raise the arms sideways, or from the front, and expand the chest, different air sacs in the lungs, which are related to different muscles, open up and we begin to breathe through these also. However, there should be no forcing or straining.

In the standing posture, the back muscles are engaged in holding the body upright, and the ribs and abdominal muscles contract. So there is a natural tendency for contraction to take place. Many emotional tensions are also held between the shoulders and the perineum. Different patterns of breathing, moving and behaviour develop according to the kinds of tensions we develop.

One way to increase awareness of the lung function is to raise the arms, which opens the chest and aids respiration. When the arms are hanging down they have an obstructive effect on the chest, creating extra weight on the shoulders. Raising the arms allows increased movement due to the reduction of this weight. As the arms rise up in front of the body, the back muscles contract to support this extra weight in the front. This frontal movement actually works more on the abdominal muscles and diaphragm than on the rib cage, although in the final position, where the arms are pulled upwards, the rib cage rises automatically.

In the second technique, rib cage expansion is enhanced. On inhalation the ribs rise upward for a few inches, like a bucket handle. So raising the arms sideways acts more strongly on the ribs than the abdomen.

In the third technique, there is a lateral expansion which works the upper lungs more strongly. If you press the point just in front of the shoulders, where the pectoral

331

muscles are attached, you will find a lot of tension is held here, even more so if the breathing is restricted, as in asthma. It is a protective contraction, a protection of the heart and emotions at the psychic level. This method has an opening effect that allows lateral expansion and release of tension along the clavicle. The abdomen is relatively constricted and the aim is to synchronize the breath with the movement. At the same time, there is an enhancement of the upper, middle and lower lungs, depending on the position of the arms.

3. Sitting pre-pranayama practices: Mudra breathing

The third group of practices which teaches us how to breathe properly is called mudra breathing. These practices can be performed while sitting in a chair, but sitting in vajrasana is recommended, or sukhasana if vajrasana is not possible.

Technique

Stage 1: Sit in vajrasana with the spine erect and the head facing forward. Place the hands on the thighs.
Join the index finger and the thumb in jnana mudra. Position the hands so that the circle of the mudra is placed in the hip area with the palms pressing down on the upper thighs.
The elbows should be pointing sideways.
In this position, with the opening of the shoulders, the breathing becomes lower abdominal breathing, which is slow and deep without any strain.
Stage 2: Clench the fists and place them in the same position, with the fingers closed instead of open.
Press down slightly with about ten percent of the body pressure against the upper thighs and continue the same breathing.
Stage 3: Place the thumbs inside the fist.
As the breathing improves, the thumbs will become more flexible. If the breathing is shallow, the thumbs will be near the third finger. If there is full control over the

breathing process, then the thumbs will touch the little finger or even go beyond it.

Press down slightly against the inside of the hips, but not against the bone, with ten percent of the body pressure. Breathe slowly and deeply.

Stage 4: Join the fists together, turning them upwards, and press swadhisthana kshetram. Breathe slowly and deeply.

Practice note: In all four mudras keep the shoulders straight, the chin up, the chest out and the elbows pointing sideways. Breathing is slow and deep.

Physiological effects

When you sit with the hands forward on the knees, there is a tendency for the back to flex a little. As the hands come further and further back towards the hip joint, even without the hand mudra, the back becomes straighter. The shoulders are supported and lifted away from the chest wall. There is easier respiratory movement. At the same time the spine must be kept straight. To elongate the spine, the chin has to be drawn in slightly, so that there is a stretching of the neck up to bindu chakra, at the top back of the head. This mudra automatically engages the back muscles, keeping them upright, allowing the ribs and abdomen to move freely and easily.

The use of hand mudras creates different patterns of very subtle nervous stimulus. The effects are most obvious. In the first mudra one can feel the lower lungs expanding, in the second mudra one can feel the middle lobe of the lung expanding, and in the third mudra one can feel the upper lobe expanding. The fourth mudra influences the whole lung. It brings together all the other mudras and gives an overall emphasis. These mudras allow for gross changes in the spine, abdomen and ribs to take place. They also allow one to go inside and begin to manipulate the organs.

The thumb governs akasha tattwa (ether element), the first finger governs vayu tattwa (air element), the second finger governs agni tattwa (fire element), the third finger governs apas tattwa (water element), and the little finger governs prithvi tattwa (earth element). The effects occur partly by manipulating the tattwas and partly by manipulating the nerves. Manipulation of the fingers creates nervous stimulation which can either relax the chest, allowing a greater freedom of breath and movement of the muscles, or constrict them. By performing these mudras, we are trying to relax and open up the respiratory system, the lungs, windpipe, nostrils, nerves and muscles that are related to the breathing process.

4. Prana Mudra (invocation of energy)

After mudra breathing comes the technique of prana mudra, which also belongs to the sitting group. It is a more advanced practice which shows how to raise the prana by the process of correct breathing.

Technique

Stage 1: Sit in a comfortable meditation posture with the spine erect and the head facing forward. Place the hands in the lap.

Inhale and then exhale as deeply as possible, contracting the abdominal muscles to expel the maximum amount of air from the lungs.

Bring the awareness to mooladhara chakra below the spine at the perineum.

Inhale slowly and deeply, expanding the abdomen. Simultaneously raise the hands until they are in front of the navel. The hands should be open and the fingers straight with the fingertips pointing towards each other, but not touching.

Feel as though the vital energy is being drawn upward from mooladhara to manipura chakra, as you inhale from the abdomen.

The movement of the hands should be coordinated with the abdominal breathing.

Stage 2: Continue the inhalation, expanding the chest.
Raise the hands from the navel region until they are directly in front of the heart.
Try to feel the pranic energy being drawn upward from manipura to anahata chakra as you inhale.
Drawing even more air into the lungs by raising the shoulders, feel the prana being raised to vishuddhi.
Simultaneously raise the hands to the front of the throat.

Stage 3: Retain the breath inside and stretch the arms out to the side, so that the hands are level with the ears and the elbows are slightly bent.
Feel the pranas spreading like a wave to ajna, bindu and sahasrara.
Concentrate on sahasrara. Try to visualize an aura of pure white light emanating from the crown of the head.
Retain the breath and the position for as long as you can without straining.
Then return to the starting position while exhaling and repeat the stages in reverse order.
Feel the prana progressively moving down through each chakra.
At the end of exhalation, the awareness should be at mooladhara.

KUMBHAKA

In Sanskrit, the word *kumbhaka* means 'breath retention'. It is derived from the word *kumbha*, meaning 'a pot' which can be empty or full. Kumbhaka is, therefore, of two types. The first is *antar kumbhaka*, or internal breath retention, where the breath is held after inhalation when the lungs are full of air. The second is *bahir kumbhaka*, external breath retention, where the breath is held after exhalation when the lungs are empty. There is also a third type called kevala kumbhaka or spontaneous breath retention, where the breath stops of its own accord, without any practice or physical effort. The word *kevala* or *kaivalya*, means 'that which is beyond duality'.

Kevala kumbhaka is, therefore, the spontaneous cessation of the breath that leads one beyond duality to the state of samadhi.

All other forms of kumbhaka are known collectively as sahita kumbhaka. The word *sahita* means 'combined with something'. *Sahita kumbhaka* comprises all the other types of breath retention that are combined with or brought about by practice. They do not arise spontaneously; it requires effort to perform them. These kumbhakas are performed in order to induce or prepare the system for spontaneous kumbhaka.

According to the *Raja Yoga Sutras* of Patanjali, pranayama is not deep breathing or breath control. It is the cessation of inhalation and exhalation, where there is only kumbhaka. When the breathing is controlled in order to retain the breath, it is called pranayama. Thus, retaining the breath either inside or outside the body is the actual meaning of pranayama. The other pranayama techniques are only adjuncts which serve to prepare for, or induce, kumbhaka.

In kundalini yoga the purpose of pranayama is to reverse the flow of prana and apana. Inhalation (pooraka or arohan) helps to reverse the flow of apana from the perineal region to the region of manipura. Exhalation (rechaka or awarohan) helps to reverse the flow of prana, so that it moves downward from vishuddhi to manipura. The aim is to merge apana with prana at samana, thereby awakening the kundalini shakti and inducing spontaneous kumbhaka.

1. Antar kumbhaka (internal retention)

There are three ways of practising internal breath retention or antar kumbhaka. These are not usually taught, as most practitioners do not have such in-depth awareness. That awareness only comes after practising the breathing techniques given in the previous section and becoming aware of the different types of breathing. Kumbhaka is not just holding the breath in or out. It is creating different pressures within the body, according to the type of breathing

336

being practised, in order to alter the physical, pranic and mental states.

Technique
Stage I: Thoracic kumbhaka

Sit in a comfortable meditation asana with the spine erect. The pelvic area should be slightly forward.

Practise yogic breathing for one or two minutes before starting retention.

Keeping the navel area still, inhale, expanding the chest. Hold the breath inside and relax the muscles of the stomach. Feel the point of pressure at the sternum, which will now be slightly uncomfortable. If there is still tightness in the diaphragm, relax more by allowing the air pressure to move down. Then the pressure in the sternum will be accentuated.

When retention is complete, pull the stomach in a little to aid the process of exhalation and breathe out, relaxing the chest.

Exhalation should be slow and continuous. Avoid releasing the breath sharply or suddenly. The transition must be smooth, so that the air in the lungs is gradually expelled.

If you are unable to control the exhalation or the subsequent inhalation, it means that you have exceeded your capacity and the duration of retention should be reduced. The entire process must be controlled and smooth, without strain.

Practice note: This technique activates the heart area. It opens the upper part of the lungs and initially pressure is felt in the spine along the middle thoracic region, between the seventh and tenth vertebrae. It induces intense activity in the anahata kshetram. When you exhale the relaxation of the nerves and pressure helps to balance the pranic activity and reverse the energy flow. That is the theory of kundalini yoga in relation to the first stage of internal kumbhaka.

337

Stage 2: Abdominal kumbhaka

Keeping the chest still, inhale and expand the abdomen. Retain the breath and relax the chest so that the navel area becomes tight. Here an effort is made to retain the breath from the lower abdomen, between the navel and the perineum.

When retention is complete, pull the abdomen in a little to aid the process of exhalation and breathe out, relaxing the abdomen.

Practice note: This practice activates the pelvic region and the lower psychic centres: mooladhara, swadhisthana and manipura. If practised regularly it will stimulate the large and small intestines, and the urogenital organs, creating pressure along the walls of the muscles covering the entire region. With exhalation there is relaxation and reduction in pressure, so that again the energy will move.

Stage 3: Thoracic and abdominal kumbhaka

This practice combines both thoracic and abdominal breathing and retention.

Inhale, expanding the lower abdomen and then the chest, so that the entire area from swadhisthana to vishuddhi is filled with a large quantity of air. Then perform kumbhaka and relax the muscles.

A solid pressure will be felt throughout the torso, from the neck down to the perineum. There should be equal pressure in the abdomen and in the chest, which helps to awaken the samana energy.

When retention is complete, pull the abdomen in a little to aid the process of exhalation, and breathe out, relaxing the chest and then the abdomen.

Practice note: There are no mudras or bandhas associated with these three stages of internal kumbhaka.

Physiological effects

In the practice of kumbhaka, air is isolated in one part of the body to create pressure. For example, in the first stage of internal kumbhaka, oxygen is retained in the chest under high pressure and this creates certain stimuli. When the abdomen is contracted or just held steady in order to expand the upper chest, high pressure is created in the chest cavity. At the same time this movement of the ribs lifts them around the spine and stimulates the nerve plexuses in the spine. Kumbhaka is a very subtle procedure. It involves neither the major stretching of asana, not the major movement of pranayama.

In the area where the breath is being expanded, the nerves are given just enough emphasis to stimulate their activity. These nerves are behind the heart in anahata, and involve the functions of the emotional system. Also remember that the chemical balance in the body is altered by retaining oxygen for as long as possible. When chemical changes have reached a certain level and the oxygen level has dropped, we have to exhale. Normally the body has a constant rhythm of inhalation and exhalation. However, in inner kumbhaka the nerves are stimulated and held steady in such a way that certain changes are created in the chemical balance.

In the first stage of inner kumbhaka, the chest is influenced and pressure is put on the lungs, so there is a very powerful effect on the heart function. In the second stage of inner kumbhaka, digestion is influenced and in the third stage, the whole spinal column is influenced.

2. Bahir kumbhaka (external retention)

External retention is more difficult than internal retention. It should not be attempted until you have mastered the three stages of internal kumbhaka and are able to perform them with ease. Begin external kumbhaka very slowly. At first the system cannot tolerate a long duration of external retention. With regular practice, however, you will be able to increase the length of retention without the feeling of suffocation.

339

Technique

Stage 1: Sit in a comfortable meditation posture. Make sure the spine is erect.

Practise yogic breathing for one or two minutes before retention.

Then inhale and exhale normally and just before you would inhale, stop breathing in and hold the breath outside.

This does not eliminate all the air from the lungs, some residue still remains inside. Relax the internal muscles. Feel the sensation in the region between the navel and the rib cage. The moment you relax this area, the stomach will move forward.

When you begin to feel breathless, allow the inhalation to proceed. Do not fight the urge.

Note

Breathlessness is felt after some time because, due to the habit of continuous breathing, the body is accustomed to eliminating carbon dioxide and other toxins through the breath. According to yoga, however, the breath is only one medium through which toxins are eliminated. Other ways become possible when we go into the advanced practices of kumbhaka with bandhas and mudras.

In the first stage of external kumbhaka, there is absolute relaxation of each and every muscle, which helps to realign and rebalance the nervous and pranic agitations. These agitations arise because we breathe in and out. Due to continual breathing, the level of prana goes up and down all the time; it is never constant. By stopping the breath for a few seconds, these agitations are stilled, allowing the pranic and nervous systems to realign.

In order to create harmony in the three main prana vayus: prana, apana and samana, this simple form of external kumbhaka is advised. Later, it can be attempted in the fourth stage of nadi shodhana pranayama. In the ratio taught initially, 1:4:2:2, external retention is half that of

340

internal retention. This creates less strain on the lungs. When this stage is perfected, then the next stage with bandhas can be practised.

Stage 2: Inhale and exhale normally, holding the breath outside. Then exhale further, so that the lungs are completely emptied. This creates an internal vacuum. Try to relax all the muscles inside.

At this time the abdomen moves inward and there is spontaneous uddiyana bandha. Feel the pressure at the base of the sternum. Be aware of the heart beat, which is becoming very prominent. Feel the heart beat slowing into a steady, strong rhythm.

When an urge to breathe is felt, gradually allow the inhalation to intervene.

This is the basic practice. When the other bandhas are combined, external kumbhaka becomes a very powerful means of stimulating manipura and raising the vital energy.

Contra-indications: People with heart ailments, stroke or blood pressure problems should avoid this practice.

Physiological effects

Internal and external kumbhaka are the opposite ends of a continuum. They both work partially by increasing proprioceptive awareness in certain parts of the body, isolating positive pressure in the case of internal kumbhaka, and negative pressure in the case of external kumbhaka. In this way, they allow internal spaces to be felt more acutely, which is the awakening aspect. In internal kumbhaka, positive pressure is created by oxygen filling a cavity and expanding it. With external kumbhaka negative pressure is produced by creating a vacuum in which even stronger pressures are created. External kumbhaka is like a quantum leap and is more difficult than internal kumbhaka. Increased prana comes from the pressure, the blood flow and the nervous stimulation. If one's attention is focused enough to feel and

341

connect the sensory, proprioceptive or informative aspect with the energy aspect, then knowledge and energy come together.

From a chemical point of view, when oxygen is held in the body, there is a period when the body is comfortable. You can sit comfortably without feeling the need to breathe. The nervous system and cells do not demand oxygen until the carbon dioxide increases to a certain level. In external kumbhaka all the oxygen is expelled, so the body needs oxygen again very soon. The increase of carbon dioxide in the body is the most potent stimulus to make you breathe. Running out of oxygen is not as strong. In kumbhaka we develop the ability to withstand the pressure and pull created by the starvation of oxygen and the build up of carbon dioxide in the body.

During internal kumbhaka there is plenty of oxygen in reserve, so we can sit relatively quietly and observe the stopping of the major biorhythms of the body. Once this is perfected, external kumbhaka can be practised. In stage one, you exhale naturally and stay as relaxed as possible, allowing the reserves of oxygen to run out slowly and the carbon dioxide to build up. When a certain level is reached, oxygen deprivation occurs and carbon dioxide builds up very quickly. The aim of staying relaxed is to slow down the formation of carbon dioxide. When tension builds up there is a hypermetabolic state, which means that oxygen is burnt up and carbon dioxide builds up very quickly.

In kumbhaka we learn to stay relaxed under this stressful condition. Stress is created by cutting off the supply of oxygen. We have to learn to stay relaxed during that process and to induce hypometabolism so that the carbon dioxide level will build up even more slowly. Therefore, conscious control is developed over a very subtle aspect of our being, the blood chemistry, and the drive to breathe emanating from the centre of the brain. If this skill can be developed, relaxation can also be maintained when other pressures occur.

342

Psychologically, the major effect of external kumbhaka occurs when, due to the vacuum created inside the body, the mental functions also stop. It is very hard to think while practising external kumbhaka. If we consider thoughts to be energy flows or forms of energy in the mind, then the most visible sign in kumbhaka is their cessation, where there is no movement of any kind of subtle pranic energy. Therefore, external kumbhaka has been used widely in the practices of pratyahara and in combination with mudras and bandhas.

Every single organ and tissue in the body has a rhythm. These rhythms are like an orchestra. In kumbhaka one of the most important vital rhythms of the body is stopped. When we begin this practice, the nerves in the brain start to increase their discharge because they are trying to make the muscles move. When the discharge stops, a state of tranquillity is experienced. By controlling and stopping one rhythm, all the other rhythms in the body are affected. These are powerful practices and should be performed with awareness and care.

NADI SHODHANA PRANAYAMA

The word *nadi* means, 'pranic flow' or 'pranic channel' and *shodhana* means, 'purification'. Nadi shodhana is thus the practice by which the pranic channels are purified, allowing the prana to flow freely throughout the body. There are four basic stages of nadi shodhana. Each stage should be mastered before proceeding to the next. Control over the respiratory system must be developed gradually over a period of time.

Nasagra Mudra
The breath through the nostrils is controlled by the fingers of the right hand, which is held straight in front of the face. This position is called nasagra or nasikagra mudra, the word *nasi* meaning 'nose'.

343

Technique

Hold the right hand in front of the face.

The elbow should be in front of the chest and the forearm vertical. The head, neck and back should be in one straight line.

Place the index and middle finger tips at the eyebrow centre, keeping the fingers straight. The thumb should be beside the right nostril. The ring and little fingers are held together beside the left nostril.

The right nostril can now be controlled, by pressing the right side of the nose with the thumb. The left nostril can be controlled, by pressing the left side of the nose with the ring finger.

Nadi Shodhana Pranayama (psychic network purification)
Technique I: Preparatory practice

Stage I: Sit in a comfortable meditation posture. Close the eyes and relax the whole body.

Raise the right hand in front of the face and perform nasagra mudra.

Close the right nostril with the thumb. Slowly inhale and exhale through the left nostril.

Be aware of the breath.

Continue breathing through the left nostril for two to three minutes. Try to utilize the full capacity of the lungs, rather than the thoracic cavity only.

Then close the nostril with the ring finger.

Breathe in and out through the right nostril in the same way for two to three minutes. Try to gain control over the flow of the breath.

Lower the right hand to the knee.

Breathe in and out through both nostrils together for two to three minutes.

Stage 2: This practice is similar to stage 1, but here you begin to count the number of breaths through each nostril, using the 1:1 ratio.

Close the right nostril with the thumb.

Breathe in and out slowly and rhythmically through the left nostril five times.

Count 1-2-3 as you inhale, and again count 1-2-3 as you exhale.

Close the left nostril with the ring finger. Breathe in and out slowly through the right nostril five times.

Count 1-2-3 as you inhale and again as you exhale.

Try to make each breath rhythmic and even.

Then lower the right hand to the knee.

Breathe in and out slowly through both nostrils together five times, utilizing the same count.

This makes one round: five breaths through the left nostril, five breaths through the right nostril and five breaths through both nostrils together.

Practise five to ten rounds.

Stage 3: This practice is similar to stage 2 except that now the ratio of 1:2 is used.

Close the right nostril.

Breathe in and out slowly through the left nostril five times.

While inhaling, count 1-2-3, and while exhaling count 1-2-3-4-5-6.

Breathe deeply, expanding and contracting both the abdomen and the chest.

After completing five breaths in this manner, close the left nostril.

345

Breathe in and out through the right nostril five times. Continue the same counting, 1-2-3 while inhaling and 1-2-3-4-5-6 while exhaling.

Then lower the right hand to the knee.

Breathe in and out through both nostrils five times utilizing the same count.

Be aware of the breath and the mental counting throughout the practice.

Here the ratio of inhalation and exhalation is 1:2. Gradually extend the count from 3:6 to 4:8 then 5:10. Practise five to ten rounds.

Practice note: If the nose is blocked, it is essential to do jala neti before beginning the practice.

Technique 2: Alternate nostril breathing

Stage 1: Sit in a comfortable meditation asana. Close the eyes and relax the whole body.

Become aware of the breath.

Feel the breath moving smoothly and evenly up and down both nostrils.

Raise the right hand in front of the face and perform nasagra mudra.

Close the right nostril with the thumb. Inhale slowly through the left nostril.

Breathe in deeply expanding both the abdomen and the chest. Fill the lungs to the maximum.

At the end of inhalation, close the left nostril, open the right nostril and exhale slowly.

While exhaling, the chest and abdomen should be gently contracted so that the lungs are emptied as much as possible.

After exhalation, slowly inhale through the right nostril, filling the lungs.

Then close the right nostril, open the left nostril and exhale, emptying the lungs.

Two complete breaths make one full round: inhalation through the left nostril, exhalation through the right nostril, inhalation through the right nostril, exhalation through the left nostril.

The duration of inhalation should be equal to the duration of exhalation. Practise 15 rounds.

Note

This practice is commonly known as *sukha poorvaka*, meaning 'simple preliminary practice' or *bhal bhati* meaning 'forehead bellows'. In English, it is called alternate nostril breathing because air is inhaled through one nostril and exhaled through the other. It is essentially a practice of slow, deep, rhythmic breathing through alternate nostrils. The emphasis is on progressively slowing down the breathing rate and balancing the flow of the breath through the two nostrils. This induces tranquillity and balance throughout the system.

Stage 2: After mastering stage 1, start to mentally count the duration of inhalation and exhalation. Try to count with a fixed timing. Each count should be about one second. It is very easy to speed up the counting when you are short of breath. Adjust the count according to your own capacity with the ratio of 1:1. If you breathe in for a count of five, then you also breathe out for a count of five. Begin with whatever count you feel is comfortable, whether it is 3:3, 4:4, 5:5 or 10:10.

However, you should not strain during the practice. If you feel any strain, reduce that count. Gradually increase the duration of inhalation and exhalation over a period of months, up to 24:24.

Stage 3: After mastering alternate nostril breathing with the 1:1 ratio, start to slowly increase the duration of exhalation. Over the space of five rounds make the exhalation one count longer. For example, if you inhale for a count of five, then exhale for a count of six. If you breathe in for a count of ten, then breathe out for a count of eleven. The actual count depends on how far you have progressed in the previous part.

Practice note: Do not use force or strain. The duration of inhalation and exhalation should be comfortable. After five rounds, add one more count to the duration of exhalation. Continue in this way to increase the count by one every five rounds, until you find it difficult to increase the length of exhalation any further without straining. Eventually the aim is to fix the ratio of inhalation to exhalation at 1:2. How quickly you attain this will depend on what your count was for the initial 1:1 ratio.

When you reach the 1:2 ratio, gradually start to increase the inhalation by one count and the exhalation by two counts, maintaining the same 1:2 ratio. For example, if you are starting with a count of five inhaling and ten exhaling, then increase to six inhaling and twelve exhaling, seven inhaling and fourteen exhaling. Over a period of months, try to increase the count to 24:48. Remember its is essential to maintain awareness of the breathing and the mental counting throughout the practice.

Note

Nadi shodhana is known as the silent pranayama. Try to breathe without making any noise as the air enters and leaves the nostrils. Noise is a sure sign that you are breathing too quickly. If you cannot eliminate the sound of the breath, go on with the practice, but keep this point in mind. The respiratory rate will gradually reduce with practice. The breathing must be relaxed and without violent heaving and movement of the body.

In technique 3, antar kumbhaka or internal breath retention is added. Techniques 1 and 2 of nadi shodhana are essential because they prepare the lungs and the nervous system for kumbhaka. It is easy to hold the breath once, but to hold the breath several times with intermittent inhalations and exhalations requires practice. Therefore, technique 2 should be mastered fully before technique 3 is undertaken. Otherwise you will feel strain and your progress will be impeded.

Technique 3: With Antar Kumbhaka (inner retention)

Stage 1: Breathe in slowly through the left nostril, keeping the right nostril closed. The duration of inhalation should be the same duration reached at the end of technique 2. At the end of inhalation, close both nostrils and retain the breath inside the lungs. Slightly contract the glottis and firmly hold the air inside for the same duration as the inhalation.

Then slowly breathe out through the right nostril. Exhalation should not be in one gasp, but controlled, the duration being equal to that of inhalation and retention. At the end of exhalation, breathe in through the right nostril, keeping the left nostril closed.

Again do antar kumbhaka, holding the breath firmly inside. Then exhale through the left nostril.

This makes one round.

Continue with the practice, maintaining the ratio of 1:1:1. After some time, when you feel comfortable with the practice, change the ratio to 1:1:2. Keep the same duration of inhalation and exhalation as mastered in technique 2, stage 3. Practise five to ten rounds.

Stage 2: The aim in this stage is to gradually extend the duration of antar kumbhaka by one count every few days, until it is the same duration as the exhalation, that is the ratio of 1:2:2. Then keeping the ratio of 1:2:2 fixed, begin to increase the duration of inhalation, antar kumbhaka and exhalation. Over a period of months, try to reach the count of 20:40:40. Gradually extend the count so that no tension or strain is produced by the practice.

Stage 3: After mastering the ratio of 1:2:2, the duration of antar kumbhaka has to be increased again until the ratio of 1:4:2 is attained. Keeping the same ratio and count for the inhalation and exhalation as you reached in stage 2, slowly extend the duration of inner retention by one count every few days until you reach the count of 20:80:40. Awareness of the breath and the mental counting is

349

essential in order to master the ratio of inhalation, kumbhaka and exhalation, and to alter it when necessary.

Contra-indications: Techniques 3 and 4 of nadi shodhana with kumbhaka are not recommended for people with hypertension or heart disease, vertigo, neurosis or psychosis, or any serious ailment.

Technique 4: With Antar and Bahir Kumbhaka (internal and external retention)

Practise the same method that you have mastered in technique 3 and add external breath retention.

Inhale through the left nostril, retain the breath internally, exhale through the right nostril and retain the breath externally.

Then inhale through the right nostril and hold the breath internally, exhale through the left nostril and hold the breath externally. This makes one round.

First begin with the ratio 1:1:1:1, using a count that is comfortable. After some time, change the ratio to 1:2:2:1, 1:2:2:2, and then to 1:4:2:2.

Practice note: At this stage the practice of bahir kumbhaka or external breath retention is added. Bahir kumbhaka is more difficult to master than antar kumbhaka because it is not a function the lungs are normally required to perform. Therefore, it should be developed slowly.

Note

These four techniques of nadi shodhana: (i) breathing through individual nostrils, (ii) alternate nostril breathing, (iii) alternate nostril breathing with antar kumbhaka and (iv) alternate nostril breathing with antar and bahir kumbhaka are the same in both the hatha yoga and kundalini yoga texts.

Physiological effects

Slow, deep, rhythmic breathing as practised in nadi shodhana has far reaching effects on the entire system. It results in fewer breaths per minute, for as one breathes more deeply, the frequency of respiration automatically decreases. In everyday life, most people breathe 15–20 times per minute. These are generally shallow gasps, which utilize only a small portion of the available lung capacity. Therefore, a lot of energy is consumed in breathing with a relatively small return in terms of energy. By breathing slowly and rhythmically, we can easily oxygenate the system and expend less muscular energy.

Inhalation is a completely different process to exhalation. During inhalation, there is muscular expansion and a balanced tension in the body. One is trying to gradually control all the muscles involved in respiration in such a way that the breath can be lengthened to the maximum. Every day this is gradually increased. Exhalation is generally longer than inhalation. Exhalation is passive, one relaxes and lets go. In order to lengthen the exhalation, one has to have control of the muscles, otherwise there will be a re-coil and the whole body will contract into its natural state. In nadi shodhana one has to be able to control inspiration and expiration, which balances out the whole respiratory cycle.

From the physiological point of view, nadi shodhana is the perfect balancing practice. Alternate nostril breathing stimulates the left and right sides of the brain equally and thereby the left and right sides of the body. It directly balances the two major nadis, ida and pingala, which play a major role in determining our thinking and behaviour, deciding whether we are introverted or extroverted. Furthermore, it is stated in the yogic texts that when ida and pingala are balanced and purified, sushumna nadi, which is responsible for spiritual experience, begins to flow. This leads to heightened awareness and spontaneous meditative states.

The addition of a ratio is what makes nadi shodhana unique. The ratio gradually superimposes a smooth and even rhythm on the normal rhythms of the brain, which are not even. Due to our lifestyle we are often alienated from nature and out of tune with the natural cycles and rhythms of the environment. It is important to remember that pranayama practice, especially nadi shodhana, is trying to rebalance the cycles of our body in order to bring them into harmony with the cycles of the environment. We do not exist outside our environment, we are not islands unto ourselves.

There are many cycles going on simultaneously all over the brain. On an EEG we can see that the patterns are irregular and haphazard. There is no obvious rhythm. When we practise nadi shodhana we impose a smooth wave on top of these irregular rhythms, which is a sine wave. The kindling effect is then used in its positive sense, gradually pushing all those other rhythms in that direction, imposing our will on the unconscious, autonomous rhythms of the body. Gradually, regular daily practice will bring all the other rhythms into harmony.

By using the ratio 1:2, we are bringing the breath to its natural rhythm of exhalation, being double that of inhalation, which allows the body more time to rest. The resting phase is double the length of the working phase, as it is in life. Every working phase should always be half the resting phase. So we work for eight hours and we relax for sixteen.

When kumbhaka is added, we are stopping at a certain point in the cycle and putting a block on the rhythms of the body. The respiratory cycle wants to move, but we do not allow it to move. This emphasizes the effect that we have been inducing. When we breathe in and retain the breath, the levels of oxygen and carbon dioxide change accordingly. The whole system, heart beat, blood pressure, digestion, is affected by this central change.

Any practice which works centrally will affect every structure in the body. By doing it regularly, it then becomes easier to hold the breath for a longer period of time. The practice of external retention is more difficult, one has less oxygen to start with. With internal retention one is emphasizing the oxygen component of the respiratory cycle. With external retention the carbon dioxide level of the respiratory cycle is emphasized.

UJJAYI PRANAYAMA (THE PSYCHIC BREATH)

From ancient times, the word *jaya* has been uttered to denote 'victory' or 'success'. The prefix *u* or *ud* means 'aloud'. Ujjayi is the technique of breathing aloud, which calms the mind and leads to success in meditation. Ujjayi is also known as 'psychic breathing' because it introverts the mind prior to many meditation practices and the kriyas of kundalini yoga.

In the hatha yoga version of ujjayi, inhalation and exhalation take place smoothly and effortlessly through both nostrils, without any feeling of tension or constriction in the chest. There is awareness of the sound being produced in the throat both by inhalation and exhalation. This sound resembles the soft snoring of a sleeping baby. It should be audible to the practitioner alone, and not to others. If the sound is very loud, it means too much effort is being made. In the hatha yoga variation, ujjayi breathing is meant to become spontaneous and subtle.

Hatha yoga technique

Sit in a comfortable meditation position, keeping the head and neck straight. Close the eyes.

Breathe slowly and deeply with the awareness at the throat.

Partially close the glottis by slightly contracting the throat. When you contract the glottis, you will automatically feel a slight contraction or pulling sensation at the abdomen. As you breathe in ujjayi, you should hear a continuous soft, snoring sound being emitted from the throat. This sound is produced by the friction of the air as it passes through the constriction you have made in the throat.

Try to relax as much as possible during the practice.

Do not contort or tense the face, neck or throat.

The contraction should be slight and the breathing effortless.

Kundalini yoga technique

In this technique the process of ujjayi breathing changes considerably.

Inhale fully and deeply through both nostrils. During inhalation there is no constriction of the throat and no sound of the ujjayi breathing.

After completing the inhalation, perform internal kumbhaka for as long as you can hold the breath comfortably, without straining or building up tension. During breath retention, relax the diaphragm allowing the air to pass down into the lower region.

At this time the stomach is pushed out and the pressure is reduced from the chest and head. The internal muscles are relaxed all the way down to the perineum, causing the inner pressure to dissipate. Breath retention here is performed without bandhas.

When you are ready to exhale, first pull the diaphragm up. Then close the right nostril and exhale through the left nostril, ida nadi, with ujjayi breathing.

During exhalation there is constriction of the thoracic cavity as well as the throat. Therefore, the ujjayi breathing during exhalation is louder and more forceful than in the hatha yoga variation.

No ratio is added in this technique. It is performed according to one's capacity, without creating tension or strain.

Note

This technique should be practised in stages. The first stage is becoming aware of the diaphragm and the contraction in this area. Then work on engaging, not the abdominal breath, but a relaxed breath around the area between the rib cage and the abdomen. When the strength of the breath is such that it creates a kind of mild contraction, then emphasize the throat.

Breathe using the whole abdomen, especially emphasizing the mooladhara chakra area, the perineum. If even a small amount of muscular tension is held in any part of the abdomen or pelvis, it will interfere with the breath and its functioning. Most people have little areas of chronic tension which they relax to a certain degree. But when the awareness is taken away, that contraction creeps up and takes over other parts of the body. So, by extending ujjayi down to the perineum, many of these deeper contractions are relaxed.

The benefits of ujjayi have been described as follows: first, it is a heating practice; second, it removes mucus or phlegm from the throat, and third, it improves the digestive functions. This third aspect is the key which describes how the technique has to be performed. In the hatha yoga variation of ujjayi pranayama, the breath is limited to the thoracic cavity, but in the kundalini yoga process, a different action takes place. After inhaling, retain the breath inside and relax the diaphragm. Then the breath will move down and the pressure will also move down and dissipate.

Before breathing out, again pull up the diaphragm in order to maintain control over the exhalation process. If you try to breathe out with the diaphragm relaxed, the exhalation will be very short. In order to have the same control over exhalation as inhalation, the diaphragm must be pulled up before exhalation. It is this movement of the diaphragm that massages the stomach muscles and associated organs. That soft gentle massage experienced with the movement of the diaphragm will rectify digestive imbalances and increase digestive power.

This is how kumbhaka should be performed in the ujjayi technique. Inhale, retain the breath inside and relax the diaphragm. When you are ready to exhale, pull up the diaphragm and breathe out slowly. If you inhale and retain the breath in the pulmonary region, then the expansion of the lung muscles and tissues within the rib cage can create a kind of pressure on the heart organ. That pressure is removed from the heart by relaxing the lower diaphragm.

Even in the hatha yoga technique, where kumbhaka is not practised, there is an effort to breathe in more using the

355

stomach while maintaining the contraction of the throat muscles in order to create the hissing sound.

Physiological effects

There are two points to consider in discussing the physiology of ujjayi. One point is related to the concept of conscious and unconscious breathing. This practice takes us into the realm of completely conscious breathing for extended periods of time, by engaging the conscious mind in the process of extending the breath.

The second point is that there are two levels of respiration. The first level is external or pulmonary respiration which goes on in the lungs. When we are engaging all our muscles, the diaphragm descends and we suck air into the lungs. Contracting the throat is like gently blowing up the lungs. We are pushing air into all the regions of the lungs, working the lungs and improving the balance between gas exchange and pocket pressure. Some parts of the lungs are more expanded and work harder than others. Ujjayi evens the pressure throughout the lungs rather than having these isolated contracted areas. The second level is cellular respiration. The oxygen goes into the blood and is carried into the cells. Every single cell is an individual which has its own life, and which also breathes.

So, in regard to these two simple points, we are engaging all our muscles, creating a strong suction of breath at the external level. This has an effect all the way down into cellular respiration, as if we are sucking the prana down into the cell and pushing it out. There is enhanced movement of oxygen and carbon dioxide all the way down to the cells. Normal respiration is very weak and only uses a very small percentage of the lung capacity. Ujjayi uses almost the complete respiration capacity and has a very powerful effect.

The next level to consider is the enhanced benefit of blood flow to all the various organs in this technique. The extended movement of the lungs is like a pump inside the body being fully depressed as one breathes in. Blood, fluid and nervous energy are moved through the body in a way they would not normally be, unless we were running. While exercising or running, the muscles contract, but in the practice of ujjayi this occurs while the muscles of the body are completely relaxed, and so it has a very profound effect.

Another level to consider is the nervous system. We are bringing our conscious awareness down into the unconscious sea of prana, which has its root at the base of the brain where the nerve centre governing respiration lies. By performing this breathing technique, we exert a smooth and flowing rhythm on the nervous system, which has a profoundly relaxing effect at the psychic level, the deepest level of our being. For this reason ujjayi is one of the most useful of all the pranayama practices in yoga therapy.

Ujjayi also affects the carotid sinuses in the region of the throat, the main artery, which supplies blood to the brain. The carotid sinuses regulate blood pressure in the arteries. When the blood pressure rises, the carotid bodies send a message to the brain. The brain in turn sends a message to the heart, which slows down, thereby bringing the blood pressure down to a reasonable level. If the blood pressure is too low, the same process is repeated and the heart speeds up to increase the blood pressure. When ujjayi pranayama is practised, a slight pressure is exerted on the carotid sinuses, which eventually lowers the blood pressure. This in turn reduces the tension and thought processes in the mind. For this reason ujjayi is conducive to meditation practices.

KAPALBHATI PRANAYAMA
(FRONTAL BRAIN CLEANSING BREATH)

Kapalbhati pranayama is the frontal brain bellowing technique. In Sanskrit the word *kapala* means 'skull', 'cranium' or 'forehead' and *bhati* means 'light' or 'splendour', and also 'perception' or 'knowledge'. Hence kapalbhati is the practice which brings a state of light or clarity to the frontal region of the brain. The word skull refers here to the frontal region of the brain which is behind the forehead.

Kapalbhati is also one of the six cleansing kriyas of hatha yoga. There are other names for this practice, such as kapalshodhana. The word *shodhana* means 'to purify', so this practice is frontal brain purification. Kapalbhati is used to create light-headedness, which is conducive to meditation. It stops thoughts and removes sensory distractions from the mind. It is also directly linked with the purification of ida and pingala nadis.

Kapalbhati Pranayama

Sit in any comfortable meditation posture, keeping the spine straight and the body firm. Padmasana is recommended for this practice because it is the steadiest position. To begin with perform ten rapid respirations through both nostrils. Each respiration should start with exhalation and end with inhalation. Inhalation should be natural and spontaneous with expansion of the abdomen. Exhalation should be forceful with contraction of the abdomen.

After completing ten rapid breaths in succession, inhale and exhale deeply, which is the eleventh breath. This is one round. After completion of each round, pause to allow the breath to return to normal. Then begin the next round. Practise up to ten rounds. Gradually increase the number of respirations per round as the lung capacity increases. In the final stage, 60–100 rapid, forceful exhalations should be performed in a sequence, followed by a rest between rounds.

Variation I: Alternate nostrils

Different techniques can be added to this basic practice, for example, alternate nostril breathing. First close one nostril and practise kapalbhati through the other nostril twenty times. Then take a deep breath in and out, which is the twenty-first breath. Repeat the same process though the other nostril, and then through both nostrils together. This constitutes one round. In advanced stages, this practice is combined with bandhas and kumbhaka.

Variation 2: Kapalshodhana pranayama

In this method the alternate nostrils are used as in variation 1, but the process is different. It begins with inhalation through the right nostril, which is the pingala or dakshina nadi. Initially, in this practice the ratio of 8:4:2 is used. Inhale for a count of eight, retain the breath inside for a count of four and exhale forcefully through the right nostril for a count of two. Repeat the same process 20 times through the right nostril, 20 times through the left nostril and then 20 times through both nostrils together. This is one round.

At first, concentrate on control of the breath and become used to the forced exhalation. Then the pace can be quickened by changing the ratio from 8:4:2 to 4:2:1, which is the ideal ratio for this practice. Once you feel comfortable with the ratio, then maintain that same rhythm throughout the practice. In the advanced stages, bandhas and mudras can be combined.

Duration: In all three practices of kapalbhati it is recommended that the number of rounds is increased rather than the number of breaths, until a point is reached where there is total control over the physiological process and activity. To reach the level of Paramahamsa Satyananda, who did 5,000 continuous bhastrika or kapalbhati breaths at one stretch, as part of higher sadhana, a very high degree of voluntary control over the physical organs and the nervous system is needed. In the basic technique 60 to 100 breaths per round is ideal. In variation 1 the ratio of breaths is 20:20:20. In variation 2 (kapalshodhana) the breathing ratio is 4:2:1 and the ratio of breaths is 20:20:20. Advanced practitioners should extend the number of rounds to ten or more.

Speed of respiration: The speed of respiration changes depending on which technique you are practising. In the hatha yoga technique, the rapid movement stimulates the lower abdominal muscles, and the practice becomes like a semi-agnisar kriya, activating the manipura region. In the kundalini yoga technique there is more in-depth awareness of the breath. Even though there may be a tendency to speed up the breath, you will have to control it in order to enter into the psychic dimension. That is the main difference between hatha yoga and kundalini yoga techniques.

Contra-indications: People with heart ailments, stroke, high blood pressure, hernia, gastric ulcer and vertigo should avoid this practice.

Practice note: When kapalbhati pranayama is practised with a combination of bandhas and kumbhaka, then only internal retention should be used with jalandhara and moola bandha. External retention and uddiyana bandha should be avoided because it will create further abdominal contraction, which will cause a lot of tension in the diaphragm. If practised for an extended period, this over-contraction will make the muscles of the diaphragm and lungs go into spasm and there will be breathlessness. You may not notice this at first, but you will notice it later. It is safe to use external kumbhaka with bhastrika, however, because in bhastrika there is equal inhalation and exhalation, so the body is not at the same level of tension or stress.

Notes on Kapalshodhana Pranayama

The upanishadic texts have always emphasized that kapal-shodhana should begin with the right nostril, because the aim of this practice is activation of pingala nadi, which in turn stimulates vata nadi to release gas. Vata nadi controls gas formation and elimination within the body. This nadi runs along the back of the neck and head and disappears inside the brain. People with control over vata nadi can belch when the point at the back of the neck is pressed.

The form of kapalbhati mentioned in the hatha yoga texts is never really taught to anybody, because most people do not even know what it is. It is not the form of kapalbhati that we know, it is kapalshodhana pranayama. The purpose of this practice is to stimulate vata nadi to eliminate excess vata from the body and to release the pressure that vata creates inside the skull. Because of the release of that pressure, the name of the practice is kapalshodhana.

Physiological effects

In every process of the body there is a dual system at work, active and passive. In the respiratory process, inspiration is considered to be active and expiration passive. During inhalation, energy is used to pull the breath inside. Exhalation is generally passive and mainly involves a recoil action. Inspiration is energizing because it requires nervous system stimulation. The elastic recoil of the lungs and the rib cage creates exhalation automatically. That is the resting phase, which is passive.

The technique of kapalbhati is a way of reversing the normal breathing cycle by making inspiration passive and expiration active. This requires consciously over-riding the usual subconscious processes. All pranayama practices aim at creating different rhythms, speeds and intensities of breathing, and a different emphasis on inhalation and exhalation, in order to change patterns that habituate in the physical, mental, emotional and deeper psychic bodies. Prana can be expanded right up to the psychic dimension by pranayama practice in hatha yoga, while in kundalini yoga one can go much further.

From a muscular point of view, the main focus in kapalbhati is on the diaphragm. During exhalation the diaphragm moves up and during inhalation it moves down. Due to the forceful upward movements with the diaphragm, the abdominal muscles are contracted forcibly. This contraction of the abdomen pushes the digestive prana, the samana energy, upwards. The upward movement is

361

emphasized to the extent that the breath comes up, hits the base of the skull and comes down through the nose. This has a very stimulating effect on the blood, nerves and celiac plexus in the gut. It also has the effect of pushing impulses through the nerves to the brain, as well as the breath up through the tubes of the lungs.

The breathing ratio is very important here. Normally we breathe in for half the duration that we breathe out. For example, in nadi shodhana we breathe in for four counts and out for eight counts. This is the normal ratio for respiration, 1:2. In kapalshodhana, however, we breathe out for a quarter of the time that we breathe in. This exercises our breath control and stretches it to its limit. It also alters the level of carbon dioxide and other chemicals, acids and alkalis in the blood. Apart from cleansing the body and the nervous system and removing accumulated gases which build up in the upper parts of the lungs, the intention of pranayama is to enable the system to withstand the build up of carbon dioxide in the lungs.

What we are trying to do in the kundalini yoga technique is to develop a rhythm in which there are two components. There is the entire body with all the tissues, prana, nerves and so on, and there is us trying to work with our bodies through our limited understanding. Often that egoic part of us pushes too hard and strains. If we strain we have to slow down because we feel tired, or if we do not feel strain we speed up because we want to go faster in order to get better results.

The important thing, however, is to have the muscles moving in a very relaxed, comfortable rhythm. The rhythm should be slow at first and then, as the lung capacity is developed, natural and effortless. It is like riding the sea of prana, working with that vast, pranic, muscular, nervous interaction. Then, as a relaxed attitude develops towards the breath, we can speed up or slow down according to the results we want to achieve.

Many times the pranayama practices have slight variations. When emphasis is put on a different aspect of the technique, the result or benefit is different because each aspect stimulates a different nadi, brain centre or part of the nervous system. The moment we stop practising as we please and begin to realize the potential that is inherent within the different tissues of the body, the total concept of pranayama changes. We do not have to control the breath – the body controls our movements. That is the final result of the practice.

Initially, an effort is made to breathe in a particular rhythm, pushing the body to the maximum limit. We practise ten rounds of pranayama when we should only do three because we think that by doing a few more rounds we will get a better result. We fail to realize that if we overstep the limit, the practice will begin to rebound, creating further stress in our system. Often that stress becomes hard to deal with later on.

An aversion is created to certain kinds of practices because we try to control the body voluntarily rather than allowing it to control itself. The body knows what it can do and what it cannot do. You have to come to that level of awareness. The moment the strength, breath, movement and concentration merge with each other, then the body comes alive. However, if you push the body to do something that it cannot do, then the body is more dead than alive at that moment, and pushing that dead body is not really worthwhile.

BHASTRIKA PRANAYAMA (BELLOWS BREATH)

In Sanskrit, the word *bhastrika* means 'bellows'. This pranayama is known as bellows breathing because air is drawn forcefully in and out of the lungs like a blacksmith's bellows. Bellows are used to fan the fire in order to produce more heat. Bhastrika pranayama has the same effect on the body. It increases the flow of air inside and fans the inner heat which burns the impurities. In Sanskrit this process of burning the impurities is known as tapasya. Bhastrika is a direct method of purification or tapasya.

Hatha yoga technique

Sit in a comfortable meditation posture, preferably padmasana or siddhasana.

Raise the right hand in front of the face and perform nasagra mudra. The left hand should rest on the knee. Close the right nostril with the thumb. Breathe in and out forcefully and rapidly through the left nostril 20 times. The pumping action should be done by the expansion and contraction of the abdomen, try not to use the chest.

Inhalation and exhalation should be of equal force. Forceful inhalation is induced by fully expanding the abdominal muscles. Forceful exhalation is induced by firmly and quickly contracting the abdominal muscles. The whole breathing process should be rapid and rhythmic. As you breathe in and out forcefully, you should hear a snuffling sound in the nose.

After completing 20 rapid respirations, breathe in deeply through the left nostril, keeping the right nostril closed. Fill the lungs as much as possible, expanding both the abdomen and the chest. Hold the breath inside for as long as is comfortable.

Perform jalandhara and moola bandhas while retaining the breath.

Do not strain.

Release the bandhas and exhale slowly through the left nostril.

Then begin right nostril respiration.

Close the left nostril with the ring finger and open the right nostril. Breathe in and out rapidly and forcefully through the right nostril 20 times. Remember to push the abdomen in and out like a bellows.

Then inhale slowly and deeply through the right nostril. Hold the breath inside and perform jalandhara and moola bandhas.

Release the bandhas and breathe out slowly through the right nostril.

Then begin respiration through both nostrils. Breathe in and out rapidly and forcefully 20 times through both nostrils together.

Then inhale slowly and deeply through both nostrils. Hold the breath inside and perform jalandhara and moola bandhas.

Release the bandhas and exhale slowly through both nostrils together.

This is one complete round: 21 breaths through the left nostril, 21 breaths through the right nostril and 21 breaths through both nostrils.

Note

This practice is very similar to kapalbhati and many beginners are unable to differentiate between the two in their practice. The main difference is that in kapalbhati the emphasis is on forceful exhalation, allowing inhalation to be spontaneous, while in bhastrika both inhalation and exhalation are equally rapid and forceful.

Breathing is always performed through the nose and the mouth should remain closed throughout the practice. Although the breathing is rapid and forceful, there is no need to grit the teeth or contort the face.

In some yogic texts it says that one should begin rapid breathing through the left nostril. However, as a general rule always begin through whichever nostril is open and flowing. If both are flowing then, depending on the type of result you want to produce in your system, you can begin with the left or the right.

Kundalini yoga technique

Stage 1: This is alternate nostril bellows breathing. Sit in a meditative asana. Raise the right hand in nasagra mudra. Breathing rapidly and forcefully, inhale through the right nostril and exhale through the left.

Inhale through the left and exhale through the right. After completing 20 rounds (40 breaths) through the alternate nostrils, inhale deeply through both nostrils together.

Retain the breath inside and perform jalandhara and moola bandhas.

Then release the bandhas and exhale slowly through both nostrils together.

Next do 20 rapid and forceful breaths through both nostrils together.

Then inhale deeply through both nostrils and retain the breath inside.

Perform jalandhara and moola bandhas during breath retention.

Release the bandhas and exhale through both nostrils.

This is one round: 40 breaths through alternate nostrils and 20 breaths through both nostrils together.

Stage 2: In this stage alternate nostril bellows breathing is also performed.

Breathing rapidly and forcefully, inhale through the right nostril and exhale through the left.

Again inhale through the left and exhale through the right.

After completing 20 rounds (40 breaths) through the alternate nostrils, inhale deeply through the right nostril (pingala nadi) and retain the breath.

Perform jalandhara and moola bandhas during breath retention.

Release the bandhas and exhale through the left nostril (ida nadi).

Next do 20 rapid and forceful breaths through both nostrils together.

Then inhale deeply through the right nostril and retain the breath inside.

Perform jalandhara and moola bandhas during breath retention.

Release the bandhas and exhale through the left nostril.

This makes one round – 40 breaths through the alternate nostrils and 20 breaths through both nostrils together.

366

In stage 2, inhalation is always through the right nostril and exhalation is always through the left nostril.

While retaining the breath internally and practising jalandhara and moola bandhas, imagine the activation of sushumna nadi, between mooladhara chakra and vishuddhi chakra. Move the mind up along the spinal passage from mooladhara to vishuddhi.

Release the two bandhas and exhale through the left nostril.

During deep inhalation, internal retention and deep exhalation, the ratio of the breath should be the same as the ratio that you have perfected in the practice of nadi shodhana. For example, if you practise nadi shodhana with a ratio of 5:20:10, then you should use this ratio; if it is 10:40:20 then use that ratio. Use the ratio mentally while moving the attention up along the spine from moola bandha to jalandhara bandha, mooladhara to vishuddhi. When one round has been perfected, increase the number of rounds as the lung capacity increases.

Duration: Bhastrika increases the blood pressure and can cause dizziness due to hyperventilation. Therefore, in the early stages a maximum of three rounds is recommended. The system tires easily because inhalation and exhalation are performed with equal force. Therefore, it is necessary to rest after each round until one again feels relaxed.

Precautions: The practice should be stopped immediately if you feel faint, or there is excessive perspiration, excessive shaking of the body, or vomiting.

Contra-indications: People with high blood pressure, heart ailments, hernia, gastric ulcer or vertigo should avoid this practice.

Note

It has also been mentioned in the yogic texts that if one perspires, or feels faint or dizzy during bhastrika, then the practice is incorrect. These symptoms indicate that the strenuous respiratory movement is creating heat. If the movement becomes very physical then the symptom of heat will manifest in the form of perspiration, or it will go to the head causing lack of coordination and light-headedness. The reason the texts have said that the perspiration should be controlled in bhastrika and that one should not become dizzy or faint is to maintain pranic rather than physical awareness. In the practice of prana nigraha there is more body consciousness.

Physiological effects

Pranayama stretches our capacity to breathe quickly and slowly, withstanding both deprivation as well as high levels of oxygen in the body. In bhastrika we can suffer from hyperventilation, which occurs when the oxygen levels increase to a point where there is dizziness and fainting. With practice we can regulate our intake so that dizziness does not occur and conscious awareness of the process is maintained. We need to learn to remain balanced and relaxed while performing a technique that is outside our normal range of experience.

Control over the diaphragm and abdomen is required to maintain a relaxed bellows breath, which fans the digestive fire and massages the internal organs. Awareness of the internal activities, ranging from the physical level of the diaphragm, lungs and abdominal organs through to the more subtle levels within the nervous system and brain, is increased. Most of the carbon dioxide in the lungs is eliminated, and we prepare ourselves for long periods of breath retention. In the kundalini yoga variation of bhastrika, the breathing skills developed in hatha yoga are used. Rapid breathing is followed almost immediately by a long slow, prolonged breath in the spine.

Physiologically, the right side of the body is different from the left side. At the base of the right side of the body are the ascending colon, which is upward moving, the liver, which governs heat in the body, and the right lung. On the left side of the body are the heart, the left lung, the stomach and spleen, which deal more with the earth and water elements, and the descending colon, which is downward moving. So, there are different energy processes in the right and left sides of the body.

With such practices that emphasize one side of the body more than the other, we are influencing this right/left balance in certain ways. For example, we know that breathing in the left nostril will affect the right brain. During rapid alternate nostril breathing, we are rapidly stimulating these two sides of the brain as well as the right and left sides of the body. Right nostril breathing emphasizes the heating aspect of the right side of the body and left nostril breathing affects the organs on the left side. Inhalation through the right nostril stimulates pingala nadi and exhalation relaxes it. Similarly, inhalation through the left nostril stimulates ida nadi and exhalation relaxes it.

The practice of bhastrika is also a powerful means of purification. There are several layers of tissues called *dhatus*. They start with serum which is called *rasa*, then *rakta*, blood; *mumsa*, muscle; *asti*, bone; *medha*, fat; *majja*, nerves; *shukra/ arthara*, the reproductive tissues. These are the different levels that have to be kept pure. When we purify the blood through the practice of bhastrika, we are also able to purify the body at these different levels. The rapid movement of the diaphragm and the breath moves vayu into the internal organs and the nerves, so that purification takes place in the cells by the fire of metabolism (agni). Once purification takes place in the deeper tissues, vayu is transported out of the body by the blood. This rapid movement of the diaphragm and the breath is one of the best ways to get deep into an internal organ.

In the yogic texts it is said that formation of the three doshas or humours of the body, which are known as vata, pitta and kapha or wind, bile and phlegm, can be controlled by the practice of bhastrika. The diseases which arise due to the accumulation of these three humours blocking the

369

generation of agni, heat or fire in the body, are removed. With the perfection of bhastrika, the yogi can pierce the three granthis or psychic knots, after which the brahma nadi begins to flow, culminating in the awakening of kundalini.

A study of the doshas reveals a relationship between the various tattwas. For example, excess wind or vata, knocks the other doshas out of balance. It may fan the fire, pitta, increasing it too much. You may get a fever because the wind element increases and fans the fire in the body. If you have too much fire, it may increase movement of the wind element. If you have too much kapha, this will block the wind from moving, which dampens the fire in the system.

By pumping air into the nadis, you move the wind or vata through a mechanical process in order to cleanse out mucus. You increase the fire in the digestive system, which burns away the impurities, thereby getting rid of excess kapha. However, the practice has to be modified according to whether your system has more wind, fire or mucus.

Bhastrika works to increase heat in the system. It is agni activating. Agni is the element that is most important from the point of view of health. When agni is kept pure, the balance of the other doshas can be maintained quite easily. Agni is there to burn away the impurities. This is the basic principle around which balancing the three doshas occurs.

When the vitality or fire in the body is blocked due to an imbalance in the doshas, the prana cannot be awakened in the psychic body. It is diverted to deal with the imbalances that are being created by the doshas. Once the doshas have been brought into balance, then the inner agni or prana begins to flow through the brahma nadi.

Brahma nadi is the subtle channel which flows through the centre of sushumna and which is responsible for the actual awakening of kundalini. Brahma nadi is the actual pathway through which kundalini rises. It is like a pipe within a pipe. Sushumna nadi deals with the balancing of ida and pingala and the prana vayus, whereas brahma nadi is responsible for the ascent of kundalini. When the pranic fire is activated, the merger of the three pranas – prana, apana and samana, takes place. With the merger of these three pranas, the subtle pranic force begins to move through brahma nadi, which is responsible for the kundalini experience.

SHEETKARI PRANAYAMA (HISSING BREATH)

Sheetkari pranayama is known as the 'hissing breath'. The sound *shee* or *sheet* is made during this practice, and the word *kari* means 'that which produces'. Therefore, sheetkari is the pranayama that produces the sound shee or the hissing sound. This is one of the pranayama practices for cooling the body and mind. Here inhalation is performed through the mouth instead of through the nose.

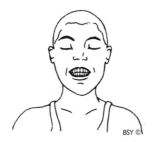

Hatha yoga technique
Sit in a comfortable meditation posture and close the eyes.
Bring the lower and upper teeth together and separate the lips as far as possible. Fold the tongue back so that the lower surface presses against the area of the front teeth. The tongue should be relaxed, not tense.
Inhale forcefully through the clenched teeth, making a hissing sound. Feel the cool air passing along the sides of the tongue into the throat.
When the inhalation is completed then close the lips, relax the tongue and breathe out through the nostrils.

371

Kundalini yoga technique

This practice begins in the same way as the hatha yoga version.

Bring the teeth together and separate the lips.

Fold the tongue back so that the lower surface presses against the area of the front teeth.

Inhale forcefully through the clenched teeth.

Feel the cool air passing along the sides of the tongue and down the throat.

After inhaling, close the mouth, release the tongue, and perform internal kumbhaka. Hold the breath inside for as long as is comfortable, relaxing the diaphragm. Before exhaling, raise the right hand and close the left nostril. Exhale through the right nostril and bring the hand down.

Duration: Start with nine rounds and slowly increase up to 60 rounds. This technique can be practised as a counter-balance to heating pranayamas, or by itself for cooling and relaxing the system.

Precaution: Breathing through the nose is a general rule in yogic practice because the nose heats and cleans the air before it enters the delicate lungs. When you breathe through the mouth this air-conditioning process is bypassed. Therefore, do not practise cooling pranayamas in cold weather or in polluted surroundings.

Physiological effects

The physiology of sheetkari concerns the cooling effect that occurs. There are many blood vessels in the mouth and under the tongue. The tongue itself is full of blood and this is the most direct way to cool the body, because blood carries heat in the body. It is a seat of pitta. So, by cooling the blood in the mouth and tongue, cooler blood is circulated to the rest of the body.

Through this practice control is developed over the temperature-regulating mechanisms in the brain. You learn to regulate the heating and cooling of the body. In ujjayi, a slight friction is produced which heats the body, while in the practice of sheetkari there is a cooling effect. This technique should be practised carefully by people who have cold bodies. It is designed to regulate the body temperature when added into a general sadhana. If you overheat when doing the major pranayamas, you have to be able to bring your temperature down. If you cool off too much in meditation, you have to be able to heat your body again. So, these techniques control the temperature regulation system.

Regarding the benefits of this technique, it has been mentioned that one gains control over sleep, lethargy, thirst and hunger. These effects are possible because of the activation of pingala nadi which takes place due to exhalation through the right nostril and the simultaneous lowering of the body temperature which automatically activates ida. Excess ida would tend to put one in a state of lethargy. This is counterbalanced by exhalation through the right nostril and the force that is created at the time of exhalation, which activates pingala further. So, with equal emphasis on pingala activation, which balances out the introversion of the senses, there is a cooling down of the body. With the introversion of the senses and the cooling of the body, there is a tendency to relax more deeply and fall asleep. That tendency is counteracted here.

The second point that is mentioned is overcoming thirst. While practising this technique, the salivary glands are activated and saliva flows copiously. Breathing this moistened air produces more juices in the cells and tissues and helps to regulate the body fluid. Furthermore, the heat in the body evaporates the moisture. Here the physical temperature is lowered, so more fluid is retained in the body. If sheetkari is practised for a long time, the coolness experienced in the tongue and throat prevents the throat from becoming dry. One of the symptoms of feeling thirsty is dryness of the throat. It is not that one does not need water but that the dryness is not felt. One can go for longer periods without having to drink. In the hatha yoga texts it says that one should practise a minimum of 50 rounds so that heat and lack of fluid do not dehydrate the body.

SHEETALI PRANAYAMA (COOLING BREATH)

Sheetali is known as the cooling pranayama. In Sanskrit, *sheetali* means 'cooling' or 'relaxing'.

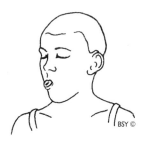

Hatha yoga technique
Sit in a comfortable meditation posture. Close the eyes and relax the body.
Roll the tongue so that both sides curl upward and inward, forming a tube. The end of the tongue should protrude outside the mouth.
Slowly inhale through the tube formed by the tongue. Breathe in deeply, but without strain.
Then withdraw the tongue, close the mouth and breathe out through the nose.

Kundalini yoga technique
This practice is the same as the hatha yoga version initially. Sit in a comfortable meditation posture. Close the eyes and relax the body.
Roll the tongue so that both sides curl upward and inward, forming a tube. The end of the tube should protrude outside the mouth.
Slowly inhale through the tube formed by the tongue. Breathe in deeply but without strain, expanding the abdomen and the chest region.

374

Then withdraw the tongue and close the mouth. Retain the breath for as long as is comfortable. Then exhale through the right nostril, activating pingala.

Note

The physiological effects and benefits are the same as for sheetkari pranayama. However, there is a genetic quality which allows the muscles of the tongue to move in this particular way and some people cannot do it right away. In this case, practise rolling the tongue around a pen or a cylindrical object. Then gradually remove the object. With practise, it can be done without any problem.

SURYA BHEDA PRANAYAMA
(VITALITY STIMULATING BREATH)

The word *surya* means 'sun', which refers to pingala nadi, and *bheda* means 'to pass through', 'to pierce', or 'to purify'. So surya bheda means to pierce or to purify the pingala nadi. The main thrust of this practice is to activate pingala in order to increase the vital energy and heat in the body. Pingala nadi is associated with the flow of breath through the right nostril. The characteristic of the practice is prolonged breath retention. In the hatha yoga texts, it says that after inhaling deeply through the right nostril, you should retain the breath inside until you feel pressure or perspiration from the hair on the head to the fingertips.

Hatha yoga technique

Sit in a comfortable meditation posture. Close the eyes and relax the whole body. Allow the breathing to become deeper.

Raise the right hand in front of the face in nasagra mudra. Close the left nostril with the ring finger.

Breathe slowly and deeply through the right nostril, pingala nadi. Try to fill up the lower part of the lungs first, and then the upper part.

Retain the breath inside and perform jalandhara and moola bandhas.

Hold the breath and the bandhas.

Release the bandhas, close the left nostril and breathe out through the right nostril, pingala nadi.

This is the basic practice. As control over the breathing process is gained, the ratio of 1:2:2 is added: one inhalation, two retention, two exhalation.

Kundalini yoga technique

Stage 1: Sit in a comfortable meditation posture. Close the eyes and relax the whole body. Allow the breathing to become slow and deep.

Become aware of the five pranas, the five vital airs situated within the body.

Withdraw the pranas to the navel and concentrate them at the agni mandala. Experience a build-up of energy and light in this area.

Raise the right hand in front of the face in nasagra mudra. Close the left nostril with the ring finger.

Inhale slowly and deeply through the right nostril, pingala nadi. While inhaling, feel the energy being drawn upward from the reservoir of prana at manipura chakra behind the navel. Feel that this prana is recharging the whole body.

Feel the entire body filling and expanding with prana.

At the end of inhalation retain the breath and do jalandhara and moola bandhas.

Retain the breath for as long as you can without straining. Release the bandhas and exhale slowly through the left nostril, ida nadi.

After mastering the practice, add the ratio 1:2:2.

Stage 2: This practice is the same as stage 1 up to inhalation. Inhale slowly and deeply through the right nostril, pingala nadi.

While inhaling, raise the prana up the sushumna passage from manipura to ajna.

Experience the intensity of prana in sushumna. As the prana is drawn upward, feel it piercing and opening each chakra junction enroute.

At the end of inhalation retain the breath and do jalandhara and moola bandha bandhas.

Retain the breath for as long as possible without straining. Release the bandhas and exhale slowly through the left nostril, ida nadi.

While exhaling, direct the prana back down through the sushumna passage from ajna to manipura.

After mastering the practice, add the ratio 1:2:2.

Stage 3: This practice is also the same as stage 1 up to inhalation.

Inhale slowly and deeply through the right nostril. While inhaling raise the prana up through the pingala passage in a spiralling pathway.

From manipura, the pingala passage curves to the right and crosses anahata. From anahata, it curves to the left and crosses vishuddhi. From vishuddhi, it curves to the right and terminates at ajna.

After terminating the inhalation at ajna, begin to exhale slowly through the left nostril.

Bring the prana back down to manipura through the ida passage following the spiralling pathway. From ajna, ida curves to the left and crosses vishuddhi. From vishuddhi, ida curves to the right and crosses anahata. From anahata, it curves to the left and comes back to manipura.

After mastering the rotation of the breath through the spiralling passage of ida and pingala, add internal breath retention and bandhas.

Contra-indications: People suffering from heart problems, hypertension and epilepsy should avoid this practice.

Balancing the swara

In the kundalini yoga version, inhalation is always through pingala nadi and exhalation through ida nadi, while in the hatha yoga version both inhalation and exhalation are through pingala nadi. The reason for this difference is due to one factor. The hatha yoga technique emphasizes the generation of heat or prana, while the kundalini yoga technique aims to balance the swara, the left and right nostrils, or ida and pingala breath flows. The build-up of heat or prana in the hatha yoga technique aids the other hatha yoga techniques to achieve purification and also to remove blockages from the nadis. In the kundalini yoga variation, at the time of inhalation the prana or vital force is generated and raised, first physically and then psychically up through the sushumna passage. At the time of exhalation ida nadi is activated in order to balance pingala activity.

The general theory behind this is that when one inhales, the body goes into a state of tension. The nervous and muscular system and even the brain activity become tense. You are injecting something into your body. Air is being pulled inside. As you breathe out, ida activity is induced. The physical and mental tensions relax. The cerebral tensions also relax, which improves memory and retention power. So, at the time of inhalation, the state of tension is very much a pingala activity and during exhalation, the state of relaxation is an ida activity.

Kundalini yoga uses the approach of balancing the swara more than hatha yoga. The theory is that kundalini yoga cannot be practised until hatha yoga and asana and pranayama have been perfected. So the system of kundalini yoga is not taught in general classes. Most of the traditional books dealing with kundalini use the same techniques with variations to balance both activities of ida and pingala. This is also the case with surya bheda pranayama.

The nostrils change their dominance every ninety minutes to three hours, and in some cases the changeover takes longer. It can be days also, depending on what is going on in our system. This reflects the cyclic movement of energy in the body, so that at one time of the day certain systems in the body are dominant and at other times other systems are dominant. For example, when eating, the digestive system is

378

active so the relaxation or ida aspect is dominant. When working, the pingala aspect dominates. When sleeping, one goes through different cycles as well. So, this function in the body, this changing cyclic pattern, is reflected in the changing dominance in the brain and in the nostrils.

Physiological effects

The science of pranayama increases our perception of physical, organic changes and adds the subtler pranic dimensions to them. First, one has to be aware of the actual change in the physical structure. Then through yogic practice, one develops deeper layers of understanding and perception. Surya bheda pranayama accentuates the functioning of pingala nadi, the left brain and all the systems in the body connected with outward movement which are not involved in perception in some sense. In the hatha yoga system the main aim is to increase physical vitality.

What are these physical structures? All the muscle systems, all the systems geared to external activity, which project outwards, like speech. The karmendriyas are accentuated over a period of time. An interesting experiment was performed in the USA on rats, in which a wire was put into the rat's brain with a very small electrical stimulus, not enough to make any obvious changes in the rat or in its perception, other than some stimulus to certain nerves and faculties. It was noticed after a period of time that if the same minute stimulus was given every day, the rat had an epileptic fit.

This does not mean that the same thing will happen with surya bheda. However, through regular practice or sadhana one is putting a small amount of stimulus into the system which, over a period of time, has an accumulative effect. If it is practised properly, the results are good. They will not be as gross and disruptive as the rat's experience. Of course, if one puts too much in too quickly or if one is not in balance or not clear as to what one is doing, it is possible to run into problems.

379

Surya bheda is a system which, over a period of time, gradually shifts one's energy in the direction of pingala. As more physical vitality is developed and more prana moves in the system, the ida nadi system works better as well. Without a high level of prana, one does not have the power or energy required to generate interest and vitality for performing mental and physical activity. This is how the practice balances out the right and left hemispheres.

The next level involves bandhas. By making a minute adjustment in the inflow of breath in the right nostril, the left brain is stimulated and the vitality of the right side, the liver and pitta is increased. By exhaling through the left nostril, the right brain and the whole left side of the system, the stomach and spleen, the cooling aspects, are relaxed. Then, by adding bandhas, we are able to magnify this effect. This is where we have to take a lot of care in this technique. Surya bheda involves not just the change in the breath flow, but also the addition of bandhas, which further raises the pranic level.

The way in which these techniques interact with the human body is very different to that rat's situation. You feel some minor changes in your system. Then you know, "I'm overheating" or "I'm feeling a strain" or "I'm breathing in too hard" or "I'm not breathing out in a way that balances the tension within the system, the contraction of the muscles, and the stimulation of the right side." Therefore, a teacher is essential. One cannot learn pranayama from a book.

You have to see these practices as long term techniques that you have to bring into your life every day and make them as normal as brushing your teeth. When you brush your teeth you do not have to try very hard. The same attitude should apply in pranayama practice. The practices are to be done with awareness and relaxation. Most of the problems that arise come at the nigraha level, never from pranayama itself. The problems come from forced control. Most people are still at the nigraha stage and so they jump over some of the basic fundamentals or forget them. They

380

are not yet even aware of prana or pranayama. Once you start to experience pranayama as a part of your life, then you will have much more respect for the practice.

Chandra Bheda Pranayama

Many people feel that if they can practise surya bheda through the right nostril, then why not do chandra bheda through the left nostril. However, chandra bheda is a restricted pranayama and is only taught at the discretion of the teacher, according to the student's progress in yoga. Chandra bheda creates extreme introversion which, if not handled properly, will turn into depression. The physical and mental faculties will be under the influence of that depression. You can become so depressed that you cannot see the light at the end of the tunnel. To come out of that situation voluntarily is practically impossible. This is the reason why chandra bheda pranayama is not taught. There is no mention of it in any of the books. Surya bheda has the opposite effect. It raises the prana and brings one out of depression.

17

Bandhas and Granthis

The word *bandha* means 'to lock', 'to hold', 'to tighten'. There are only three bandhas and they are related to the three psychic knots, or granthis, in our personality.

1. *Brahma granthi* is the first knot, or psychic block, where energy and consciousness interact and manifest in a certain way. It is supposed to be the lowest knot, covering the areas of mooladhara and swadhisthana chakras. It is also known as the perineal knot and is awakened and stimulated by the practice of moola bandha.

2. *Vishnu granthi* is the second knot and covers the areas of manipura, anahata and vishuddhi chakras. It is also known as the navel knot and is activated by the practice of uddiyana bandha.

3. *Rudra granthi* is the third knot and covers the areas of ajna and sahasrara chakras. It is also known as the neck knot and is activated by the practice of jalandhara bandha.

These three knots prevent the free flow of prana along sushumna nadi and, therefore, hamper the awakening of the chakras and the rising of kundalini. It has been the experience of advanced practitioners in the higher techniques that, with the awakening of prana and sushumna, certain spinal contractions can be experienced at these three points. There is a tightening of the nadi, where the body adopts different postures such as bending backwards and losing the sense of balance. This occurs because at the time of pranic awakening, the blockage is being experienced in either brahma granthi, vishnu granthi or rudra granthi.

Brahma granthi is the knot of Brahma. Brahma is the manifest force of life and creation. In relation to the world in which we live or, according to tantra, in the world of yonis or different life forms, Brahma controls the energies of mooladhara and swadhisthana. It is linked with the urge to procreate and with deep instinctive knowledge, awareness and desire. This experience is known as the blockage of Brahma because it holds our consciousness at a level related to desires of the physical dimension, sensuality, procreation and the instinctive urge to survive, which we generally cannot transcend. Once this blockage is removed from the realm of consciousness and energy, instincts of the so-called deep-rooted karmas, samskaras or desires do not affect or alter the other patterns of consciousness and energy. The kundalini or primal energy is able to rise beyond mooladhara and swadhisthana without being pulled down by the other attractions to which our consciousness is attached.

Vishnu granthi is the area where the personality and the body are sustained. Manipura sustains the physical body in a practical way. The food we consume is converted to energy and distributed throughout the body. The process of conversion of matter into energy in a form which can be used for maintenance and growth of the body is a function of manipura. In the same way, anahata sustains the mental structure in the form of emotions, which are raw, unrefined, intense expressions of subtle energy, and which can manifest as anger, compassion and so on. This pure unadulterated energy is the force which sustains manomaya kosha and pranamaya kosha. Vishuddhi, the all-pervading space, is the subtle energy which sustains vijnanamaya and ananda-maya koshas.

The sustenance aspect of all human dimensions is governed by these three chakras which vitalize, feed, balance and nurture the subtle bodies. This is the function of vishnu granthi. Once the vishnu granthi blockage is removed, we begin to sustain ourselves from energy drawn from the universe and not from a localized centre. The energies of the body become harmonious with the energy of the cosmos. The interaction between the human personality and the cosmos happens naturally and spontaneously.

Rudra granthi, or the knot of Rudra, governs ajna and sahasrara chakras. It represents the transformation of an existing form, idea or concept into its universal aspect. Therefore, the dropping of individuality happens when rudra granthi is pierced. The word *rudra* means 'howling energy'. It is derived from the root *rud*, which means 'to cry', and also the word *roodan* meaning 'the cry'. The process of detaching from our deeply fused attachment to the whole of life and to our individuality is known as the breaking apart or tearing asunder. The howling which takes place here is the piercing of rudra granthi.

To leave the known, manifest consciousness and enter unmanifest consciousness, where vijnanamaya and anandamaya become active, is the tearing of rudra granthi. Here there is a breaking away of the old, the ego awareness, the mental awareness, the physical awareness, and an evolving of the sixth sense or the eye of intuition, the third eye. This sixth sense and beyond is a state where the omniscient nature of consciousness is experienced, where past, present and future become known. With that omniscient awareness we move on to sahasrara, where the final merger of the individual soul and the universal cosmic soul occurs.

So, bandhas aim, firstly, at eliminating these three psychic blocks which hamper the awakening of prana at the pranamaya kosha level; secondly, at eliminating boundaries which are created in the consciousness by the world of the senses; and thirdly, at allowing the consciousness to become more free flowing rather than a limited perception. These bandhas are to be practised in conjunction with other yoga practices. Initially, it may be necessary to practise them individually and independently in order to perfect them. Once mastery is attained, they can be practised in conjunction with pranayama and mudra techniques, and then they become even more powerful.

Psychophysiological aspect

Granthis are 'ways of being' which somehow limit our energy. They are physical as well as pranic and mental contractions which create individuality and prevent us from understanding our real cosmic form. Psychophysiologically, all our physical and mental experiences arise out of the granthis which tie us to the world. The three granthis correspond to the three major connecting areas of the body. Brahma granthi is the lowest part of the body where both the legs and digestive tract connect to the pelvis. Vishnu granthi is the area of the diaphragm where the chest and abdomen connect.

These connecting areas also overlap. The manifestation of rudra granthi will affect other chakras and granthis; for example, a problem at the level of ajna chakra comes down to vishuddhi chakra and interferes with expression, such as speech. A problem at the vishnu granthi level can also manifest in speech. We can use the voice to express the intellect and also to express the heart. In singing, the flow of energy is upwards from the heart through the throat. To express ideas and concepts, energy moves from the area of rudra granthi down into the throat. These flows are interrupted by physical, mental, emotional and pranic contractions at various levels.

At a muscular level, contraction at brahma granthi may result in unconscious, prolonged contractions of parts of the perineum, especially when we are tense or involved in a relationship with someone. These psychophysiological contractions maintain our limited state. Similarly, with the diaphragm; in this area we are protecting our heart and not expressing our power. Psychophysiological problems at manipura arise because we diminish our own strength, tighten the stomach, contract the energy and create illness and weakness. This may be due to a fear of expressing our power and strength.

In the area of rudra granthi, blockages are expressed in contractions of the jaw and the back of the neck. At a psychophysical level, there is a lot of interconnection between the three granthis. All illnesses arise from these contractions. For example, with rudra granthi, contractions at the base of the skull will affect the ears and jaw muscles and perhaps create sinus problems. The bandhas help to energize, straighten and reconnect the flow between various levels of our being.

JALANDHARA BANDHA (THROAT LOCK)

Jalandhara bandha is a technique that frees the blockages of rudra granthi. It is known as the throat contraction. In Sanskrit the word *jala* means 'net' and *dhara* means 'stream' or 'flow'. Jalandhara bandha is thus the physical contraction or lock which controls the network of nadis, nerves and blood vessels flowing through the neck to the brain. Jalandhara bandha is the most important bandha associated with pranayama as it accompanies all practices of kumbhaka, prolonged breath retention.

Technique
Stage I: With internal kumbhaka
Sit in siddhasana or padmasana, with the knees firmly touching the floor. Make sure the spine is erect.
Place the palms of the hands on the knees. Relax the body.
Inhale deeply and fully. Retain the breath inside.
Bend the head forward. Press the chin against the chest at the top the sternum between the collarbones, so that tension is felt in the back of the head and neck.
Hold the concentration where this tension is felt. Simultaneously straighten the arms and lock them into position with the palms pressing down firmly on the knees, and hunch the shoulders forward.

386

This will lock the posture and increase awareness of the area between the chin and the top of the sternum.

Remain in this position for as long as you are able to hold the breath without straining.

When releasing the bandha, relax the shoulders, bend the elbows, slowly raise the head and exhale.

When the respiration has returned to normal, repeat the practice.

Practise ten rounds.

Stage 2: With internal and external kumbhaka

Jalandhara bandha can be performed with both internal and external kumbhaka by a normal, healthy, long-term practitioner.

Inhale and retain the breath inside. Perform jalandhara bandha. Raise the shoulders and lock the arms.

Count mentally from one to ten.

Release the shoulders, raise the head and exhale.

Again perform jalandhara. Retain the breath outside and count from one to ten.

Release the shoulders, raise the head and inhale.

This is one round.

Relax and allow the respiration to normalize. Do not perform the next round until the breathing returns to normal. Do not practise when there is shortness of breath. You will need to breathe normally several times after each round. Practise ten rounds.

387

Precautions: Never inhale or exhale until the head is upright, otherwise you may injure the muscles which are compressed and experience sharp pain.

Contra-indications: Jalandhara bandha is not recommended for people with heart ailments, stroke or blood pressure problems.

Physiological effects

Holding the breath for a period of time with jalandhara bandha creates a strong nervous stimulus, which distracts the attention from the need to breathe. At the same time, contracting the throat affects the trachea and the blood vessels going to the brain. The blood supply to the brain is slowed down as pressure is placed on these blood vessels in the neck, especially the carotid sinus. Therefore, the breath can be held longer than normal with this technique.

At the same time, as we bend the head forward we are also pulling up and elongating the spine, which gently stretches the meninges around the brain. This subtle pressure opens up the knots in the physical structure around the brain and spine. Stimulus at the throat level also helps to balance out the thyroid function, which regulates metabolism. With regular practice, there is a gentle, repetitive stimulus at the thyroid, not a major stimulus as in sarvangasana, for example.

In discussing the physiological effects, we should keep in mind that yoga is absolutely holistic in theory and practice. We cannot say that any one practice directly influences any particular organ or gland, etc. All yogic practices just stretch and squeeze, contract and expand. So, in jalandhara bandha the neck is placed in one posture and then in another. Each vertebra, muscle, nerve channel, gland, etc, creates a self-contraction. In the course of time, this gentle compression and expansion alters the total functioning of an organ, in the same way as a sponge is filled with water and squeezed dry repeatedly. There are certain practices which are said to affect a particular organ directly, such as the liver, kidneys, stomach, etc. This is an indication of the organ on which the asana is supposed to work and improve the function. So it is not a question of whether we can improve thyroid and parathyroid functioning by practising jalandhara bandha, although it has been seen to happen.

In physiology, one person will practise a bandha and it will affect a particular part of the body. Another person will practise the same bandha and it will affect a different part of the body. Research and experiments average out the results obtained from a number of people. The physiological and psychophysiological explanations are mechanical. They provide a deeper understanding of which structures are involved and which energies may be involved, but we do not really know how the practices work. For example, respiratory physiologists do not really understand how the respiratory muscles work. We do not understand simple functions, let alone the extremely complicated processes and manoeuvres. Yogic explanations and physiological explanations try to complement each other, but it is important not to over-simplify mechanical research results.

Yoga allows us to access our nervous system directly and deeply with controls that allow us to self-regulate. If yoga practices, such as bandhas or kumbhaka, are added to other existing methods and techniques, then the core of the system is somehow strengthened and stabilized with long lasting effects.

MOOLA BANDHA (PERINEAL CONTRACTION)

In Sanskrit, the word *moola* means 'root'. Here this refers to the root of the spine or the perineum where mooladhara chakra, the seat of kundalini, is located. Therefore, moola bandha is generally known as the perineal lock. It is effective in the releasing of brahma granthi and for the locating and awakening of mooladhara chakra.

Moola bandha is an important practice of hatha yoga and kundalini yoga. At the physiological level, it is the contraction of certain muscles at the pelvic floor. At the subtle level, however, it is the contraction of mooladhara chakra itself. The perineal body acts as a trigger point to enable us to locate the psychic centre of mooladhara. At the pranic level moola bandha is responsible for redirecting the downward flow of apana. By steady contraction of the perineum, the apana force is drawn upward and merged with the agni mandala in the region of samana in order to facilitate the awakening of kundalini.

Area of contraction
The area to be contracted is the physical trigger point for mooladhara chakra, which has a different location in the male and female bodies. In the male body, the trigger point is at the perineum, between the anus and the sexual organ. In the female body, it is at the cervix, where the vagina and the uterus meet.

In order to understand moola bandha, first we must look briefly at two other associated practices: ashwini mudra and vajroli/sahajoli mudra. Ashwini mudra is contraction of the anal sphincter. Vajroli/sahajoli mudra is contraction of the urinary passage. These two contractions must be performed independently in order to perfect them. You must become aware of the internal pressure point which is being affected by each contraction.

At first when practising moola bandha, both contractions must take place. At this time you will become aware of a third point slightly inside the body, which is very sensitive. It tickles a bit when you contract this point. Maintaining the contraction at this exact point is the practice of moola bandha. When you discover this exact point, the practice of moola bandha begins. Then you have to leave ashwini and vajroli, and concentrate on moola bandha. For a better idea of the area of concentration for these three practices, see the following diagrams.

Location of the Psychic Points

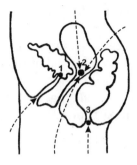 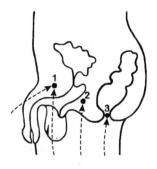

Female body
1. Sahajoli mudra
2. Moola bandha
3. Ashwini mudra

Male body
1. Vajroli mudra
2. Moola bandha
3. Ashwini mudra

Hatha yoga technique
Stage 1: Without retention

Sit in siddhasana or siddha yoni asana. Place the hands on the knees. Close the eyes and relax the whole body. Move your awareness, to the point of contact where the heel is pressing into the perineum or yoni.

Centre your awareness at this point.

Breathe slowly and deeply. With each inhalation, contract the perineum or the inner walls of the vagina. Feel the upward pull of this area towards the navel.

With each exhalation, release the contraction and relax. At this stage there is no breath retention and the contraction is not prolonged.

It follows the rhythm of the breath. Breathe in, contract; breathe out, release.

Continue the practice for five minutes.

Stage 2: With internal retention

Sit in siddhasana or siddha yoni asana. Close the eyes and relax the whole body.

Inhale deeply. Hold the breath and practise jalandhara bandha.

Contract the mooladhara chakra area.

Draw the area upward as much as you can without excessive strain. Keep your attention fixed at the point of contraction.

Hold the contraction for as long as is comfortable.

Then release the contraction, release jalandhara and slowly exhale.

This is one round. Allow the breathing to return to normal before beginning the next round.

Practise ten rounds.

Stage 3: With external retention

Begin the practice in the same way.

Inhale deeply and exhale fully. Hold the breath outside and perform jalandhara bandha.

Contract the mooladhara chakra area.

Hold the contraction for as long as is comfortable.

Then release the contraction, release jalandhara and slowly inhale.

This is one round. Practise ten rounds.

Contra-indications: People with heart ailments, stroke or high blood pressure problems should avoid this practice.

Kundalini yoga technique
Stage 1: Locating mooladhara

Sit in siddhasana or siddha yoni asana. Place the hands on the knees. Close the eyes and relax the whole body. Move your awareness to the point of contact where the heel is pressing into the perineum or yoni. Become intensely aware of the distinct pressure at that point. Centre your awareness at that point.

Become aware of the breath.

Feel or imagine that you are breathing in and out of this pressure point.

Feel the breath moving through the perineal body becoming finer and finer, so that it pierces the point where mooladhara chakra is located.

At this point you will feel it as a psychophysical contraction.

If you are able to locate mooladhara, visualize a yellow square at this point. Inside the square see a red inverted triangle. Visualize this while continuing to breathe in and out through the trigger point. Continue this practice for five minutes.

Stage 2: Mooladhara Anusandhana

Sit in siddhasana or siddha yoni asana. Make sure that the heel is pressing firmly against the perineum. Straighten the spine and hold the head erect. Relax the entire body and close the eyes. Become aware of the natural, rhythmic breathing for a few moments.

Focus your awareness at the mooladhara chakra point. Breathe in deeply and as you breathe out repeat the mantra *Lam-Lam-Lam-Lam-Lam*. Run one repetition into the other, forming a mala of unbroken sound. Feel the vibrations emanating and resonating at mooladhara chakra. Continue this practice for fifteen rounds.

Next, inhale deeply and exhale with one long smooth repetition: *Lam-m-m-m-m* the long 'm' sound should taper off as exhalation is completed. Feel the resonance at mooladhara and try to experience the exact location of the chakra.

Practise fifteen rounds.

Stage 3: Mooladhara Dhyana

Sit in siddhasana or siddha yoni asana. Straighten the spine and hold the head erect. Feel the heel pressing into the perineum or yoni. Intensify your awareness of the mooladhara trigger point. Become acutely sensitive to the chakra point itself.

Visualize mooladhara as a dark red lotus with four petals. See the lotus clearly. Slowly the lotus begins to turn. Four red petals going around and around. See the spinning lotus a whirling red vortex of primal energy and light. Feel the vibrant energy of this whirling vortex of light pulsating through you.

Experience this vortex of energy being drawn upward and contracting spontaneously, spreading waves of light

393

and energy to the brain. At first these contractions occur at the mooladhara level, but gradually the sensation spreads throughout the whole body.

You can feel the whole body contracting, spontaneously, without any effort. The waves of energy and bliss intensify with each contraction, becoming unbearable.

This is the awakening of mooladhara.

Continue this experience until the awareness begins to fade.

Physiological effects

Mooladhara chakra lies in very close proximity to a point called the perineal body, which is a small area where all the many muscles and ligaments of the perineum converge. It is around this area that you will find the sensation of mooladhara chakra stimulation. By practising vajroli/sahajoli and ashwini mudras and trying to separate the two muscle groups, mooladhara chakra is automatically stimulated. Then, by isolating that contraction we can pull up this point. We are normally unaware of this area, and it is quite contracted a lot of the time due to various psychological and environmental stresses. These muscles are very reactive to stress as well as to psychological tension.

Through the practice of moola bandha, we gain control over the muscles of the perineal body. The base of the brain, especially the reticular activating system, is also stimulated. This part functions like a filter, allowing only so much energy to go through to the brain. It is this part of the brain which keeps the rest of the brain awake, conscious and alert. Regular stimulation of this area has the effect of stimulating the reticular activating system, thereby creating a greater sense of whole body awareness, taking us out of our heads and into the whole body.

You can think of the spinal cord as an extension of the base of the brain, descending down the back of the body. It is really a part of the brain. If you stimulate the base of the brain with moola bandha, you will also make the spinal cord more conscious, which will revitalize all the other organs as the energy passes through them.

Moola bandha is also useful for digestive problems, especially in the colon and for treating haemorrhoids. Moola bandha is especially useful for toning and strengthening the pelvic organs. In the female it strengthens the ligaments, preventing prolapse of the uterus, and releases blood congestion, which helps to regulate menstruation. In the male it helps deal with prostate problems, premature ejaculation and impotency. It also sublimates the instinctive drive and the sexual drive, with the raising of consciousness from the level of brahma granthi to the area of vishnu granthi.

UDDIYANA BANDHA
(ABDOMINAL CONTRACTION)

The third bandha is uddiyana, the abdominal lock. The word *uddiyana* means 'to raise up' or 'to fly up'. This practice is so called because the physical lock applied to the abdomen causes the abdomen and the diaphragm to rise towards the chest. It also directs the prana into sushumna nadi, and causes it to 'fly' upward.

Technique
Stage 1: Standing Uddiyana
This practice can be done in the standing position, which is easier for beginners.
Stand upright with the feet about half a metre apart. Inhale deeply through the nostrils. Bend forward from the waist, and exhale all the air through the mouth.
Try to empty the lungs as much as possible.
Keep the spine straight and bend the knees slightly. Place the palms of the hands on the thighs just above the knees, so that the knees are supporting the weight of the upper body.
Make sure the arms are straight.

In this position there is an automatic contraction of the abdominal region.

Then bend the head forward, but do not press the chin against the chest. Pull in the abdomen and try to join the navel with the vertebrae at the back. Hold the breath outside and the abdominal lock for as long as is comfortable without straining.

Release the abdominal lock and relax the chest.

Straighten the knees and raise the head. Stand upright and breathe in slowly.

Remain in the standing position until the breath has returned to normal.

Then begin the next round.

Practise ten rounds.

Stage 2: Sitting position

Sit in siddhasana or padmasana with the spine erect and the knees on the floor. Place the palms of the hands flat on the knees. This posture is necessary in order to apply pressure with the arms in the final pose.

Breathe in deeply through the nostrils.

Exhale through the mouth in one loud blast, emptying the lungs as much as possible. Hold the breath outside.

Raise the shoulders and press down on the knees with the palms of the hands, straightening the elbows, allowing further extension of the spinal cord.

Perform jalandhara bandha by pressing the chin against the top of the sternum. Contract the abdominal muscles inward and upward.

Hold the abdominal lock and the breath outside for as long as you can without straining.

Then release the abdominal lock. Bend the elbows and lower the shoulders.

Raise the head and slowly inhale.

Remain in this position until the respiration returns to normal.

Then begin the next round.

Practise ten rounds.

Stage 3: Sitting in vajrasana

This is the variation of uddiyana bandha described in the Upanishads.

Sit in vajrasana with the knees apart. Make fists with your hands on each side of the navel.

Inhale deeply through the nose. Bend forward and exhale through the mouth. This pushes out all the air from the lungs.

Hold the breath outside. Place the hands on the knees to support the spine. Raise the shoulders and bend the head forward.

Practise uddiyana bandha and hold it for as long as you can without straining.

Then release uddiyana, relax the shoulders and raise the head. Bring the navel forward and breathe in slowly.

In this technique extra assistance is given to the elimination of all the air from the lungs by pushing the diaphragm externally with the fists.

Practice note: Always exhale through the mouth before performing uddiyana in order to completely empty the lungs of air. There is a more forceful expulsion and less resistance when you breathe out through the mouth. After performing the practice make sure you do not begin inhalation until you have released uddiyana and jalandhara bandhas, and returned to the starting position. Relax after completing each round. It is easy to remain in a contracted state and continue the practice, which will lead to adverse effects.

Precautions: Uddiyana bandha must always be practised on an empty stomach. Wait for four to five hours after meals. Try to evacuate the bowels before starting the practice.

Contra-indications: People with heart problems, high blood pressure, stroke, ulcer, colitis, hernia, and other serious abdominal problems, should avoid uddiyana bandha.

Physiological effects

In uddiyana bandha, one creates a negative pressure inside the body by exhaling fully. Then, by flexing the spine, there is an automatic contraction of the abdominal wall inward. Of the two segments of the abdominal wall, the upper segment is easier to contract than the lower one. One of the mistakes many people make is to work the upper abdomen and not the lower one. It is necessary to work around the navel as a central point, which entails working the lower abdomen as well. Sometimes one needs to put more force on the lower abdomen. This in turn puts pressure onto the nerve plexuses, the celiac plexus (the solar plexus) and the sacral plexus. When uddiyana is performed, there is an automatic suction of the throat inwards and a pulling up of mooladhara, owing to the negative pressure. This makes jalandhara and mooladhara bandhas much easier to perform.

Uddiyana bandha works very much on the adrenal glands. Therefore, it helps us to handle stress better. In fact, all the bandhas work on the glands: jalandhara affects the thyroid and pituitary glands, and moola bandha affects the uro-genital system. Uddiyana also puts strong pressure on the liver, stomach, spleen, pancreas and intestines. It tones the reproductive system as well, pulling up the internal pelvic organs and strengthening them. It removes constipation, helps treat haemorrhoids and is useful in respiratory conditions like asthma and hay fever.

MAHA BANDHA (THE GREAT LOCK)

Maha bandha means the 'great lock'. It is the combination of jalandhara bandha, moola bandha and uddiyana bandha:

Hatha yoga technique
Sit in siddhasana or siddha yoni asana. Inhale slowly and deeply through the mouth and exhale all the air through the mouth. Perform jalandhara, uddiyana and moola bandhas, while holding the breath outside. Hold the bandhas and the breath for as long as is comfortable without straining. Then release moola, uddiyana and jalandhara bandhas, in this order. When the head is upright then breathe in slowly. Allow the breath to return to normal before starting the next round. Practise ten rounds.

Kundalini yoga technique
Stage I: In meditative posture
Sit in siddhasana or padmasana with the spine erect. Place the palms of the hands on the knees.
Inhale through the nose and exhale through the mouth.
Perform jalandhara, uddiyana and moola bandhas.
Hold all the three locks.
Take the awareness to the point of mooladhara for a few seconds. Feel the point of pull and mentally repeat 'mooladhara' three times in order to become more aware

of the region. Then raise the awareness up along the spine to manipura. Repeat mentally 'manipura' three times, feeling the pressure in this region. Now move the awareness up to vishuddhi. Repeat 'vishuddhi' three times, feeling the contraction at the throat and the pressure moving up and down.

If you are able to retain the breath for a longer period, repeat the process two or three times.

Then release moola, uddiyana and finally jalandhara bandha.

Raise the head to the upright position and breathe in slowly.

This is one round.

Allow the breath to normalize before starting the next round.

Practise five to ten rounds.

Stage 2: In Utthanpadasana

Sit with both legs stretched out in front. Place the hands on the knees.

Inhale first and as you exhale, bend forward. Do not perform paschimottanasana. Here you are only bending forward enough to catch hold of the toes. Keep the spine straight and the head up.

In this posture practise jalandhara, uddiyana and moola bandhas.

The process is similar to stage 1. Rotate the awareness to: mooladhara, manipura, vishuddhi; mooladhara, manipura, vishuddhi; mooladhara, manipura, vishuddhi. Then release moola, uddiyana and jalandhara bandhas. Return to the sitting position with the hands on the knees and breathe in.

It is advisable to rest for some time after each round until the breath returns to normal and there is no agitation. Then practise the next round.

Contra-indications: People with heart ailments, stroke, high blood pressure, hernia, gastric ulcer or serious abdominal problems should avoid maha bandha.

400

Physiological effects

Maha bandha manipulates and refines external kumbhaka. If external kumbhaka is performed well, then as one goes into jalandhara bandha, uddiyana should begin to occur automatically. Once uddiyana occurs, then isolation of moola bandha is very easy because there is an automatic lifting up of the perineum through suction. The effects are as before.

The three bandhas act upon three of the five pranas. Moola bandha raises the apana energy. Jalandhara reverses the flow of prana and sends it downward to the navel region. When these two forms of energy meet samana in the navel, manipura is activated. The activation of manipura then stimulates sushumna.

With the practice of uddiyana bandha, a vacuum is created in the lower abdominal region. The Upanishads mention that when practising uddiyana bandha the heart should be held at the throat region. This means that the force of the contraction should create a total vacuum. Once the vacuum is released, the air fills it up with force. The same kind of principle is applied here with prana. When we create a vacuum in the region of samana, for a short time only, the pranas fill up that empty space. This kind of contraction also has a deep influence on the nervous system.

One of the subjective experiences, which applies to everyone with the practice of bandhas, is that when we hold a bandha for a long period, its effect is also noticed on the activity of the mind. If we practise moola bandha at a time when the mind is very active, it will calm down. If we practise jalandhara bandha when the mind is hyperactive, the mind calms down. So, the locks, or bandhas, stop mental dissipation and assist the mind to achieve a point of concentration, internal harmony and balance.

18

Mudras

Mudras have been called psychophysiological postures, movements or attitudes, and are divided into different categories. Yoga mudras aim at rebalancing the energy field or pranic structure. *Natya*, or dance, mudras, express different attitudes or moods such as anger, love and so on, through various facial expressions, eye movements or hand gestures. Each mudra has a different effect on the body, mind, feelings, emotions and prana. Therefore, we can consider mudras to be psychophysiological gestures which connect the psyche and body, the keys which create that link. The diversification of names given for these practices shows that mudras are not just one type of technique or practice, like asanas, pranayama, bandhas or kriyas. They are a combination of subtle, physical movements that alter the mood, attitude and perception, and deepen awareness and concentration.

Traditionally, according to tantric texts, it is believed that Lord Shiva was the first exponent of mudras. These texts describe over a hundred forms of mudras. Of these, yoga has utilized approximately twenty-five major mudras, which are also referred to in the hatha yoga texts, such as *Gherand Samhita* and *Hatha Yoga Pradipika*.

The tradition states that the practice of mudras alone can bestow any and all kinds of siddhis on the practitioner. Mudras create a link or connection between an attitude, posture or movement adopted by the external, physical body and the internal body. In other words they connect annamaya and pranamaya koshas together, and this later influences manomaya kosha. The yogic tradition also states that there are sixteen *adharas* or bases that support the body. These sixteen bases are physical as well as pranic and mental in nature. Their representation corresponds to human anatomy.

From Kirlian research we can conclude that the extremities of the body constantly discharge energy which manifests in the physical body as the electro-magnetic field. That is one form of manifestation of the prana being discharged through the body. It is possible to increase the radiation around the fingers, for example, by practising certain techniques like asana, pranayama, bandhas, mudras or relaxation. However, there are subtle discharges or manifestations of this prana at other levels, which have been given different names. The aura that is seen around our psychic body is one. It is also known as bio-plasmic energy. This is a deeper interpretation than that of the electro-magnetic field.

Such terms have been applied without the actual realization that they represent a subtle aspect of the pranic force. The continual discharge of pranic force and the tension in pranamaya kosha caused by coordinating the activities of annamaya, manomaya and vijnanamaya kosha depletes the pranas manifesting through the body and mind. Therefore, we experience mental lethargy, fatigue, tiredness and other symptoms of energy depletion. The mind is supposed to be constantly active, but if we do a lot of mental work we feel exhausted. This is because we have overused the mental prana.

When we do a lot of physical work, it often happens that the physical body is extremely tired but the mind is fully active and charged. This is because we have overused the physical manifestation of prana. If we analyze the situation properly, we will find such depletion at every level of our life. It is possibly for this reason that yogis considered the use of mudras to be very valid and important in rebalancing the flow of prana in the annamaya, manomaya and pranamaya systems. These mudras are specifically designed to create a movement, a posture and an attitude in the major extremities of the body.

Psychophysiological interaction

To understand what lifts a simple posture, movement or gesture into the realm of mudra, where you are unifying the internal levels, requires an awareness of the psycho-physiological interaction. The best way to understand this is to look at the brain.

In the process of human evolution, we are trying to link up the cortex with the deep primitive structures of the brain. We need to lift the focus of the primitive, sensory life out of the base of the brain back into consciousness, back into the cortex. When the cortex links to the base of the brain, this process is called telencephalization, which means bringing what normally is instinctive into conscious control.

When prana falls from manipura into mooladhara, we fall back into instinctual living. The aim of mudras is to create fixed, repetitive postures, gestures and attitudes, which can snap us out of these old, instinctive habit patterns and bring us back into a more refined state of consciousness. To understand this, there are a few points we need to remember about the brain.

What is the cortex for? You can destroy a large part of the cortex and still receive sensations. You may be able to feel sensations, but the cortex gives depth, meaning and understanding to the signals that you are receiving. When you bring the cortex in, you are no longer just in the realm of sensations; you are in the realm of higher functions. If the frontal cortex where the thinking process takes place is destroyed, thoughts will come, but you will no longer be able to plan or grasp abstract concepts; there will be no depth to your thoughts. The cortex adds a huge dimension to the sensory input that we receive from the world around us.

The brain consists of two basic systems. One is a generalized system that is going on automatically all the time, and the other is a specific system. For example, I can be sitting very quietly, but my brain is still active; the whole brain is still functioning. If I touch something, I will get a specific sensation and it will go through the nervous system to the brain. Within that generalized, unconscious mass of energy which can be described as the physical representation of the psyche, there is a specific sensation, task or focus of attention that I am working on.

There are two other systems to remember. One is the dopamine system, which awakens the body. When you take dopamine into your system, you want to eat more and you are much more aggressive. The other is the serotonin system which, when it is active, puts you to sleep, reduces pain and makes you calm. So, there is a generalized and specific system, and there is an activating and a depressing system.

What we are trying to do with the various mudras is to create an attitude in which we make a specific signal. Let us look at chin mudra. When you hold the hands in the position of chin mudra for a period of time, a signal goes to the brain. After some time you become used to it and the signal becomes less. Even though the signal is still going to the brain, you no longer feel it. You have then entered the generalized system of the brain. In a sense, the mudra is a pathway into the generalized system. It allows you to enter and then to develop control over the generalized system of the brain.

Yoga mudras
Yoga mudras can briefly be categorized into five groups: (i) head mudras, performed by the eyes, tongue and ears; (ii) hand mudras; (iii) postural mudras; (iv) locked or bandha mudras, and (v) perineal or adhara mudras. These are the five categories within the structure of yoga mudras.

When the dissipation of prana stops through the practice of mudras, introversion of the mind takes place. Tantric literature states that one can attain the stages of pratyahara and dharana by practising introversion of consciousness through the various mudras. This seems logical when we consider that these practices rebalance the hemispheres of the brain and regulate their activity, so that there is no dissipation, distraction or disturbance in the nerves and nadis. Nervous impulses are electrical in nature. With the balancing and adjustment of the nerves and nadis, there is greater possibility of attaining one-pointed concentration.

1. POSTURAL MUDRAS

In our practical discussion of yoga mudras, we will begin with the postural mudras because they are more physical in nature and we can understand them more easily.

VIPAREETA KARANI MUDRA
(INVERTED PSYCHIC ATTITUDE)

The word *vipareeta* means 'inverted'. In this practice, the position of the sun (manipura chakra) and the moon (bindu chakra) are reversed, so that the sun is above the moon. Normally, the life-giving nectar flows downward from bindu to manipura, where it is burnt up by the physical activities. In vipareeta karani, however, the process is reversed. The nectar of subtle life force is redirected from manipura back to bindu, its source, which leads to the expansion of consciousness and revitalization of one's entire being. In fact, it is said that even the aged can regain their youth and vitality by this practice.

Vipareeta karani mudra is also an asana, the simple form of sarvangasana.

Body position
Lie flat on the back with the arms at the sides. The legs should be in a straight line.
Relax the whole body.
Breathe in deeply and raise both legs, keeping them straight and together.
Bring the feet over the head.

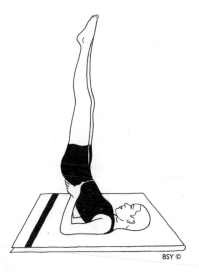

Press the arms against the floor and raise the buttocks off the floor.

Bend the elbows and place the hands at the hips, so that the trunk is supported by the arms.

Raise the legs so that they are vertical.

The chin does not press against the chest in the final pose. There is no contraction and no pressure on the area of the epiglottis.

The weight of the body is distributed on the top of the shoulders, the neck and the elbows. This is the base for supporting the body weight. The back is at a 45-degree angle with the floor.

In this posture the body should be as relaxed as possible.

To return to the starting position, lower the legs over the head, then place the arms and hands close on the floor, palms facing down.

Slowly lower the spine along the floor.

Hatha yoga technique

Assume the inverted position of the body. Make the legs vertical. Close the eyes and relax.

Become aware of the breath.

Practise slow, rhythmic ujjayi breathing, which should be natural due to the slight constriction at the throat.

Be aware of each inhalation and exhalation.

Bring the awareness to mooladhara chakra point, at the perineum. This is the starting point of every round. While inhaling, the breath flows from mooladhara to manipura. While exhaling, the breath flows from manipura to vishuddhi.

Then bring the awareness straight back to mooladhara. This is one round.

Begin with 10 rounds and slowly increase up to 21.

Practice note: Here we become aware of three regions: (i) mooladhara, the perineal base, (ii) manipura, the lumbar base, and (iii) vishuddhi, the base connecting the body to the brain. The consciousness is moved from one base to the next with inhalation and exhalation. The movement of consciousness is always from mooladhara to vishuddhi, not the reverse. You become mentally aware of these bases when you stop momentarily between inhalation and exhalation.

Kundalini yoga technique

Assume the inverted position of the body. Make the legs vertical. Close the eyes and relax the body.

Become aware of the breath. Practise slow, rhythmic ujjayi. Bring your awareness to manipura chakra point in the spine. This is the starting point for every round. While inhaling, feel the flow of prana moving from manipura chakra to vishuddhi chakra. Imagine the prana moving through the sushumna passage as a stream of hot golden nectar.

Allow the nectar to collect at vishuddhi. Hold the breath for a few seconds and feel the nectar going cold. Then exhale and eject the cold nectar from vishuddhi through ajna to bindu. When the nectar reaches bindu, bring your awareness straight back to manipura.

This is one round. Practise 21 rounds.

Physiological effects

Both the hatha yoga and the kundalini techniques are described in the Upanishads. In vipareeta karani mudra, the inverted posture is used to reverse the flow of prana. Physiologically we are linking up the limbic system with the cortex. The limbic system controls the vegetative functions in the body, all the activities which go on automatically. It is also known as the pleasure centre. During experiments with rats when electrodes were inserted into pleasure centres of the brain, the rats went on stimulating that centre until they died. They stopped eating and drinking, and just went on pressing this centre.

These brain centres are very powerful. The brain is a kind of hologram of the whole body. It is like a little mirror of everything else that is in the body. Continually rotating your awareness and breath along a fixed pathway is what takes the practice from being just a posture to being a mudra; the intention is to manipulate the prana. When vipareeta karani mudra is practised for a period of time, the attention moves through the brain circuits from the limbic system up through the thalamus towards the cortex. In this way, you become more conscious of all these various functions, and gradually link them up. That is basically what happens, apart from all the benefits of inversion. Control over pleasure, sexuality and all the other basic vegetative functions of the body is developed.

Vipareeta karani mudra gives a gentle inversion. There is no hard compression as in sarvangasana. Physiologically, there is a greater flow of blood in the cerebral capillaries and blood vessels which helps to activate the brain. For this reason, it is believed that this posture gives a fresh charge to the brain. When it is used as a mudra, the pranic dimension is added. With the rotation of awareness, the concentration and mental faculties are directed to a particular pathway in your being. As your awareness evolves, you can feel the actual movement happening at various levels. This shows the intensity of mind working at the pranic level.

409

YOGA MUDRA (ATTITUDE OF PSYCHIC UNION)

Yoga mudra, although also practised as a part of the padmasana group, has never actually been considered to be asana.

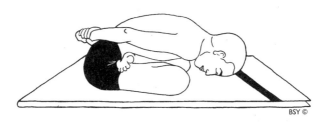

Hatha yoga technique

Sit in padmasana. Close the eyes. Clasp the left wrist with the right hand. Relax the whole body.

Inhale deeply in the upright position. Exhale while slowly bending forward. Try to bring the forehead down to the floor. Relax in the position as long as is comfortable.

Concentrate on manipura chakra.

Then slowly raise the body to the starting position while inhaling.

This is one round. Repeat the practice five times.

Kundalini yoga technique

Sit in padmasana. Hold the right wrist with the left hand, or the left wrist with the right hand. The hand you hold should always be opposite to the nostril which is flowing more freely. If the right nostril is flowing more freely, then hold the left wrist with the right hand. If the left nostril is flowing more freely, then hold the right wrist with the left hand. The purpose is to balance the swara.

In the starting position, inhale deeply and exhale.

Hold the breath outside and bring your awareness to mooladhara chakra. Mentally repeat 'mooladhara' five times with concentration at the perineum.

Then slowly inhale, raising the awareness up the spinal passage from mooladhara to ajna.

At this point the awareness is at ajna, at the top of the spine, just below the bindu centre. Without retaining the breath inside, begin to exhale and bend forward until the head touches the floor. While bending forward, move the awareness from the back of the head to the forehead. As the forehead touches the floor the awareness should be at bhrumadhya. Retain the breath outside and mentally repeat 'ajna' five times. There should be total relaxation of the entire body in the pose. The body should be loose like a rag doll.

Inhale and come up with the breath, bringing the awareness from bhrumadhya to ajna in the centre of the head. Slowly exhale and take the awareness down along the spine from ajna to mooladhara. Hold the breath outside, and with the awareness at mooladhara, again mentally repeat 'mooladhara' five times. This is one round. During the practice the movement of the body should be coordinated with the breath and the movement of the consciousness up and down the spine. This is very important.

Practise 5 to 10 rounds, slowly and gently with total awareness.

Benefits: Yoga mudra is the best antidote for anxiety, tension, mental pressure, fatigue, lethargy, drowsiness or dullness. It should be practised first thing in the morning, so that the prana begins to flow through the chakras and the entire chakra system becomes active.

Note

If you are unable to sit comfortably in padmasana, you can try practising in vajrasana. This is like the technique of shashankasana with the hands clasped behind the back. If you have difficulty bending forward due to stiffness in the back, you will find it easier to bend forward into shashankasana. If you find it difficult to bend forward in vajrasana, because of the legs supporting the entire trunk, then separate the knees slightly, allowing the chest to come closer to the floor. That is also a very comfortable posture and the same results are experienced.

Physiological effects

Vipareeta karani mudra and yoga mudra are two ways of taking your awareness through the brain, from the limbic system to the cortex. However, the two positions have different effects. In vipareeta karani mudra, you are stimulating the dopamine system, which is activating, and in yoga mudra you are stimulating the serotonin system, giving a calming effect.

In vipareeta karani mudra there is a point where the legs are perfectly balanced. When you bring your legs up, suddenly something clicks into place and your know you are perfectly balanced. At this point, the pressure comes off the legs and automatically there is a sensation of opening in the throat. This is called an alignment of joints and angles, which opens up certain nadis and chakras.

In the inverted posture, we use the weight of blood coming down into the brain to create pressure. In yoga mudra we use the forward bend to bring the legs into position, thereby exerting a slight pressure on the perineum, which opens sushumna.

There are a few reasons why yoga mudra is so comforting. Firstly, it brings the body in touch with the ground. Touching the front of the body with the legs is very comforting. The resulting pressure along the abdomen and chest has a very calming effect on the adrenal system, as in shashankasana and pranamasana. Also, in this posture the front of the body is protected while the back is exposed. The back of the body is harder; it is the soft front that we feel the need to protect. So, in yoga mudra we take a very protective attitude in which we come into contact with the earth and close ourselves off, exposing the back.

In padmasana the heels press against the groin and create a spontaneous contraction of the relaxed muscles towards the centre, creating a semi-nauli effect. In nauli the muscles are pushed together, here they are relaxed. It is the heels which press the muscles towards the centre. This nauli effect is important in yoga mudra. You do not have the nauli effect and the stimulation of manipura kshetram with other cross-legged postures.

2. HAND MUDRAS

The hand mudras number sixteen in total. Some are used to denote an attitude of mind, while others help to channel and redirect energy. Examples of attitudinal hand mudras are *abhaya mudra*, (the gesture of fearlessness), which is seen in statues of Buddha, and *shankha mudra*, the conch mudra, where the thumb is held between the fingers.

There are many different attitudinal hand mudras which denote a projection of mind and prana for the well-being of another person. The meditation mudras have a common aspect, which is to channel the flow of prana being emitted by the fingers into the environment, and to redirect it within the body.

JNANA MUDRA
(PSYCHIC GESTURE OF KNOWLEDGE)

The word *jnana* means 'intuitive knowledge'. Thus jnana mudra is the gesture of intuitive knowledge. This hand position has a symbolic meaning. The little finger, ring finger and middle finger represent the three qualities of nature: tamas, rajas and sattwa. These three states have to be transcended in order to pass from ignorance to knowledge. The index finger represents the individual consciousness and the thumb symbolizes the universal or supreme consciousness. In jnana mudra, individual consciousness is joining or uniting with supreme consciousness, which symbolizes the culmination of yoga.

413

BSY ©

Technique

Sit in any meditation posture.

Bend the index fingers of both hands so that the tips touch the root of the thumbs. Straighten the other three fingers and separate them slightly. Place the hands on the knees with the palms downward.

Relax the arms and hands.

Folding the thumb over the index finger helps to retain the mudra.

Jnana mudra can also be performed with the tip of the index finger touching the middle joint or the tip of the thumb, so that the thumb and index finger form a circle. This variation is as effective as the basic position.

Physiological effects

The palms are the most sensitive areas of the body. If two pins are placed half a millimetre apart on the palm of the hand, the two points will be felt pricking the skin. But if the two pins are placed one inch apart on the back, for example, the two points will not be felt. The palms and fingers have many nerve root endings which are constantly emitting energy. They sensitize the knees when placed on top of them. By keeping the fingers and hands on the knees, the pranic circuits are closed, so that the prana remains inside the body rather than being lost. There is a nadi known as gupta nadi which runs from the knees up the inside of the thighs into the perineum. Gupta nadi is supposed to be connected with mooladhara chakra. The sensitizing of that nerve channel helps to stimulate the energies at mooladhara.

414

CHIN MUDRA
(PSYCHIC GESTURE OF CONSCIOUSNESS)

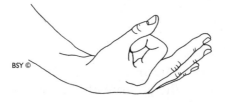

BSY ©

The word *chin* is derived from *chit* or *chitta,* which means 'consciousness'. Thus chin mudra is the attitude of chitta or consciousness. This mudra is very similar to jnana mudra, only the position of the hands is reversed, the backs of the hands being placed on top of the knees with the palms upward. It has been said that when the palms face upward, there is a slight stimulation of the nerves along the inside of the upper arms which helps to open up the lungs and chest cavity. When we begin to breathe in and out more easily, it is easier to control the mind. Breathing also relates to the different mental moods, which can be controlled by regulating the breath.

YONI MUDRA
(ATTITUDE OF THE WOMB OR SOURCE)

The word *yoni* means 'womb' or 'source'. Therefore, yoni mudra is the attitude by which we invoke the primal energy inherent in the womb of creation.

Technique
Sit in a comfortable meditation posture.
Place the palms of the hands together with the fingers and thumbs straight and pointing away from the body.
Interlock the middle, ring and little fingers of both hands.
Place the pads of the index fingers together, so that these two fingers form a triangle.

415

The apex of the triangle is pointing forward and the thumbs are placed together to form the base of the yoni or womb shape. The thumbs can also be crossed.

Another variation is to bring the pads of the thumbs together, so they point upward or inward.

Physiological effects

Yoni mudra helps to balance the activities of the right and left hemispheres of the brain. With the interlocked fingers, there is a complete cross connection of energies, the energy of the right hand going into the left and the energy of the left hand going into the right. The index fingers and the thumbs are also placed together, forming a triangle which further intensifies the flow of prana. While performing this mudra, it is natural for the elbows to point sideways, which helps to open up the chest cavity.

Hand mudras aim at providing greater concentration, awareness and internal physical relaxation, with the channelling of prana and the gentle opening up of the different muscles and cavities. Through the use of those mudras, the body is made more stable than when the fingers are left open.

Mudras are techniques which require very subtle awareness. We come to mudras after we have practised and understood asana, pranayama and bandhas, which remove gross blockages. When we come to the practice of mudras, we can appreciate and feel what is going on at this very subtle level. We have already gone through whole body awareness and integration of the body parts, and we are now back into cellular level consciousness. We are coming out of the 'doing' techniques and coming into the 'being' techniques. Asanas and pranayama require a lot of manipulation and effort, a lot of 'doing'. Mudra techniques are much more within the scope of just 'being'. We can now flow with the energy that we have created in our previous practice and develop experiences that come up into the consciousness.

Bandhas are used to slow down the physical and mental energy, thinking process, brain waves and metabolism.

416

Through mudras we enter the cellular level where energy or prana is manufactured, stored and utilized. The manufacture of energy is called anabolism, building up of tissue. The breakdown of energy is called catabolism, the using up of all the stores. The aim of yoga is to store prana, to build up and hold as much energy as possible. So the 'doing' techniques utilize more energy, while the 'being' techniques store it up.

In dealing with cellular level consciousness and the manipulation of the brain, awareness is brought into the cortex, into the conscious, from the unconscious. In the motor cortex, the entire body is represented. The area from the shoulder to the ankle is given only about a quarter or a fifth of the space that is designated to the hand. The hands and the head alone take up about fifty percent of the cortex, and the rest is for all the other parts of the body. The sensory information and the motor output from the hands and head enable very refined movements of the fingers, mouth and eyes. There are mudras for the eyes, hands, tongue and genitals. These techniques are aimed at controlling and bringing the awareness to large areas of the cortex. Mudras cover most of the cortex and sensory motor area.

Hand mudras, where the thumb and index finger are joined, engage the motor cortex at a very subtle level. Once pingala nadi is engaged a signal goes back through ida nadi to the brain. By holding these incredibly sensitive areas in a certain fixed position, a loop of energy moves from the motor cortex down to the hand and then back to the brain. With this minimal use of energy, a large part of the sensory and motor cortex can be stimulated at the same time. After about one or two minutes, the brain habituates and blocks out the signal. Therefore, consciousness of the mudra needs to be maintained for a period of time, so that when the sensory information is dissolved into the general system, you can go with it consciously.

3. HEAD MUDRAS

The head mudras are seven in number. These practices are related to the eyes, ears, nose, tongue and lips. They form an integral part of kundalini yoga and many of them are meditation techniques in their own right.

SHAMBHAVI MUDRA
(EYEBROW CENTRE GAZING)

Shambhavi is the name of the wife or consort of Shambhu (Shiva). She has many other names such as Parvati, Shakti and so on. It is believed that Shambhu taught Shambhavi the practice of shambhavi mudra and urged her to practise it diligently if she wanted to attain higher awareness. It is said that the practice of shambhavi will stir Shambhu (super-consciousness) and make him appear before you.

This practice is also known as *bhrumadhya drishti*, which means 'eyebrow centre gazing'. By this practice ajna chakra is awakened, which enables us to transcend the fetters of the individual ego and see the significance and essence behind all manifest things.

There are seven stages of shambhavi, according to the vedic system: with coordination of the breath, with breath retention, first dharana, second dharana, third dharana, fourth dharana and fifth dharana.

Technique
Stage I: With normal breathing
Sit in a comfortable meditation posture.
Straighten the back and head. Place the hands on the knees in chin or jnana mudra.
Close the eyes for a short time and relax the whole body.
Relax all the muscles of the face, including the forehead, eyes and behind the eyes.
Breathe normally for the duration of the practice.

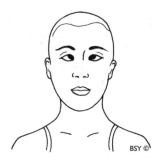

Slowly open the eyes and look straight ahead at a fixed point. Fix the head in that position.

Then look upward and inward. Try to focus both eyes at the eyebrow centre. If this is done correctly, you will see two curved images of the eyebrows which merge with each other at the centre forming a V-shaped point at the root of the nose. The head should not move.

Be aware of the V-shaped formation which is the approximate location of the eyebrow centre. If you do not see this V formation, it is a sure indication that the eyes are not converging as they should.

When you begin to feel strain, close the eyes for a few moments and relax them.

Then resume the practice. Do not strain the eyes.

Initially the eye muscles will begin to pain after a few seconds. Therefore, you should perform each round for a short period only.

Practise 10 to 15 rounds.

Stage 2: With coordinated breathing

After mastering the eye movement, try to coordinate the movement of the eyes with the breath.

Breathe in slowly and look up and in towards the eyebrow centre. Then breathe out slowly and lower the gaze. Practise 15 to 20 rounds.

Stage 3: With kumbhaka

Once the eye movement is coordinated with the breath, gradually train the eye muscles to remain in shambhavi without any kind of eye tension.

419

Continue coordinating the eye movement with the breath. Retain the breath either inside or outside, maintaining shambhavi mudra for the duration of the retention. The head should remain straight throughout the practice.

In the final stage, with breath retention, concentration should be on the image of the self. Practise ten to fifteen rounds.

Introduction to Stage 4

There are five levels of experience in shambhavi, according to the vedantic approach, through which the image of the self is developed. These experiences manifest as we perfect each stage. This kind of imagination or visualization also helps to focus the mind to a greater extent, so that sublimation can take place. The normal thoughts, ideas and visions, which constantly distract our concentration must be eliminated so that a different kind of experience can arise.

Stage 4: The five dharanas

1. *Agni mandala*: In the first visualization, or dharana, concentrate on the entire body in the form of agni, fire. The whole body is to be viewed as agni mandala. Feel the body as fire. This is not just a visual or mental imagination, but a sensorial experience. The flames and heat can be experienced along the spine and the front of the body. The different experiences of fire must be felt in this body.

2. *Surya mandala*: In the second dharana, concentration is on surya mandala. Here the image of the sun is visualized in shambhavi mudra at the point between the eyebrows.

3. *Chandra mandala*: In the third dharana, awareness is of chandra mandala, which is also called ajna mandala. Here the symbol of ajna chakra is visualized at the gazing point in shambhavi.

4. *Prakasha mandala*: In the fourth dharana visualize the light at the centre of ajna chakra. This light does not radiate any sensation of heat or coolness. It is pure, white light.

5. *Vidyut mandala*: In the fifth dharana visualization is of lightning within the white light.

These are the five levels of experience in shambhavi mudra.

Precautions: The eyes are very sensitive and, therefore, the final position should not be held for too long. If the nerves are weak, retinal detachment can even take place. As soon as you feel strain, release the position.

Psychophysiological effects

Because of the different stages of experience that can be attained by this practice, it is highly regarded in all yogic, tantric and vedantic texts. It has been stated that one who becomes proficient in this technique can awaken ajna chakra. This enables one to transcend the faculties of the lower mind and establish oneself in higher consciousness.

The practice strengthens the eye muscles and gradually releases the tension that accumulates in the nerves and muscles of the eyes. Mentally there is reduction of anxiety, stress and emotional stress. It is easier to achieve concentration, mental stability and the state of thoughtlessness by this practice than by other techniques for controlling the mind.

NASIKAGRA DRISHTI (NOSE TIP GAZING)

In Sanskrit the word *nasika* means 'nose', *agra* means 'tip' and *drishti* means 'gazing'. So nasikagra drishti means nose tip gazing, which describes the practice perfectly from the practical point of view. The other name for this practice is *agochari* mudra, which is derived from the Sanskrit word *agocharam* meaning 'beyond sensory perception', 'unknown' or invisible. In other words, this practice takes one beyond the normal limits of consciousness. It calms the mind and develops introversion. If practised regularly, nose tip gazing is an excellent form of concentration.

Technique
Stage 1: With normal breathing

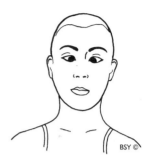

Sit in a comfortable meditation posture. Close the eyes and relax the whole body. Breathe normally throughout the duration of the practice.

Open the eyes slightly and focus on the nose tip. Keep the head straight. Do not strain the eyes, but try to hold the gaze steadily at the tip of the nose. If the eyes are correctly focused, then you should see a double outline of the nose. These two lines converge at the tip of the nose, forming a V.

Try to hold the gaze at the apex of the V.

When you begin to feel strain, release the gaze then relax the eyes for a few seconds.

Then repeat the practice. Gradually increase the duration as the eyes become accustomed.

Continue for up to five minutes.

When you can gaze at the nose without the slightest difficulty, then become aware of the breath as well. Be aware of the breath flowing in and out at the nose tip. Try to become completely absorbed in the practice to the exclusion of all other thoughts.

Practice note: Initially it is very difficult to focus the eyes at the nose tip. To check if you are practising properly, hold the index finger in front of the eyes and focus on it. Then slowly bring the finger to the nose tip, keeping the eyes focused on it. When you remove the finger, both of the eyes will be correctly focused on the nose tip.

Stage 2: With kumbhaka

Close the eyes and become aware of the breath at the nose tip.

Inhale with the eyes closed. Retaining the breath inside, open the eyes slightly and gaze at the nose tip.

422

Concentrate on the point of the V.

Then release kumbhaka and breathe out slowly.

Close the eyes and relax them. Continue the practice for five minutes.

Practice note: Nasikagra drishti is always practised with inner retention, not external retention. During inhalation and exhalation, the eyes remain closed. While gazing at the nose tip, you are actually activating mooladhara. The theory regarding this is that the bridge of the nose represents the spinal cord. Just as different centres in the body are represented in the brain, the different psychic centres are also represented along the bridge of the nose. At the top of the bridge is ajna and at the tip is mooladhara.

Contra-indications: People suffering from glaucoma should not practice this mudra. Those with diabetic retinopathy or who have just had cataract surgery, lens implant or other eye operations should not perform nasikagra drishti without the guidance of a competent teacher.

Those suffering from depression should avoid this practice.

MANDUKI MUDRA (GESTURE OF THE FROG)

The word *manduki* means 'frog', so manduki mudra is the frog attitude. It was given this name because the sitting pose resembles the natural position of the frog. Manduki mudra is an advanced variation of nasikagra drishti.

Technique

Sit in vajrasana with the feet pointing outward and separate the knees as far apart as possible.

Let the buttocks rest firmly on the floor, so that pressure is felt at the perineum, stimulating the region of mooladhara chakra.

Feel pressure at the perineum.

Place the hands on the knees with the palms downward.

Hold the spine and head upright.

Close the eyes and relax in the posture.

423

Breathe in and out slowly and rhythmically, with equal inspiration and expiration. There is no breath retention in this practice.

Open the eyes halfway and gaze at the nose tip. While gazing steadily, be aware of the flow of the breath through the nostrils.

Simultaneously become aware of different smells. Concentrate on the sense of smell in the air you breathe in and out. The aim of the practice is to smell the astral body, which has the subtle fragrance of sandalwood.

While concentrating at the nose tip be aware of the flow of breath and the sense of smell.

If your eyes become tired, close them for a minute and relax them. Then resume nasikagra drishti.

Continue the practice for five to ten minutes until the mind and senses become introverted. Do not lose yourself in the practice.

Practice note: If you find it difficult to sit in manduki asana, then sit in bhadrasana with the toes pointing inward and the soles upward. The buttocks should rest on the floor. If you still find difficulty, place a folded blanket underneath the buttocks. This will apply firm pressure to the region of mooladhara.

424

Physiological effects

The sense of smell is a faculty of mooladhara. Therefore, concentration on smell is a way to activate this centre. Whether you use the faculty of smell wilfully and consciously or it happens naturally, there is a change in the energy structure at mooladhara, and the corresponding centre in the brain is affected by it. By directing the attention to the experiences of smell, while keeping the vision focused at the nose tip, you are also stimulating certain nadis which help to awaken mooladhara. If you concentrate hard enough, you will feel a tingling sensation at mooladhara. Smell a rose and see what happens at the perineum. Mooladhara and the area of smell are one of the most powerful regions for storage and recovery of memory. A smell can trigger a memory from childhood. Smell is the most primitive of all the senses. This area is very deep inside the primal brain.

BHOOCHARI MUDRA
(GAZING INTO NOTHINGNESS)

Bhoochari means 'gazing at nothingness'. This mudra should be practised facing a blank wall so that there is nothing to distract the vision.

Technique

Sit in a comfortable meditation posture.
Keep the eyes open.
Raise the right hand in front of the face.
Hold the hand horizontally, so that the palm is facing downward, with the fingers together.
The side of the thumb should be touching the tip of the upper lip. The right elbow should point to the side of the body.
Focus the eyes on the tip of the little finger for a minute or so, without winking or blinking.
Then remove the hand but continue to gaze at the place where the little finger was situated.

When the vision dissipates raise the hand again, and concentrate on the tip of the little finger. Then remove the hand and continue to gaze intently into the space, the nothingness. Practise for five to ten minutes.

Practice note: This technique helps to tranquillize and concentrate the mind. It is very beneficial for people who express a lot of anger. Whenever you are angry, practice bhoochari mudra and feel yourself calming down.

AKASHI MUDRA (AWARENESS OF INNER SPACE)

The word *akashi* means 'inner space'. Akashi mudra is awareness of the inner space. This practice induces mental tranquillity by withdrawing the senses. It renders the mind free of thoughts and leads to states of trance. Akashi mudra is a combination of ujjayi, khechari, kumbhaka, shambhavi and nasikagra.

Technique

Sit in siddhasana or padmasana. Hold the spine and head straight. Relax the whole body.
Fold the tongue back into khechari mudra.
Practise shambhavi mudra.
Inhale slowly and deeply with ujjayi pranayama.
Simultaneously bend the head backwards.
Synchronize the movement of the head with inhalation.

At the end of inhalation, the head should be leaning backward, but not fully.

Straighten the arms and lock the elbows, pressing the knees with the hands.

Practise internal kumbhaka for as long as possible, without straining.

Continue to practise khechari and shambhavi.

Fix your whole awareness on the eyebrow centre.

Then bend the arms and slowly exhale with ujjayi, while bringing the head forward.

Gently lower the eyes.

At the end of exhalation, the head should face forward. Practise external kumbhaka and nasikagra drishti. Concentrate at the nose tip.

At the end of external kumbhaka, close the eyes, breathe normally for a few seconds and relax. Be aware of the inner space.

Then begin the next round.

Continue the practice for 5 to 10 minutes.

When you feel a fainting sensation, stop the practice.

Contra-indications: People with high blood pressure, vertigo or brain haemorrhage should not do this practice.

Physiological effects

Akashi mudra aims at developing control over the senses. When you concentrate on the nose and the sense of smell, you are actually focusing your attention on the most primitive of all the senses, which is located deep down inside the primal brain. Vision, on the other hand, is the most developed sense. As you take your attention to the eyes, you are moving from the lowest part of the brain to a very highly developed part of the brain. There is a theory that at some stage along the evolutionary path, choices had to be made about which senses would be developed; for example, dogs developed smell much more actively that vision.

In the brain there are two main areas for vision. One is the occipital cortex, an area about the size of the hand which controls involuntary vision. We have no choice but to keep moving our eyes in order to continue receiving sensory information and input. The second area, which is located in the frontal lobe, is involved in voluntary vision. It helps in directing the eyes where you want them to look for a specific purpose, like looking ahead, in the same way as the purpose of the frontal lobes is thinking ahead, looking to the future. This is the physical level of the mental activity.

This mudra fixes the eyes, stops involuntary movement, stops the use of energy and brings all the brain cells into entrainment. They go into a simple alpha rhythm. If you close your eyes, you will get an alpha rhythm, which is a relaxed state in the back of the head. But when you focus into these mudras, you not only get that relaxed rhythm in the back of the head, but also in the frontal lobes. This is the main reason why these mudras are very tranquillizing. They stop the thinking process almost instantly. Thought and thought waves are very much connected to metabolic activity in the cells, the rate of breathing, the rate of movement of the eyes and also the rate of movement of the tongue. These activities have a reflex in the frontal lobes, so that when movement is slowed down the brain is also slowed down, for example, during meditation.

Akashi mudra involves different forms of manipulation, either looking upward at the eyebrow centre, directing the energy to the higher centres in the brain, or looking downward at the nose tip, and fixing the attention on the lower, more primitive centres in the brain, whereas practices such as bhoochari mudra take us away from our point of focus. Just as shambhavi and nasikagra mudras increase concentration, bhoochari mudra takes us into a field of vision that is no longer focused on a point, but on the entire visual field.

KHECHARI MUDRA (TONGUE LOCK)

Khechari mudra, the tongue lock, is regarded as a very important practice in all the hatha yoga, raja yoga and vedantic texts because of its effect on the body and mind. It is also known as *nabho* mudra, and is generally combined with ujjayi pranayama and other meditation practices.

Raja yoga technique
Sit in a comfortable meditation posture. Close the mouth. Roll the tongue back so that the lower surface touches the upper palate.
Bring the tip of the tongue as far as possible towards the back of the throat.
If the tongue is long enough, try to insert it into the nasal cavity from inside.
Do not strain.
When you feel discomfort bring the tongue forward and relax it for a few seconds.
Then repeat the practice.
Some people try to elongate the tongue by massaging it with butter and then turning it backward.
Precaution: If a bitter taste is experienced during khechari mudra, the practice should be terminated. It is due to physical impurity and is experienced when there is too much kapha dosha, mucus element, in the body. As a general rule, if you go through the process of hatha yoga, elimination of toxins and balancing of the doshas can be achieved, then the bitter taste will not be experienced.

429

However, if you take up the practice without purification, you will have that bitter taste, like rotten egg going down the throat.

Hatha yoga technique

This form of khechari mudra should be attempted only under the guidance of a guru. The tendon beneath the tongue is slowly cut, week by week. A sharpened stone can be used for this purpose. The tongue is massaged for long periods daily with butter until it is long enough for the tip to touch the eyebrow centre. Then the full khechari mudra can be practised, in which the tongue is inserted inside the sinus cavities where it stimulates the nerve centres, thereby altering the brain function.

Precaution: Once the tongue is cut, control over the faculties of speech and swallowing is impaired, which cannot be reversed. Therefore, the hatha yoga technique was traditionally done only by those yogis who were totally dedicated to spiritual awakening and no longer involved with worldly life.

Physiological effects

The head, hands and tongue cover a very large part of the sensory area of the cortex. In the motor area, the area given for the tongue is three or four times greater than that given in the sensory area. The area allocated to the lips, mouth and vocal cords for the communication of thought into words through vishuddhi is given tremendous importance. The hand is another very important area. Therefore, most of the cortex is given to the head, hands, tongue, eyes and voice.

When we practise any of the mudras, we bring our attention to these important areas. Folding the tongue back and holding it still has the effect of bringing it into the consciousness. The tongue is an organ that moves a lot, often unconsciously, especially when we talk. By folding it back into khechari mudra we stabilize and fix muscles that

430

are normally never still. This act produces stillness and quiet throughout the whole system, and has a profound effect on the consciousness. A lot of energy that would normally be utilized in cortical activity is free for other functions.

It is believed that by this practice one gains control over the major functions of the body. As the tongue is inserted into the nasal cavity, many tiny nerve endings, hormones and glands are activated, which give greater autonomic control. Yogis who go into extended periods of meditation use khechari mudra to overcome the physical needs of hunger and thirst. It is also believed that when khechari is practised in its full form, then the astral body detaches itself from the physical body. With this detachment one's mind or consciousness experiences the akasha tattwa.

According to kundalini yoga, another benefit attained through khechari is rejuvenation of the physical cells of the body. Kundalini yoga states that bindu visarga, at the top back of the head, is an important centre. From there the amrit, nectar or elixir of life, is secreted in tiny quantities which drip down into the body. When the lower centres metabolize this nectar the body undergoes the process of decay, old age, disease and death. With the practice of khechari mudra, yogis have tried to reverse this process, by stimulating bindu visarga, and trapping the drops of hormone or amrit at vishuddhi, by folding the tongue back.

When that hormone is retained in the vishuddhi region, it becomes purified and creates a different effect on the body. It does not combine with the acids of the stomach and become poison. It retains its purity and is distributed throughout the body after being percolated by the mucus membranes and salivary glands lining the mouth. Once that happens, the nectar begins to rejuvenate the body. The lifespan can thus be increased through the practice of khechari mudra.

431

SHANMUKHI MUDRA
(CLOSING THE SEVEN GATES)

Bindu visarga is traditionally considered to be the centre or source of individual creation, from where the psychic vibrations first emanate. These vibrations are known as *nada*, or 'psychic sound'. They are the first manifestation of creation from the unmanifest source. Shanmukhi mudra, or the attitude of the seven gates, is used to withdraw the mind from the external environment and to focus it at bindu visarga, the source, in order to experience psychic sound.

By taking the awareness to bindu one begins to experience the inner silence, in which the psychic sounds are heard. Shanmukhi mudra is used in nada yoga. It is a mudra of introversion through which one experiences the different layers of psychic sounds. The word *shanmukhi* means 'seven gates'. Here the seven gates refer to the seven sensory apertures: two eyes, two ears, two nostrils, one mouth. These are the seven doors of perception through which information is received from the outside world. In shanmukhi mudra these gates are closed, allowing the awareness to be redirected to the source.

Technique

Sit in padmasana or siddhasana with the spine and head straight.

Raise the hands in front of the face with the elbows pointing sideways.

Close the ears with the thumbs, the eyes with the index fingers, the nostrils with the middle fingers, and the mouth with the ring fingers above the upper lip and the little fingers below the lower lip.

The fingers should gently but firmly close the seven gates.

During the practice, the middle fingers should release the nostrils during inhalation and exhalation.

Inhale deeply and slowly.

At the end of inhalation, close the nostrils with the middle fingers and practise antar kumbhaka.

Concentrate at bindu visarga and listen to the inner sound or nada emanating from that region.

When you can no longer retain the breath comfortably, release the pressure of the middle fingers, and slowly breathe out.

This is one round.

Breathe in again immediately to start another round.

Physiological effects

Shanmukhi mudra is also a technique of prana vidya where the energy which is emitted from the hands and fingers is absorbed by the nerve endings in the face. The energy and heat from the hands and fingers stimulates and relaxes the nerves and muscles in the face, which are very sensitive to any kind of external change. In this way a circuit is created between the hands and eyes, nose, mouth and ears.

Neurological connections are created between all of these senses, the awareness introverted, and enough pressure is applied to stimulate the ida/pingala flow. The pressure on the sensory organs is the pingala aspect, while the sensory component is the ida aspect. Through this practice, areas of the cortex are consciously brought into relationships which

433

would otherwise not normally occur. This accounts for the simultaneous potency of internalization and the maintaining of wakefulness. How it affects the inner sound, how it creates nada, is an experience outside the area of physiology.

4. LOCKED MUDRAS

These practices are a combination of mudras and bandhas. Utthanpadasana is used as the sitting posture. One leg is stretched forward and the other leg is bent with the heel pressed against the perineum, exerting direct pressure on mooladhara. In maha mudra, shambhavi and khechari mudras are combined with moola bandha. In maha bheda mudra, nasikagra and khechari mudra is combined with maha bandha. These two practices charge the whole system with prana and prepare it for kundalini awakening.

MAHA MUDRA (GREAT ATTITUDE)

Maha mudra means 'the great attitude'. Utthanpadasana, the sitting position for this practice, has three variations:
1. Right leg straight and left leg folded, so that the left heel presses against the perineum.
2. Left leg straight and right leg folded, so that the right heel presses against the perineum.
3. Both legs straight.

Hatha yoga technique
Sit in utthanpadasana with the right leg straight and the left leg folded. The left heel should be pressed against the perineum. Keep the back straight. Try to keep the knees together.
Place both hands on top of the right knee.
Fold the tongue back in khechari mudra.
Bend forward just enough to be able to clasp the right toes with the fingers of both hands. Keep the head up.
Inhale deeply.

434

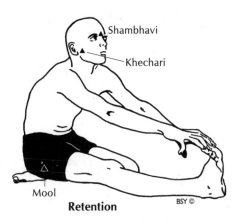

Retention

BSY ©

Practise moola bandha and shambhavi mudra, gazing at the eyebrow centre.

While retaining the breath inside, rotate the awareness through the spine from mooladhara to vishuddhi to ajna.

The awareness should remain at each centre for one second.

Bring the awareness back to mooladhara and begin the next rotation.

Repeat the name of each chakra point mentally as you come to it: mooladhara, vishuddhi, ajna.

Continue the rotations for as long as you are able to retain the breath comfortably.

Then release moola bandha and shambhavi mudra and exhale slowly.

Return to the starting position with both hands placed on the outstretched knee.

Relax in this position and allow the breathing to normalize.

Then repeat the process.

Practise five rounds on each side and then five rounds with both legs outstretched.

MAHA BHEDA MUDRA
(GREAT PIERCING ATTITUDE)

Maha bheda mudra means the 'great piercing attitude'. This
is a powerful practice for uniting with the inner being or
self.

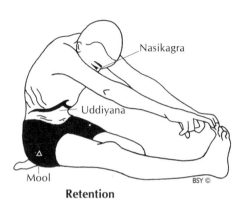

Retention

Hatha yoga technique

The starting position, utthanpadasana, is the same as for
maha mudra.

Bend forward and clasp the right toes with both hands.
Inhale and exhale deeply.

While retaining the breath outside, practise jalandhara,
uddiyana and moola bandha.

Fix the gaze at the nose tip in nasikagra mudra.

Rotate the awareness up through the spine from
mooladhara to manipura, to vishuddhi, corresponding
to the location of the three bandhas: moola, uddiyana
and jalandhara.

Repeat the name of each chakra in turn: mooladhara,
manipura, vishuddhi, as you rotate the awareness.

Do up to five rotations.

Then release nasikagra, release moola bandha, uddiyana
and jalandhara. Return to the starting position with both
hands on the outstretched knee, and inhale slowly.

436

Relax in this position until the breathing normalizes. Then begin the next round.

Do five rounds on each side and five rounds with both legs outstretched.

Physiological effects

The locked mudras combine bandhas, eye practices and kumbhaka. In this process of bringing the body into alignment and stopping these organs, the entire brain is affected. When performing bandhas with kumbhaka, the body is squeezed like a bag of fluid. Stimulation of mooladhara chakra works in the area of the upper brain stem where the reticular activating system is located. By squeezing the perineum, an immediate reflex of energy comes up and illumines the whole brain. Because so many different structures are stopped simultaneously, the cortex is pushed very rapidly into a single, pulsating unit. In meditation practice, the brain waves are synchronized but normally this is a slow process. With these locked mudras, the brain and the catabolism are slowed down immediately, like putting on the brakes too quickly. This has a powerful effect on the metabolism, which can be disturbing if the constitution or psyche is weak.

Theory of prana

Both maha mudra and maha bheda mudra are performed in the same posture, sitting in half vajrasana with one leg outstretched in front of the body and the knees together. The heel of the folded leg is pressed against the perineum, exerting pressure directly on mooladhara. As you bend forward the spine is extended and held straight. The prana from the hands goes into the toes, creating a circuit. Pressure is exerted on vajra nadi and there is focusing on the ocular nerves. Along with contraction, a circuit is created in the movement of energy from mooladhara to ajna. Therefore, these mudras stimulate the channels of prana, circulate the movement of prana within the body and awaken prana.

Yogis have always maintained that the different types of experiences of the human consciousness can be easily monitored and controlled through the channelling of prana. A mental attitude can alter the movement of prana. The external environment can influence the movement of prana because everything is constantly and continuously influencing, affecting and altering the biorhythms. Both thought and emotion alter our physical and pranic biorhythms. Controlling the body by rebalancing the thought process is a mental approach. This is the approach of raja yoga with the practices of pratyahara and dharana. In raja yoga we practise observation of the vrittis, thoughts and desires, and try to control them. Gradually, by reducing their influence on our behaviour and expression, we find a greater balance and harmony in the mind-body complex.

At the same time, another approach has been adopted to work directly on the levels of nadi, chakra and prana. Working from this level, we use techniques for manipulating and raising the prana in order to alter the condition of the mind, thoughts and emotions, so that a physical technique can induce pratyahara or dharana and a combination of physical techniques can induce dhyana. This is where mudras come in. By a change in our physical posture, joining the fingers or pressing a certain part of the body, or closing certain areas of the body, the flow of prana being directed to that part can be diverted to another area. It is like shining a torch at night on a blank wall. The light will hit the wall and then spread out in all directions because there is a block.

The theory of prana works in a similar way. The nadis and chakras are like torches that are constantly shining and radiating their energy into infinity. How far that energy radiates we do not know. Maybe it gets lost or becomes invisible at some point. However, when we are able to put up a barrier within the field of our body, like closing the eyes with the fingers, then the prana that is being radiated through the eyes, hits that barrier and is reflected back. By closing the nostrils, the prana responsible for the expulsion of breath hits that barrier and bounces back. By closing vajra nadi, the sexual energy hits that barrier and rushes upward to the brain. Each mudra has a purpose, which is to reverse that energy expression of our being and divert it back into the body.

When prana is in the process of rebalancing itself, then there is an automatic experience of mental tranquillity. Therefore, most of the mudras are used for going deep into a meditative state. They aid the processes of pratyahara and dharana. That is what we experience superficially. At a deeper level of our personality something else happens. We have discussed the four basic instinctive tendencies – fear, sexual urge, desire for sleep and desire for food. These are the corresponding physical manifestations of the mental vrittis that are being experienced on the level of consciousness. For example, the sexual urge is a desire, a force, a thought and expression. It is being experienced in the region of mooladhara. That form of consciousness is actually activating that physical part of the body known as the mooladhara, swadhisthana region.

Sleep does not affect any one organ in the body. It slows down the activity of the nervous system. As the activities cease, we move into another state of consciousness or sleep. We go through different stages of drowsiness, lethargy and somnambulism, from dream to deep sleep. Hunger is not felt in the pancreas, kidneys or liver, it is felt in the stomach, the abdomen. The desire for food actually stimulates the digestive system. Through the digestive system we can control that vritti. By controlling the physical region of manipura, the solar plexus, we can control that vritti. Similarly, by controlling the autonomic nervous system, we can control the vritti of fear, palpitation, secretion of adrenaline, rapid breathing, etc.

Mudras work within these areas in order to control the corresponding physical aspects of consciousness by altering and channelling the flow of prana, the energy that is manifesting in the body. Mudras become a process through which we begin to experiment with ourselves and try to see the relationship with the different koshas – annamaya kosha, manomaya kosha and pranamaya kosha. When harmony and integration of the various faculties of these koshas has taken place, then the psychic or spiritual aspect becomes known to us. So, bandhas are more physical in nature and mudras are more subtle than bandhas.

19

Holistic Physiology

Professor Edward Denning once said, "All models are wrong, but some are useful." He was a systems analyst who went to Japan after the Second World War and reconstructed their economy.

Using the old models of physiology to convey the physiology of the yoga practices, which are intricate and subtle self-regulatory processes, is very limited. It is mechanistic physiology, one which looks at a part of a system or organ and breaks it down into its parts. This mechanistic approach is useful and important, but it is only partial, not holistic. It is not a physiology that gives us an understanding of what is going on in the whole body and mind.

When we are examining yoga practices, we need to have both a partial and a holistic view. The emphasis in yoga is on pinpointing parts and maintaining whole body awareness at as many subtle levels as possible. We are trying to feel energy in the body at increasingly more subtle levels, and trying to gain knowledge as well as energy. We are trying to get an expanded experience of ourselves. A proper model of physiology can help us understand what is going on and which direction we should take in order to enhance the process.

To do this we have to clarify two main misconceptions. The first is the conception that we are 'solid'. The second is to realize that all the parts of our body are interconnected, not separated into 'parts'. We think of ourselves as being parts, – "I am a head", "I am a neck", "I am a chest", and we do not experience these parts as interconnected and interacting.

Intercommunication

Though we think of ourselves as being solid, we are actually bags of water. The human body is eighty percent water contained within more solid membranes. Inside this bag of water there are lots of smaller bags called organs, and inside those smaller bags there are tiny little bags of water, which we call cells. Inside these cells are smaller bags of water, which may be called mitochondria, and so on.

We are communities of cells interacting. Each cell is like a little individual which has its own function, its own karma yoga. Whether you are a liver cell and have to digest poison, or a colon cell and have to deal with wind and faeces, or a heart cell facing the task of pumping endless litres of blood, it does not matter; you have your own function. A heart cell cannot want to be a colon cell, otherwise cancer would develop. Each cell must communicate with all the other cells. The colon communicates with the heart and brain. This communication can be experienced as a supreme intelligence, an overall appreciation of who we are. Intracellular communication creates an experience of our physiology.

There is an outer physiology and an inner physiology. We have an outer body which is the skeletal system, the muscle system and the nerves which regulate that body. We have a complete system of nerves coming down from the brain to regulate the outer body. The inner physiology is the physiology of the heart and lungs, the digestive tract and so on. How these inner and outer systems communicate is one of the subjects of yoga, and many of the practices of hatha yoga relate to enhancing this communication.

For example, in asanas we use our 'outer' physiology to create pressures and to communicate with our inner physiology, with the deeper subtle processes that we normally cannot feel. We connect various systems together, and this is the important issue here. In the old paradigm we tended to think of the body as separate segments connected by wires. These wires are the nerves. However, this is a limited way of thinking.

Every single part of the body communicates with every other part, not just through the nerves but also through the connective tissue and through chemicals, such as hormones. Of all the connecting systems of the body, connective tissue is the least well understood. It is not given much emphasis in normal physiology. However, connective tissue is extremely important. It is the stuff that separates and creates the first 'big bag'. Then it creates a bag around the lungs, around the heart, and all those other bags. These bags or containers join up, so there is information continually going from one section of this connective tissue to the next section, and it must be remembered that this connection goes right down to the intracellular level.

If you try to trace a line from a point at the top of the head to any other point in the body, you will find a connecting path for information. This is the area of physiology where the really subtle techniques of bandha and mudra start to work. When we talk about asana and pranayama, we are talking about major, large scale movements. When we push or press a nerve, organ or muscle, there is an obvious change. When we talk about the more subtle effects of yoga, we are talking about subtle interconnections and effects which reach down into the intracellular level. This is something we really need to think about and understand.

As well as nervous and connective tissue connections, every organ and cell is bathed in a chemical sea. These chemicals are responsible for moods and feelings, and their intensity. They are also partially responsible for how much information we can get from ourselves. How conscious we can be of those cells will depend on how intact the communication pathways are. If there is a break in communication, we lose contact with an area of the body, for example, our toes or legs.

Breaks in communication

How do we break communication between the parts of our body? The most obvious way to do this is around the joints. The joints are areas that create segments. The body is segmented to allow for movement, and that movement can only take place when muscles wrap around a joint. If there is excess tension in the joint, we will cut off a lot of the intercommunication between the various parts of our bodies. This is why the pawanmuktasana series and yoga nidra are so important. These practices release tensions from these areas of contraction and allow improved communication via nerves, fluids or connective tissue.

Basically, contractions occur around joints and fluid movement is stopped because the connective tissue becomes restricted, crinkled, folded over and pressed upon by other structures. We cannot function efficiently and our function and flow stops. The experience we get when we practise asanas is that our body feels more alive.

When we get these contractions and lose function, there is a build-up of various chemicals, for example, lactic acid. This build-up creates pain in our tissues, burning sensations and dysfunction. Lactic acid build-up is a gross event. There are other more subtle reactions going on which are much more diffuse and hard to define, but we can feel their effect if we look for it.

Two major areas of intercommunication are in the neck and pelvis. Many joints, muscles, organs and structures interconnect here. At the hips and perineum, and at the head, neck and shoulders, there is complex muscle interaction and this is often where information becomes blocked. We can use asanas to undo gross, major blockages in communication within muscles, connective tissue and fluids. Once tensions are reduced and we become reconnected and can begin to feel the different parts of the body

444

again through asanas, we might realize, "Yes, I have a back" or "I didn't realize that I was tensing my hip."

This means that we start to get information from a part of the body that before was unconscious and blocked. Once we get that information and begin to reconnect our awareness through the tissues and fluids, we can use pranayama to reset the rhythms in the brain, which may have been put out of synchronicity by these blockages in the joints and muscles.

The diaphragms

Other important areas of segmentation and contraction occur at the three diaphragms. In the body there are long muscles and flat muscles. The long muscles are usually found in the limbs and are used for movement. The flat muscles are used for both movement, especially short, small movements and for pulsation and rhythm. The three diaphragms are the respiratory diaphragm, the perineal diaphragm and the diaphragm underneath the brain, which is a tight sheet of connective tissue. These diaphragms create divisions between segments and can amplify signals in the same way that the diaphragm at the end of a doctor's stethoscope amplifies the sound of the heart. For example, the diaphragm under the ribcage creates an upper thorax and a lower abdomen. It has pulsatory movement and also holds things together. If you are tense and you want to make sure that you are braced and protected, then your posture will change, your diaphragm will contract and you will stop breathing for a short period of time.

The three segments can communicate with each other, sending signals and information through their movement by amplifying body signals, pressures and vibrations, if we are relaxed and aware. The diaphragm beneath the brain is a powerful amplifier of vibrations and is connected to the muscles in the neck, jaw and shoulders. A lot of people carry tension at the base of the skull where it joins the neck. This tends to occur when we think in excess or worry. Awareness then tends to contract and locate itself in the head. Whole

445

body awareness is forgotten. When this happens the other diaphragms will also contract to some degree.

Re-establishing communication

In holistic physiology we try to experience ourselves as a life force in a fluid filled bag. This bag is divided into segments which are trying to communicate with each other. However, due to tensions and stresses we often cut off parts of ourselves, so as not to experience something or to protect ourselves because of various dangers, real and imagined. For example, when we go into intellectual mode, we start to focus on our thoughts and may forget about the rest of our body. In this situation the whole body might contract. We then cut ourselves off from 'reality'. It is, in effect, cutting off the head from the rest of the body where most of the information about life is contained. The body is like a big thermometer or measuring device which is measuring life. By cutting off the head from the rest of the body, we ignore a lot of signals and also deprive and starve ourselves of a lot of energy.

It is very important that we have ways of re-establishing communications, of self-regulation and breaking down these blockages, especially if we have the tendency to jump energetically into our heads and intellect when under stress. Asanas, pranayama, bandhas and mudras are ways of achieving this. Before we can really perform pranayama and bandhas properly, however, we need to practise asanas. We need to unblock the nadis in the various joints. We need to practise pranayama to re-establish movement and relaxation in the diaphragms, to get fluids circulating again so that poisons trapped can be metabolized.

We are fluid and we circulate. We are not just two-dimensional static beings. We are dynamic creatures with constant fluid movement, energy movement, nerve pulsation. It is very important that we understand this and find ways to break down blocks and re-establish communication. Then we must find finer and finer ways to go in and consciously manipulate the nerves, fluids and chemicals in a healthy way.

446

20

Causes of Imbalance and Disease according to Yoga

Physical imbalance

According to yoga, the physical causes of imbalance and disease are as follows:

1. *Biological agents which include*:
   a) Viruses, bacteria, infections etc., all of which come under micro-organisms.
   b) Internal and external parasites.
   c) Organisms such as snakes, scorpions, insects and mosquitoes.
2. *Climatic and environmental factors such as*:
   a) Extremes in temperature, altitudes, etc.
   b) Pollution of air, water, noise, etc.
   c) Contamination or adulteration of food, or food which has artificial chemicals and additives.
3. *Trauma*, including chronic postural trauma, e.g. sitting badly.
4. *Abuse, addiction and medication*: the intake of chemicals and toxins which do not conform with body requirements.
5. *Nutritional imbalance*.
6. *Genetic traits and defects*.
7. *Ageing process*.

These are the seven major points, all of which create physical imbalance. Apart from these there are many other minor points such as immunological reactions, disturbances in cellular functions and so on.

447

In the yogic system different methods are given to overcome these physical causes of imbalance. It is said that for diseases caused by biological agents, such as micro-organisms or parasites, the shatkarmas should be practised. It is possible to eliminate the poisons that accumulate in the body due to these biological agents in the following ways: (i) by maintaining a state of physical purification through regular practice of shatkarma, (ii) by taking a balanced diet to induce health, and (iii) by awakening of certain chakras, like manipura. The *Hatha Yoga Pradipika* even states that poisons from snake and scorpion bites can be neutralized with the practice of the shatkarmas. Most of the yogic texts mention this benefit, so we can understand that when the body reaches a state of total harmony and purification there is an automatic rejection of any foreign agent in the body, including that of a noxious chemical or poison.

Regarding climatic and environmental factors, yoga suggests common sense and choosing a place which is relatively free of pollutants for one's yogic practice. For trauma, e.g. chronic postural trauma, yoga suggests awareness of one's physical posture and the practice of asanas. For abuse, addiction and medication, which are again a toxic area, we can use various combinations of the shatkarmas along with asanas and bandhas.

Regarding nutritional imbalance, yogic theory states that the body has the capacity to produce its own minerals and chemicals for preserving itself. What we take in from outside, such as vegetables, fruits, lentils, grains and other natural foods, is enough to sustain the body. In cases of illness, such as a cold, where the body requires an additional dose of vitamin C, then it is better to depend on natural resources such as fruits, rather than taking vitamin C tablets. When we take a vitamin or chemical in the form of a tablet which has been mixed with other agents, it reduces the body's capacity to produce its own supply. So, for this reason ayurveda has been very specific in describing the nutritional value of different items. We should be aware of the nutritional value of all foods and try to keep our diet as balanced as possible so that the body can maintain its natural balance.

Genetic traits and defects is an area which is very hard to overcome. It is only by faith and guru's grace that such defects can be removed. In 1986, a man came to the ashram suffering from hypertension. He asked Paramahamsaji what he should do about it. Paramahamsaji closed his eyes for a few minutes and said, "Stop all medication and practise the headstand for five minutes every day." We could not believe our ears. How could the headstand help a hypertensive condition? Logically it did not sound possible, but a month later the man turned up and said he was now perfectly all right. When things like this happen, which go against normal expectations or logical, scientific concepts and techniques, what can it be due to other than God's grace or guru's grace. Genetic and organic defects, as well as defects caused by the ageing process, fall into this category.

Mental imbalance

The mental causes of imbalance and disease are as follows:
1. Unresolved conflicts which have taken the form of either fear, anxiety, worry or tension, and which have become some kind of complex or inhibition.
2. Emotional reactions such as elation, sadness, anger, hatred, jealousy or other mood swings, according to different situations.
3. Ego-related problems such as:
   a) Creation of false ideas about oneself, others, diseases or situations
   b) Non-acceptance of the present
   c) Self-identification with pain and pleasure, success and failure.
4. Psychosomatic/psycho-sexual problems, including stress, which is created due to some kind of suppression or over-indulgence.
5. Psychiatric disorders such as hallucination, mania, depression, paranoia, schizophrenia, criminal tendencies.

6. Low IQ, indecisiveness, confusion, lack of creativity, dullness in understanding.
7. Over-emotional or over-intellectual approach to a life situation, reacting either too emotionally or too intellectually.

Mental imbalance is caused by over-identification with surrounding situations or conditions. It is a well known fact that we tend to over-identify and react intellectually and emotionally on the level of buddhi. First there is reaction and then analysis. This is very much at the level where pratyahara becomes effective. As the mind follows the senses, so, with mental problems, analysis follows reaction. That is the general trend.

Normally we react and become too involved in the reaction to stand back from the situation and analyze it. This is the main aspect of mental imbalance, which will be experienced differently according to the faculty that is active or that has reacted. If there is an emotional reaction, there will be emotional imbalance. If there is a thought reaction, there will be mental imbalance. So, according to the faculty that is being used, an imbalance will be experienced.

Ego is predominant in the mental dimension. Ego is understood as 'I' or 'me'. It relates to the subtle dimension where we find the categories of ego, desire, thought, motivation and implementation as the structure. Implementation is always reactive. Motivation is very much linked with wanting to fulfil or wanting to satisfy, and that is ego-satisfaction, self-satisfaction. This idea is an extension of that ego, the seed of that ego, so ego is always very active in the mental dimension.

According to yoga, most mental problems are caused by ego involvement and over-identification with pain and pleasure, failure and success. They also arise due to non-acceptance of the present; creation of false ideas about the self, others or different situations; reactions in the form of anger, jealousy, hatred or indifference; and reactions coming back in the form of conflict, fear, anxiety, repulsion, etc.

450

There is a very deep and strong connection with this chain of experiences. A chain reaction takes place, from the level of action at one end to the ego at the other end. All these things happen in between: pain, pleasure satisfaction, dissatisfaction, repulsion, attraction, fear, inhibition, complexes, desire to improve, desire to achieve, desire to leave, etc. All this happens in the subtle dimension. It is like using a mala. You start from one end, from the sumeru, and go to the other end, where you again find the sumeru.

A mala is a very apt description of the subtle dimension. No matter which way you go, you will always have the sumeru on top, representing the ego. Each bead that you move is a reaction of that ego. Malas have one hundred and eight beads and yogis have identified one hundred and eight different kinds of ego reactions. When you repeat a mantra on one bead, you are overcoming one aspect or trying to influence, alter or change one aspect of the ego. One bead may represent insecurity, a complex, a phobia, fear, desire, ambition, attraction or repulsion and so forth. Each bead represents something and so the potential is to pass through all the different reactions.

Pranic imbalance

The pranic causes of imbalance and disease are listed as follows:

1. Disturbance of the entire pranic system, where the energy is either:
   a) Too high, resulting in hyperactivity, restlessness and sexuality, or
   b) Too low, resulting in lack of vitality, lethargy and susceptibility to disease.
2. Imbalance of the ida and pingala flow, causing:
   a) Temperature variation, either hot or cold\
   b) Mind/body incoherence
   c) Mental/physical growth retardation
   d) Introversion/extroversion
   e) Concentration, memory or sleep problems.

451

3. Blocks in the pranic flow to a particular organ or part, producing a physical disease in that part like hormonal imbalance, epilepsy, neuromuscular traumas, organ failure.
4. Sushumna blockage, which prevents further evolution.

One kind of pranic imbalance is the overall blockage in the flow of prana which manifests either as hyper-nervous or hypo-nervous activity. Here the corresponding emotions and reactions of anxiety, depression, anger and frustration are experienced.

Another kind of pranic disturbance is ida and pingala imbalance. Ida-pingala imbalance has been described as continuous, mental or physical activity which cannot be stopped. We have encountered such situations at different times in our lives. For example, with ida imbalance our mind goes into overdrive and many, many ideas and thoughts begin to arise. This happens especially at night when there are no distractions and one is more aware of the mental process. This overdrive of the mind deprives one of sleep, as there is a very fast, continuous mental process going on. Pingala imbalance is similar except that there is physical, not mental, hyperactivity. Even after a long day of hard physical work, there will be an excess of physical energy. There is also a blockage in sushumna, which stops the further evolution of consciousness.

These are some of the areas where pranic imbalance can take place, although it can become difficult to differentiate between a pranic activity and the corresponding physical, mental or emotional activity. We may think it is pranic, when it is actually a mental state affecting the pranic level. Or when we believe an imbalance is mental, it is the pranic state affecting the mind. There is a hairline difference which can only be observed through increased sensitivity to prana. Until one experiences the flow of prana and becomes aware of the pranic blockages, it is not possible to distinguish between pranic imbalance and physical, mental or emotional imbalance.

Pranic imbalance is a relatively new concept for this modern age, because all our lives we have been geared to look at ourselves only from the physical or mental viewpoint. So the pranic structure is not usually understood by the normal modern mind. However, yogis have attributed the cause of most of the mental, emotional or physical imbalances as originating in the pranic body or structure. This is where the basic understanding between science and yoga differs concerning the human body. Yoga sees everything from the pranic perspective and science sees everything from the physical and mental perspective.

The pranic perspective is seen or felt more in terms of the vibrations that we receive from other people, places or things, or that we project ourselves. We get a vibration from somebody and we either like or dislike it. Therefore, this vibration theory is the first step towards understanding pranic imbalance. In anger, for example, a very powerful vibration emanates from the personality, like a rush of energy. In depression or fear, there is a reversal of this rush. Instead of going out, the energy is withdrawn deep within.

In the pranic dimension, ida, pingala, and sushumna nadis are not just concepts but actual experiences. Without that actual experience, it is not possible to understand pranic imbalance analytically or intellectually. There is no way to express, define or understand prana theoretically. Through practice certain people develop energy spasms or energy flows in different parts of the body. However, yoga says that in order to understand the pranic structure, it is necessary to perfect the techniques of prana vidya. These techniques are specifically directed to awakening the experience of pranic flow in the pranic body and removing pranic blockages.

The basic aim of prana vidya is to sensitize the mind to such an extent that energy within the body is experienced in the form of an electrical current. This current is experienced in the form of tingling sensations, not on the surface but in the inner body. These sensations travel from one part to the next, from one end to the other. Different temperature variations and fluctuations are also experienced physically. Some parts of the body become extremely hot while others become extremely cold. Sometimes there are autonomic convulsions or spasms, or the body naturally adopts an asana or performs a mudra or bandha.

Prana vidya further describes ways of locating energy blocks in the body by observing the spontaneous mudras and bandhas that are performed. For example, when you are practising prana vidya lying down in shavasana and there is a rush of energy, one arm may begin to lift automatically without you even knowing. When it is raised, you become aware of it and let it drop. Such occurrences indicate that there is a blockage in certain areas, in certain nadis which carry the prana. The accumulation of prana in one part creates a contraction of muscles which in turn raises the arm.

Abdominal convulsions can also happen, where the abdomen begins to pump up and down without control. This is caused by a blockage in the nadis situated in the abdominal region. Unless such physiological experiences happen, one cannot understand the imbalances of ida, pingala and sushumna. The things which we experience externally, such as hyper-mental activity or hyper-physical activity may be attributed to ida or pingala awakening or imbalance. It requires experience, sensitivity and the development of a subtle range of perception in order to judge each condition correctly.

We do not know the minute details of how the mind and emotions function or what kind of reaction they create. All we can do is guess and attribute a reaction to some cause we think might be right. Yogis have always emphasized the importance of experiential knowledge. First of all, awaken the pranas, experience the flow of energy, try to direct the prana through the different nadis, know the pranic blockages. Only then is it possible to relate the pranic dimension to the corresponding experience on the level of intellect or emotions, and to recognize the symptoms which are expressing themselves on the external level.

Yogic literature describes this kind of pranic imbalance as being more on a subtle than on a physical level. There are three points to remember regarding pranic imbalance as follows:
1. General depletion, which is the lack of energy in the overall prana.
2. Energy blocks causing excess in one area and its lack in another area.
3. Uncontrolled, excessive fluctuations.

Energy blocks causing excess in one area and depletion in another will be experienced in the form of physical sensations, for example, temperature variations, shooting pains, or shooting sensations of bliss or pleasure. This is described in the prana vidya process, for example, how to heal the part, how to remove the blockage, how to rectify the imbalance. So pranic imbalance will be known and understood only after actually experiencing the flow of prana on the physical level, through the movement of the body and awareness of the electrical current flowing from one end of the body to another. Apart from this, anything not coming from the physical pranic experience is just speculation.

When we say that, generally, an imbalance in ida causes mental problems, an imbalance in pingala causes physiological problems and an imbalance in sushumna causes or retards the growth of consciousness, all of this is just the upper layer of what could happen. We have not gone into the deeper layers of pranic manifestation at all.

Psychic imbalance

The psychic causes of imbalance and disease are as follows:
1. Psychic experiences or ESP (visions, sounds, etc.) which occurs without control or knowledge of their source or cause.
2. Blocks and obstacles in the path of sadhana, higher experiences and evolution.

455

3. Acquisition and demonstration of siddhis or psychic powers.
4. Kundalini experiences in uncontrolled, unguided or unsupervised situations.

Some people speak of siddhis. The presentation and use of siddhis can cause a very big psychic imbalance. As we go deeper into the consciousness, the energy which is dormant, or the potential or qualities of the mind of which we are not aware at present, become active. Many things begin to happen spontaneously, for instance, healing or an idea which materializes itself without any effort.

When we look at people we can see their whole personality turned inside out, even their thoughts can be seen. We know without asking what the other person is thinking about. This is called telepathy. Or, we may be thinking about something happening back home. We may see certain events taking place in a dream or vision, either while we are awake or asleep. Later on, we realize that those events were really happening, we were actually there. This is called clairvoyance. We may be sitting in one room and someone may be talking in another room, when our mind suddenly goes there. We can actually hear with our ears what this person is talking about. This is called clairaudience.

Siddhis manifest naturally and spontaneously. As long as we are not aware of them as siddhis, they will not cause an imbalance. We might think there is something wrong with our mind, that is all. However, the moment we realize that this is a siddhi, there will be a tendency to use it according to the nature of our personality, whether we are sattwic, rajasic or tamasic. Then the power play begins on the psychic level and the grandiose idea of, "I'm great!" develops. The idea, "I am superior", "I know what is happening" comes, and then after some time depression sets in.

Depression sets in because when psychic experiences of this kind come in contact with our external nature, which is tamasic, rajasic or sattwic, that nature overshadows the psychic manifestation and after some time it stops. By the time these manifestations have stopped, you may have already advertised your qualities and abilities to the extent that you are giving demonstrations of your powers in front of people, when there is a short circuit and no results. Then a psychic depression begins, which is the worst kind, as there is no cure for it. Therefore, yoga emphatically states that one should not hanker after siddhis, and that if one does acquire them one should not even think about or use them.

There are many levels of kundalini awakening. Before this can take place, first of all there has to be physical purification. Kundalini awakening can happen spontaneously but this is very rare. After physical purification there has to be control over the mental vrittis, which is even rarer. How can we have control over even five percent of the mental vrittis when we are unable to control the manifestations of the mind, or our reactive nature on the external level? There has to be nadi shuddhi, purification of the nadis, which happens with the practice of asanas. This can also happen naturally but again it is rare. These are the first three stages of kundalini awakening.

In the fourth stage, the pranas have to be awakened. Pranic awakening can be spontaneous, self-willed or induced through practice. If it occurs spontaneously, without one's conscious knowledge and without one knowing how to channel the energy, it will not go any further. The sensations will be too strong and powerful. If the awakening is self-willed, there is a possibility of going beyond the level of pranic awakening using willpower. If it is awakened through practice, and there is a systematic process of instruction, with guidance and observation, then one will be able to move from one stage to the next.

After pranic awakening, there is chakra awakening. A minimum of three chakras have to be activated, namely mooladhara, swadhisthana and manipura, before kundalini becomes active within us. Mooladhara represents the instinctive nature, which has to be brought to a level where the instincts are recognized. Swadhisthana represents the

457

deeper mind, the unconscious. When the deeper mind is realized then one gains awareness and insight into samskaras and karmas.

The next stage is the ability to control vitality in order to channel the kundalini energy. Without controlled vitality, the kundalini will flare up like a match and then die down, because it will not be able to find a passage to go through. The kundalini texts describe this symbolically, saying that the kundalini becomes active but then it goes to sleep again. Until it crosses manipura, kundalini rises a short distance and then falls back down to mooladhara.

Then comes the stage which concerns the sushumna passage and the ability to link the mind from mooladhara to sahasrara via this passage. In the final stage kundalini awakens and travels from mooladhara up to sahasrara.

Kundalini imbalance can happen at the level of mooladhara, swadhisthana or manipura. If it takes place at the level of mooladhara, the kundalini energy wakes up and begins to manifest. If the instinctive nature has not yet been realized, the instincts manifest in a tamasic way which is detrimental to the evolution of consciousness. It would be like a reversal from the normal state of perception to even lower states of existence. Mental degeneration can take place. It is quite possible for a human being to become mentally like a primate.

If mooladhara is all clear and kundalini moves up to swadhisthana, which happens to be completely blocked, then kundalini will go back to mooladhara and fizzle out. However, if the gate into swadhisthana is open even a tiny bit, it will go in and create havoc in the unconscious and subconscious dimensions. Then one will have no control over what is experienced, seen or observed. Only tremendous faith in God can save one from the influx of unconscious and subconscious activity at this point. Fighting against this mental process only makes it worse; it is better just to surrender and concentrate on trying to maintain sanity, which would give a greater chance of surviving a swadhisthana reaction. The practice of ishwara pranidhana has been described in kundalini yoga in order to overcome swadhisthana imbalance.

If kundalini reaches manipura and finds it blocked, then it will short circuit anything and everything with which it comes into contact. Kundalini awakening creates a static field around the body that is so strong and powerful that anybody walking into this room would blow all these lights out. There have also been recorded documentaries of autocombustion, where a normal person is reduced to ashes in a matter of minutes. Therefore, kundalini should not be taken lightly.

According to the yogic disciplines, kriya yoga used to be considered as the final system for awakening the kundalini, and it was taught by the guru to the aspirant only after he had undergone hard training in other yogas under the guru's observation.

21

Yoga of Common Sense

Yoga is the culture of tomorrow. It is a science which deals with the development of the human personality and which leads to the awakening of untapped energy sources within the brain and mind. The practice of yoga is not new. Ancient rishis, saints and sages have been talking about it for the last fifty thousand years. They spoke about it, not as a religion or philosophy, but as a way of life that could lead to the development and awakening of our consciousness and energy.

The ancient civilizations of South America, Northern Europe, Egypt and Africa used to practise techniques of yoga. These techniques were depicted in various stages in works of art and were also mentioned in traditional books. Today, going through the art and literature of these ancient civilizations, we find that the people practised the same yoga practices as we use today, for their inner discovery, for the introversion of their consciousness. They talked about the mental and spiritual aspects of yoga, rather than the physical and health aspects. These civilizations died out due to natural calamities, war and different political colonizations. However, yoga was somehow preserved in India. Today yoga is again coming to light from India, but it is not Indian. The credit goes to India because it has preserved this science. However, it is our duty to understand yoga in its universal form.

460

Personality development

When we think of yoga, we mean development of the human personality in every aspect. When we practise yoga, we practise it for attaining balance, harmony and equilibrium in all aspects of our personality and expression. We do not believe that by inducing certain states of consciousness or by making moral changes, we can improve the quality of our life. We believe that by experiencing life as it is, and by discovering and knowing our limitations, we can evolve mentally, intellectually and psychically.

There is an urge in every one of us to find happiness, tranquillity and harmony. We would like to attain psychological balance and avoid the tensions and conflicts of daily life. Many scientific investigations have been made into yoga, and we have seen that with the practice of asanas, pranayama and other yogas, we can attain this balance, harmony and tranquillity.

Today, in our world, we find that we need two items to make our lives a complete success. The first item which we lack is vitality, which is not physical strength, but inner strength, willpower, clarity of mind and the ability to perform every action with perfection. The second item we lack is tranquillity. We are so engrossed in our day to day activities, in our intellectual and emotional tensions, that we have lost contact with our inner nature.

Man has two forms of expression. External development is one aspect and internal development is the other. In yoga we try to combine both aspects. On the external level we develop the faculties of the intellect and the senses. We also develop our emotional expression, but on a very superficial level. On the internal level, many yogic techniques bring about a state of inner awareness. By becoming aware of our mind and our mental perceptions, and by integrating this awareness into our day to day life, we can become more balanced, harmonious and complete.

Through yogic techniques we can develop the ability to relax in any situation and under any condition. We can also

461

develop the capacity to concentrate, to collect all our dissipated energies and focus them at one point. Then the combination of mental force and vital force becomes a very powerful tool in opening up the different dimensions of the human personality.

Personality has always been a problem of mankind. We do not know how to face ourselves. We become depressed and we do not know how to handle our depression. We become happy and we do not know how to handle our happiness. We become tense and we do not know how to handle our tension. We have an emotional outburst, we get angry and we do not know how to handle our anger.

Psychology tells us that in different states of mind we have different experiences. Some are sensory and some are mental. When we try to become aware of the difference between the external and the internal experience, we get lost. There are external situations which influence our life, and internal situations created by our own selves, which also influence our life. Whatever we try to do or to achieve, there is always a lack of harmony and coordination between the different faculties of our personality.

Yogic culture

When we talk about yogic culture, we do not mean culture in a philosophical sense. We do not mean a way of life which is moral or puritanical, or a way of social living. We mean that yoga is part and parcel of our life, something we do spontaneously. Every morning we get up, brush our teeth and take a bath. The day we do not brush our teeth, how do we feel? We feel that there is something missing. This is called the process of habituation. After we have become used to a certain way of living and then we do not follow that way of life, we miss it. When yoga becomes a part of life, just like sleeping, waking up, eating and drinking, then we can say that yoga has truly become the culture of humanity.

The yogic culture of tomorrow is something for which we have to strive. Yoga has been the culture of ancient India

462

and the ancient civilizations of the world, and it is going to be the culture of tomorrow. It is the science of today which we have to learn, which we have to accept and which we have to understand.

Understanding the mind

Yoga begins when there is conflict and tension, when there are disruptive forces working in our life and personality. In the *Bhagavad Gita*, Krishna taught yoga to Arjuna on the battlefield, when Arjuna was full of conflict and tension, and unsure of his course of action. At that moment of conflict, Krishna said, "Now you have to practise yoga in order to understand your position in life." So, in order that Arjuna could understand his position, course of action, emotions and behaviour, all the techniques of yoga were taught there, on the battlefield.

The same practices were later evolved and developed by the different saints and rishis. One was Patanjali, who claimed in his verses on yoga, the *Yoga Sutras*, that yoga is a form of discipline. It is a form of controlling mental conflicts, different patterns and fluctuations of mind. It is a way of controlling the dualities that we face in life. Patanjali does not say that yoga is for the health and beauty of the body. Krishna did not tell Arjuna to do yoga for health and beauty. They both geared the whole practice of yoga towards knowledge and understanding of the human mind. In this sense, there is no difference between the yoga of Krishna and the yoga of Patanjali. In Krishna's yoga we find the war taking place outside, but in the yoga of Patanjali the war takes place within.

Know yourself

The first principle of yoga we have to remember is to know ourselves. Socrates said, "Know thyself." Shakespeare said, "To thine own self be true." There are dormant centres of perception, of energy, which we can know and tap inside ourselves. We can awaken these centres after we have

463

understood the expressions of our personality, after we have resolved the conflicts that go on in our personality, after we have resolved the conflicts that go on in our emotional and intellectual areas. There are many people who have been practising meditation for the last twenty, thirty, forty or fifty years, but they have not been able to gain anything, because they fight with their minds and with themselves.

Accept yourself

The second principle of yoga is to watch, observe and accept ourselves. There is a beautiful poem by St Francis, which reads:

> *God grant me the serenity to accept*
> *the things I cannot change,*
> *the courage to change the things I can,*
> *and the wisdom to know the difference.*

We have to learn to accept and to observe objectively, not subjectively. When we become subjective towards a problem, what happens to the mind and awareness? What happens to the consciousness and to the level of energy in our system? It is all dissipated and we reach a state of very high tension.

However, if we just sit back and observe for a few minutes with a cool mind, without becoming agitated or involved with the problem, then we can easily discover the solution. So, observe and accept is the second principle in yoga. Due to our inhibitions and ambitions we struggle in life, we want to fight with life. Because of our rashness and hard-headedness, we go through life like a bull in a china shop. This is where we fail. How do we develop mental clarity and objective awareness? There is only one answer – yoga.

Non–attachment

The third principle of yoga is non-attachment. Whatever we do, whether it is very simple or very complicated, we should do it for the sake of experience; we should not expect any result from it, either positive or negative. When we perform an action, there is an expectation behind it. To have an expectation is part of our nature. Whether we call it selfish or selfless, in both there is expectation. We expect the result to be beneficial, to give satisfaction, and we expect to gain name and fame.

Name and fame is not the problem here; we all want name and fame. But when we do not achieve what we want to achieve, then there is conflict because of the expectation. Whatever actions we do, whatever thoughts we think, whatever emotions we feel, again there is conflict. So, in yoga it is said that we should perform all actions with perfection, but without expectation. We should develop this attitude if we want to have clarity of mind and discover the different dimensions of our mind.

Relaxation

The fourth principle of yoga is relaxation. How should we relax? Not by sensual pleasures or enjoyment, not by acquiring things, not by experiences that give us some temporary happiness or feeling of peace. Relaxation in yoga does not mean physical or emotional relaxation. Relaxation here means letting go of our personality, letting it run wild, letting it express itself. But in order to do this one part of our self has to be relaxed. Now you might be holding a cigarette in one hand and a drink in the other hand, but that is not really a state of relaxation. Relaxation here simply means letting go.

Let yourself go in all the different areas of your work; let yourself go in all the different channels that are open to you. Mentally find out which is the best channel and which is the best course of action. With a cool mind, first think of the problems, not of the benefits. If you can work out the problems, if you can find the solutions, you will have attained inner relaxation. But, of course, we try to look at all the benefits before and all the problems later, and there is no relaxation in that. There must be relaxation of awareness.

You are aware, fully alert, fully awake, but in that state of alertness there is complete relaxation.

Seer's yoga

These are some of the principles of yoga. If we can adopt them in our daily lifestyle, our awareness will awaken gradually and slowly, and we will be more in control of our mind. Right now, the mind is the master and we are the slave. If the mind says, "Do this," we do it. If the mind says, "Do not do this," we do not do it. If the mind says, "Accept this," we accept it. If the mind says, "Do not accept this," we do not accept it. Most of our life is governed by the mind and the different manifestations of mind.

In yoga there is a reverse of this process. We try to control, we try to become the master of the mind. In the world, we find many different types of yoga: hatha yoga, raja yoga, karma yoga, bhakti yoga, jnana yoga, kriya yoga, kundalini yoga, etc. But, out of all these, one yoga is the most important for everyone to practice. It is known as seer's yoga. In this yoga the practices are really simple. If you get an opportunity, learn them. They are very beneficial and very helpful for dealing with the tension in which we live. They are more effective than hatha yoga, raja yoga or karma yoga.

The process here is that through certain other practices of yoga, we develop an attitude towards our actions, thoughts, feelings and behaviour. We practise karma yoga, the yoga of action, intuitively not physically. Mentally, we work, we act and we develop the dynamism within us. As we do so, we gain experience in life, so that our next action is supported by the experience of the first and so, of course, it is better. We practise raja yoga, not to master its eight limbs, but to develop the attitude of an objective observer. We must observe everything that takes place in our life, in our mind, in our surroundings, in our family, in our work. We must become the observers. We practise jnana yoga, the yoga of right knowledge, right awareness, and right action. We practise bhakti yoga, the yoga of devotion, to channel the emotional manifestations of the mind. How do we do it?

Yogis have always believed that man is not only thought, desire or ambition, but that within us there are different dimensions which can be experienced in the form of vibration, sound and colour. So, the yogis developed different yogas to experience these different dimensions. They developed the science of nada yoga for becoming aware of the vibratory aspect of the personality, and laya yoga for becoming aware of the unconscious aspect.

Which science, which philosophy, which religion in the world tells us how to become aware of our unconscious personality? Only the yogis have told us. To become aware of those areas of the subconscious and unconscious mind which are dominated by archetypes or symbols, they have developed the science of yantras and mandalas. In this way, the yogis have developed a form of yoga for every experience of the personality. Not many people are aware of these different types of yoga. When we are able to integrate all four types of yoga in our life, when we are able to awaken the energy in our personality, then we practise the real yoga, which is the seer's yoga.

The seen and the unseen

Yogis have said that there are two forces which govern the body, mind and psyche – prana shakti, the pranic or vital energy, and chitta shakti, the mental energy. When we awaken the experience of the vital energy, our consciousness is extrovert. Psychology explains that we have two types of experience: one which we can see and feel, and the other which we cannot, although it is taking place all the same. We can perceive through our senses in the external area, but in the internal area we cannot. In yoga these two experiences are known as *drishya* and *adrishya*, 'the seen' and 'the unseen'. So, the mental aspect here means the unknown, the invisible.

In the relationship between the play of energy and the invisible action, these two forces, the vital and the mental, are

467

awakened. All the yogic techniques are geared towards the awakening of these two energies. Whether we practise asana, pranayama or any other yoga techniques, these two forces, which are known as the solar and the lunar force, the positive and negative force, or simply the known and the unknown, are awakened. When these energies are merged at ajna chakra, we transcend the limitations of the conscious mind.

Removing the barriers
In psychology we have the conscious, subconscious, unconscious and superconscious. These same states of experience are known in yoga as jagrit, swapna, nidra and turiya. The aim of the yogi is to reach the turiya state by going through the conscious, subconscious and unconscious, and becoming aware of the different expressions, impressions, actions and reactions. This awakening of the mind is known as self-realization.

When you are able to remove the barriers which separate the conscious mind from the subconscious, the subconscious from the unconscious and the unconscious from the superconscious, then the expression of consciousness becomes one unbroken line, one continuity. There are no distinctions. That removal of all the barriers is known as the awakening of consciousness, the union between Shiva and Shakti, or between purusha and prakriti. This is the real yoga.

Yoga for the body, yoga for the emotions, yoga for the mind, yoga for meditation, yoga for youth, yoga for ageing, it all amounts to one thing – the human personality is evolving. One group of people at the dawn of civilization evolved in one direction, the next group of people evolved in another direction. One expressed its qualities and faculties in external life. The other group expressed its qualities and faculties in internal life. Both evolved. Human evolution has been the theme and aim of mankind. We are different from our forefathers, and our future generations will be different from us in all respects: technologically, intellectually, emotionally, psychologically and internally.

Today we are able to rationalize, to know, to think, to judge and to criticize. The knowledge that we have today, Stone Age man did not have. The knowledge which our future generations will have, we do not possess at this moment. Even science tells us that our brain is not fully active, not fully awake. Out of the total capacity of the brain, only about ten percent is active and the remaining ninety percent is dormant.

The awakening of the dormant ninety percent of the brain is self-realization. Finding God is not self-realization. Awakening the remaining dormant brain centres and removing the barriers which divide the consciousness is realization. This leads to the perfect expression of the finely tuned instrument which we know as the human being. When there is perfect expression of this instrument, then there is oneness. In order to practise seer's yoga, as I have previously described, you need to know it in its full form, as the yoga of common sense.

Glossary

Abhaya mudra – gesture of fearlessness
Abhinivesha – fear of death
Adhara mudra – perineal mudra
Adharas – sixteen bases which support the body
Adharma – disharmony; not fulfilling one's natural role in life; that which is against the natural order
Advaita – non-dual experience; unity of the individual soul
Agama – testimony
Agni – fire; representing heat or fire of metabolism
Agni mandala – zone of fire, visualizing the entire body in the form of agni
Agnisar kriya – practice of emptying the lungs and pumping the stomach to strengthen the diaphragm and lower stomach region
Agocharam – beyond sensory perception
Agochari mudra – another name for nasikagra drishti
Aham Bhramasmi – vedic mantra, 'I am Brahman'
Ahamkara – ego
Ahimsa – absence of violence from within the personality; non-violence
Ajapa japa – continuous, spontaneous repetition of mantra
Ajna chakra – 'third eye', command centre, seat of intuition
Ajna mandala – ajna chakra symbol at the eyebrow centre
Akhanda kirtan – ongoing, unbroken kirtan
Akara – form, link, continuity

471

Akasha – space; ether

Akasha tattwa – ether element

Akashi mudra – awareness of inner space; practice of the external stage of dharana; gazing into space with the head tilted back

Amaroli – auto-urine procedure; drinking of one's own urine in order to detoxify the body and develop stamina and vitality

Amrit – nectar

Anadi – endless

Anahada nada – unheard, unstruck sound

Anahata chakra – heart chakra or emotional centre

Anahata kshetram – trigger point of anahata chakra

Ananda – everlasting bliss

Anandamaya kosha – sheath or body of bliss, beatitude

Ananda samadhi – fourth state of samadhi; blissful absorption

Annamaya kosha – sheath or body of matter

Antah – inner

Antah karana – inner instrument; experienced or manifest mind which includes the four aspects of manas, buddhi, chitta and ahamkara

Antar kumbhaka – internal breath retention

Antar lakshya – internal aim to be aspired for in dharana

Antar mouna – inner silence; meditative technique

Antar trataka – inner gazing

Antaranga yoga – inner yoga; four internal stages of raja yoga: pratyahara, dharana, dhyana and samadhi

Anuman – inference

Anusandhana – discovery

Apas – water

Apana – sub-prana which is located in the lower abdominal region, responsible for elimination and reproduction

Aparigraha – non-possessiveness

Ardhanareshwara – form of Shiva which is half-male and half-female

Arjuna – one of the five Pandava brothers to whom Lord Krishna addressed the Bhagavad Gita

Arohan – inhalation; ascending passage in the subtle body

Artha – material need; wealth

Asamprajnata samadhi – transitional stage of samadhi where the traces of the mind become active according to their intensity

Asamprayoge – 'not coming into contact'

Asana – a physical posture in which one is at ease and in harmony with oneself

Asevitah – faith

Ashrama – four stages of life

Ashtanga yoga – eight-fold path of yoga

Ashwini mudra – contraction of anal sphincter

Asmita – state where the ego and the sense of individuality are completely transcended and there is only pure awareness

Asmita klesha – feeling of 'I' identified with an action

Asmita samadhi – fifth state of samadhi; dissolution of ego; merging of body, mind and soul

Asteya – honesty

Asthi – bone found in the body tissues

Atadroop pratishtha – knowledge of false identity; inability to link name with form

Atma – individual soul; spirit

Aum – primordial sound; mantra

Avachetana – subconsciousness

Avidya – ignorance; lack of conscious awareness; mistaking the non-eternal for the eternal; confined cognition

Avyakta – unmanifest; unseen

Awarohan – exhalation; descending passage in the subtle body; spinal passage

Ayurveda – vedic system of medical diagnosis and treatment

Bahir – external

Bahir kumbhaka – external breath retention

Bahir lakshya – concentration upon an external object or point in space

Bahiranga yoga – external yoga; four stages of raja yoga – yama, niyama, asana and pranayama

Baikhari – audible sound produced by striking two objects

Bandha – psychic lock that concentrates the flow of energy in the body at one point or plexus; postural contraction of the body

Basti – excretory cleansing technique for the intestines and colon

Bhadrasana – gentleman's pose or gracious pose

Bhagavad Gita – Lord Krishna's discourse to Arjuna delivered on the battlefield of Kurukshetra during the great Mahabharata war

Bhaja Govindam – ode to Shakti by Adi Shankaracharya

Bhakti – devotion

Bhal bhati – forehead bellows

Bhastrika pranayama – 'bellows' breath

Bhati – light, splendour; to shine

Bhava samadhi – absorption in meditation due to emotional cause, e.g., kirtan

Bheda – to pass through, pierce, purify

Bhoochari mudra – practice of the external stage of dharana; gazing into space after focusing on the finger nail of the hand

Bhoota – unmanifest element

Bhramari pranayama – pranayama technique using a humming sound

Bhrumadhya – eyebrow centre

Bhrumadhya drishti – eyebrow centre gazing

Bhu loka – first basic dimension of the subtle body

Bija – 'seed'

Bindu visarga – centre of source of individual creation from where the psychic vibrations first emanate

Brahma – Lord of creation; manifest force of life and creation; potentiality of mooladhara chakra

Brahmacharya – one who lives in a state of higher consciousness; sexual control; redirection of sexual energy towards spiritual or meditational practices

Brahamacharya ashrama – first stage of life up to twenty-five years, which is devoted to study and learning

Brahma granthi – perineal knot or psychic block covering mooladhara and swadhisthana chakras

474

Brahma nadi – subtle pranic flow within sushumna nadi through which kundalini ascends

Brahman – absolute reality; 'ever-expanding consciousness'

Brahman dhyana – meditation on the concept of Brahman

Buddha – the enlightened one

Buddhi – discerning, discriminating aspect of mind; from the root 'bodh', 'to be aware of', 'to know'; higher intelligence

Chaitanya jyoti – eternal flame of spirit

Chakra – psychic centre in the subtle body, seven in number; circle, wheel or vortex of energy; conjunction point of the nadis

Chakrasana – wheel pose

Chandra bheda pranayama – breathing technique that pierces and purifies ida nadi

Chandra mandala – another name for ajna mandala

Charvaka – one of the six darshana or systems of Indian philosophy; philosophy that accepts only the perceivable phenomena as valid, not the unperceivable

Chaturmas – four months of the rainy season

Chetana – consciousness; unmanifest aspect of consciousness and energy

Chidakasha – space of consciousness, experienced in the head region between vishuddhi, ajna and sahasrara chakras

Chidakasha dharana – technique of meditation involving awareness of chidakasha

Chin mudra – attitude of chitta or consciousness; upward hand position with thumb and first finger touching

Chit – eternal consciousness

Chit shakti – mental force governing the subtle dimensions

Chitta – individual consciousness, including the subconscious and unconscious levels of mind; memory, thinking, enquiry

Chitta vritti – mental modification

Daharakasha – lower or deep space, encompassing mooladhara, swadhisthana and manipura

Daharakasha dharana – concentration on the symbols of chakra and tattwa within the lower space

Dakshina nadi – another name for pingala nadi

Danda dhauti – hatha yoga method of cleaning the oesophagus

Danta dhauti – hatha yoga method of cleaning the teeth

Darshana – glimpse; sight; vision; system of Indian philosophy

Deerghakala – for a long period of time

Dehasamya – body stillness

Desha – place

Deva tattwa – first tattwa: the divine element

Devadatta – minor or upa-prana responsible for yawning and sneezing

Devata – deity; shining one; aspect of consciousness manifest in a life form

Devi – female deity; goddess; aspect of energy manifest in a life form

Dhananjaya – minor or upa-prana that remains in the body after death

Dhara – stream, flow

Dharana – holding or binding of the mind to one point; concentration

Dharma – the natural role we have to play in life; ethical law

Dhatu – layers of tissue in the body, consisting of blood, bone, marrow, semen, fat, muscle and serum

Dhauti – hatha yoga cleansing practices for the eyes, ears, tongue, teeth, forehead, oesophagus, stomach, rectum and anus

Dhyana – the final meditative state, culminating in the experience of samyama

Divya – divine

Divyabhava – divine feeling

Divya loka – plane of divine or transcendental experience

Doshas – humours of the physical body

Drashta – seer, observer; awareness; witness

Dridha bhoomihi – solid foundation

Drishti – vision, eyesight

Drishtisamya – stillness of vision

Drishya – the seen

Drona – teacher of the Pandava and Kaurava princes from the Mahabharata epic

476

Durga – devi; goddess; representing energy

Dwesha – repulsion, aversion, dislike

Gayatri mantra – vedic mantra of twenty-four matras or syllables

Gherand Samhita – traditional yogic text by Rishi Gherand

Gomukhasana – cow's face pose

Granthi – psychic knot in the subtle body

Grihastha ashrama – second stage of life from twenty-five to fifty years; householder stage

Guna – attribute, quality or nature of the phenomenal world

Guna rahita akasha – one of the five mental spaces of vyoma panchaka; attributeless space

Gupta nadi – pranic channel running from the knees along the inside of the thighs into the perineum

Guru – one who dispels the darkness of ignorance

Ha/Ham – syllable or sound representing the pranic force; sound of pingala nadi

Hasta utthanasana – hand raising pose; pre-pranayama exercise

Hatha – combination of two mantras: ha or ham representing pingala, the solar force, and tham or ksham representing ida, the lunar force

Hatha yoga – yoga of attaining physical and mental purity, and channelling of the pranas in the body

Hatha Yoga Pradipika – yogic text by Swatmarama; 'light on hatha yoga'

Himsa – anything that disrupts the natural flow of human perception and consciousness, violence

Hiranyagarbha – golden womb of creation; cosmic subtle body

Hreem – bija mantra

Hridayakasha – space of the heart, experienced between manipura and vishuddhi chakras

Hridayakasha dharana – vedic meditative process involving space

Ida nadi – major pranic channel in the body; passive aspect of force, chit shakti; lunar force governing the manifest subtle dimension

Indra – king of the vedic gods

Indriyas – sensory organs

Ishwara – higher reality; non-decaying principle of Samkhya philosophy; unmanifest existence; being; non-changing principle or quality

Ishwara pranidhana – cultivation of faith in the higher reality

Iti – 'through' or 'thus'

Jada samadhi – state of samadhi induced by the hatha yogic process, in which there is no awareness or illumination

Jagriti – wakefulness, waking or conscious state

Jala neti – nasal cleansing practice in which saline water is passed through each nostril alternately

Jalandhara bandha – throat lock or contraction; technique that frees the blockages of rudra granthi; controls the network of nadis, nerves and blood vessels flowing to the brain

Janma chakra – wheel of life

Japa yoga – yoga of mantra repetition

Jaya – victory, success

Jihva dhauti – hatha yoga method of cleaning the tongue

Jiva – individual identity

Jnana – intuitive knowledge

Jnana kanda – path of knowledge

Jnana mudra – gesture of intuitive knowledge; hand position in which the index finger and thumb are joined

Jnana yoga – yoga of knowledge and wisdom attained through investigation of abstract or speculative ideas

Jnanendriyas – five organs of sense perception and knowledge: eyes, ears, nose, tongue, skin

Jyoti mandir – temple of light

Kagra – tip

Kaivalya – state of consciousness beyond duality

Kala – time

Kala loka – plane that comes under the influence of time and its secondary aspect, space

Kama – emotional need or fulfilment

Kapalbhati pranayama – frontal brain cleansing breath; technique used to raise the pranic energy of the body and centre it at ajna

Kapalshodhana – frontal brain purification, variation of kapalbhati

Kapha – phlegm, one of the three doshas described in ayurveda

Karana – cause

Kari – that which produces

Karma – action; law of cause and effect, which shapes the density of each individual

Karma kanda – path of ritual

Karma shaya – deep layers of consciousness where the karmas are stored in the form of impressions, symbols or archetypes

Karma yoga – yoga of action; action performed with meditative awareness; yoga of dynamic meditation

Karmendriyas – five physical organs of action: feet, hands, speech, excretory and reproductive organs

Karna dhauti – hatha yoga method of cleaning the ears

Kevala kumbhaka – spontaneous cessation of the breath which leads one beyond duality

Khechari mudra – tongue lock

Kirtan – singing of God's name

Kleem – bija mantra

Kleshas – fivefold afflictions, tensions or fears accompanying human birth

Koorma – tortoise; minor prana which causes the eyelids to blink

Koormasana – tortoise pose

Kosha – sheath or body

Krikara – minor prana responsible for sneezing and coughing

Krishna – incarnation of Vishnu

Kriya – action or motion

Kriya yoga – practices of kundalini yoga

Kukkutasana – cockerel pose

Kumbha – pot

Kumbhaka – internal or external retention of breath

Kundalini – 'serpent power'; spiritual energy; evolutionary potential

Kundalini yoga – path of yoga which awakens the dormant spiritual force

Kunjal kriya – method of cleansing the stomach by voluntary vomiting using warm saline water

Kuru princes – opponents of the Pandava princes in the Mahabharata epic

Laghoo shankhaprakshalana – short form of shankhaprakshalana

Lakshya – aim; stage

Lalana upa chakra – minor chakra at the back of the throat

Lam – bija mantra of mooladhara chakra

Laya – dissolution

Laya yoga – yoga of conscious dissolution of individuality

Lokas – seven planes of consciousness

Madhya – intermediate

Madhya lakshya – intermediate stage

Maha – great

Maha akasha – one of the five mental spaces of vyoma panchaka; bright like the middle of the sun

Maha bandha – great lock; combination of moola, uddiyana and jalandhara bandhas with kumbhaka

Maha bheda mudra – great piercing attitude

Maha mudra – great psychic attitude

Maha prana – prana in its cosmic, unmanifest aspect

Maha samadhi – final liberation experienced on the departure of the spirit from the body

Mahabharata – great epic of ancient India

Mahamrityunjaya mantra – universal mantra for healing

Mahat – greater mind; supreme intelligence

Majja – nerves found in the body tissues

Mala – garland; impurity

Mananat – mental bondage

Manas – analytical, rational mind

Manasi – mental

Mandala – zone; area; pictorial representation

Manduki mudra – gesture of the frog

Mandukya Upanishad – one of the major Upanishads which describes the three states of consciousness represented by the three syllables of AUM

Manipura chakra – psychic centre behind the navel, associated with vitality and energy; 'city of jewels'

Manomaya kosha – mental sheath or body

Mantra – sound or vibration of power that liberates the mind from bondage

Mantra yoga – path of yoga that liberates the mind through sound vibration

Mantraha – force of vibration

Maya – illusion; partial understanding; wrong or false notions about self-identity

Mayurasana – peacock pose

Medha – fat found in the body tissues

Mehdra – plexus of the pranic body; nadi plexus located just a few centimetres below the navel

Mitahara – balanced diet

Moksha – liberation; freedom

Moola – 'root'

Moola bandha – perineal contraction; technique for locating and awakening mooladhara chakra; used to release brahma granthi

Mooladhara anusandhana – discovery of mooladhara chakra

Mooladhara chakra – root chakra, situated at the perineum; seat of the primal energy

Mooladhara dhyana – practice involving visualization of mooladhara chakra and sensing the vortex of energy at this point

Mouna – silence

Mrityu tattwa – decayable element; manifest aspect of tattwa

Mudra – psychic gesture; psychophysiological posture, movement or attitude

Mukti – liberation

Mumsa – muscle found in the body tissues

Mumukshutva – desire for liberation

Nabho mudra – another name for khechari mudra

Nada – internal psychic sound

Nada yoga – yoga of internal psychic sound

Nadi – pranic flow or channel

Nadi shodhana – purification of nadis

Nadi shodhana pranayama – practice of alternate nostril breathing by which the pranic channels are purified

Naga – minor prana responsible for belching

Nairantarya – continuously without a break

Nara – decaying principle

Nashwara – decaying principle described in Samkhya philosophy; manifest existence; becoming; changeable

Nasi – nose

Nasikagra drishti – nose tip gazing

Nasikagra upa chakra – minor chakra at the nose-tip

Natya mudras – dance mudras that express different attitudes or moods such as love or anger

Nauli – abdominal massage; the rotation of the abdominal muscles

Neti – hatha yoga nasal cleansing practice using either saline water, oil, ghee, milk, yoghurt or amaroli

Nidra – deep sleep

Nigraha – control

Nirbija samadhi – final state of samadhi where there is absorption without seed; total dissolution

Nirguna dhyana – meditation without gunas or qualities

Nirvichara samadhi – transitional stage of samadhi; absorption without reflection

Nirvishesha dhyana – meditation without special attributes

Nirvitarka samadhi – transitional stage of samadhi involving purification of memory which gives rise to true knowledge of the object of perception

Nishkama karma – action performed without desire or personal motive

Niyama – inner discipline; second step of ashtanga or raja yoga

Nyaya – one of the six darshana or systems of Indian philosophy; 'logic'; recognition of the real spiritual experience by the omniscient mind

Om Namah Shivaya – Shiva mantra; 'I salute Shiva (consciousness)'

Om Namo Bhagavate Vasudeva – Krishna mantra; 'I salute Krishna (consciousness)'

Om Namo Narayana – Narayana or Vishnu mantra; 'I salute Narayana (consciousness)'

Padmasana – lotus pose

Pancha bhoota – five elements

Pancha klesha – five afflictions (ignorance, ego, attraction, aversion and fear of death

Panchaka – five

Pandavas – the five brothers in the Mahabharata epic

Para nada – transcendental sound

Param – supreme

Param akasha – one of the five mental spaces of vyoma panchaka; 'deep dark space with a twinkling star-like light'; state of shoonya, nothingness

Parigraha – collection, accumulation

Pashubhava – instinctive personality, animal instincts

Pashyanti – mental

Patanjali – ancient rishi who codified the meditative stages and states into the system of raja yoga; author of the Yoga Sutras

Pawanmuktasana – series of wind releasing postures divided into three groups: anti-rheumatic, digestive/abdominal and shakti bandha or energy releasing asana series

Pingala nadi – major pranic channel in the body which conducts the dynamic force manifesting as prana shakti

Pitta – bile, one of the three humours described in ayurveda

Pooraka – inhalation

Poorna – full

Poorna dhanurasana – full bow pose

Poorva Mimamsa – one of the six darshana or systems of Indian philosophy in the form of answers; contains theory of karma

Prajna – knowledge with awareness; the seer who observes the state of nidra; the all-knowing; what is known; represents the 'M' of AUM; awareness of the 'one without a second'

Prajna purusha – identity of prajna at the unconscious level

483

Prakasha – light
Prakasha mandala – white light at the centre of ajna chakra
Prakriti – individual knowledge
Pramana – knowledge based on direct experience
Prana – vital energy; inherent vital force pervading every dimension of matter
Prana mudra – invocation of energy; a technique of raising prana
Prana nigraha – control of prana
Prana shakti – dynamic solar force governing the dimension of matter
Prana tattwa – third element representing the vital or life giving force
Prana vidya – knowledge and control of prana
Pranamaya kosha – energy sheath or body
Pranava – mantra AUM; primal sound vibration
Pranava dhyana – meditation on the mantra AUM
Pranayama – expansion of the range of vital energy
Pranidhana – 'to believe in'
Pranotthana – awakening of the pranas in the different chakras
Pratishhta – awareness of identity
Pratyahara – withdrawal of the mind from the senses
Pratyaksha – direct cognition
Pratyaya – seeds or impressions in the field of consciousness which do not disappear even in samadhi
Pravrittis – four instincts: (i) desire for food, (ii) desire for sleep, (iii) desire to procreate and (iv) fear of death
Prithvi – earth or matter
Purusha – totality of consciousness
Purusharthas – four efforts which a human being must make in order to fulfil his individual existence, namely:(i) artha (wealth), (ii) kama (emotional fulfillment), (iii) dharma (duty), (iv) moksha (liberation)
Raga – attraction, liking
Rahita – without
Raja yoga – yoga of awakening the psychic awareness and faculties through meditation

Rajas – one of the three gunas; dynamism, state of activity and creativity combined with full ego involvement

Rakta – blood found in the body tissues

Rasa – serum found in the body tissues

Rechaka – exhalation

Rishi – seer; realized sage; one who contemplates or meditates on the Self

Ritam – the changing principle

Roodan – the cry

Roopa – form

Rud – to cry

Rudra – howling energy; name of Shiva in his fierce aspect

Rudra granthi – psychic knot or block between ajna and sahasrara chakras

Sadhaka – spiritual aspirant

Sadhana – spiritual practice

Saguna dhyana – meditation to develop awareness of the transcendental qualities

Sah – with

Sahaja – spontaneous; easy

Sahaja samadhi – spontaneous meditative experience where the mind is totally withdrawn from the external world

Sahajoli mudra – contraction and release of the urinary passage in the female body to stimulate swadhisthana chakra and promote brahmacharya

Sahasrara chakra – abode of Shiva or superconsciousness; 'the thousand-petalled lotus'; highest chakra or psychic centre located at the crown of the head, which symbolizes the threshold between the psychic and spiritual realms

Sahita – 'combined with something'

Sakama karma – ego-inspired actions

Sakshi – witness; drashta aspect; observer

Sam – perfect, balanced

Samadhi – culmination of meditation; state of unity with the object of meditation and universal consciousness

Samana – one of the five sub-pranas; situated between the navel and diaphragm

485

Samapatti – complete absorption; samadhi

Samkhya – one of the six darshana or systems of Indian philosophy, associated with yoga, and based on the division of all existence into purusha, prakriti and a number of elements

Samprajnata samadhi – first state of samadhi; transcendental state where there is knowledge with awareness

Samskara – unconscious memory; impression in the consciousness that does not fit into the known categories of our present personality

Samya – stillness

Samyama – harmonious control; culmination of pratyahara, dharana and samadhi

Sanatan – 'eternal'

Sankalpa – resolve

Sannyasa – renunciation; dedication

Sannyasa ashrama – fourth stage of life from the age of seventy-five onwards; total renunciation

Sanskrit – 'language of the gods'; original vedic language

Santosha – contentment

Sapta – seven

Saptavatan – awareness of seven things

Saraswati – goddess of learning

Sat – true

Satchitananda – three divine attributes of truth, consciousness and bliss

Satkaara – with faith

Satsang – gathering in which the ideals and principles of truth are discussed; association with truth

Sattwa – one of the three gunas; pure unadulterated quality; state of luminosity and harmony

Satya – truth, reality

Satya loka – seventh dimension of the subtle body

Satyam – the unchanging principle

Savdhan – attention; alert

Savishara samadhi – third state of samadhi where the mind alternates between time, space and object

Savishesha dhyana – meditation with special qualities; awareness of the concept of Shakti as a powerful force equal to that of Brahman

Savitarka samadhi – second state of samadhi where there is alternating association of the consciousness between word, knowledge and sensory perception

Shaiva – one who worships Shiva as the supreme reality

Shaivism – practice of worshipping Shiva

Shakta – one who worships the various manifestations of Shakti in the form of Kali, Saraswati, Durga etc.

Shakti – primal energy; manifest consciousness

Shaktism – practice of worshipping Shakti as the supreme

Shambhavi – name for Parvati, consort of Shiva

Shambhavi mudra – eyebrow centre gazing

Shambhu – name for Shiva

Shankhaprakshalana – cleaning the conch; shatkarma that uses saline water to clean the small and large intestines, which resemble the interior of a conch

Shankha mudra – the placing of the hands to form a conch shape

Shanmukhi mudra – closing the seven gates of the body, namely the ears, eyes, nostrils and mouth

Shat – six

Shatkarmas – group of six purificatory techniques of hatha yoga

Shaucha – cleanliness of the body

Sheetali pranayama – 'cooling breath'; breathing technique where the breath is drawn in through the folded tongue

Sheetkari pranayama – 'hissing breath'; practice of drawing the breath in through the closed teeth

Shiva – pure consciousness

Shmashan bhoomi – cremation ground

Shodhana – purification

Shoonya – nothingness; void

Shuddha – pure in nature

Shuddhata – virtue; purity

Shuddhi – purification

Shukra/arthata – reproductive tissues in the body
Siddha – perfected being
Siddha yoni asana – accomplished pose for women
Siddhasana – accomplished pose for men
Siddhi – paranormal or supernormal power; accomplishment
Simhasana – lion pose
Smriti – memory; memory field
Soham – mantra of the breath; used in the practice of ajapa japa
Sthiti – steadiness, stability
Sthoola – gross
Sthoola prana – upward moving energy
Sukha poorvaka – 'simple preliminary practice'
Sukhasana – easy pose
Sukshma – subtle
Sumeru – mountain; tassel on mala
Surya – sun
Surya akasha – one of the five mental spaces of vyoma panchaka; luminous space of the sun or the soul
Surya bheda pranayama – vitality stimulating breath; pranayama that pierces and purifies pingala nadi
Surya mandala – image of the sun visualized at the eyebrow centre
Surya namaskara – 'salute to the sun'; series of twelve asanas for revitalizing prana
Surya tantra – path of realization through visualization and evocation of the vital energy of the sun
Surya vijnana – another name for surya tantra
Sushumna – central nadi in the spine which conducts the kundalini or spiritual force from mooladhara to sahasrara
Sutra – thread; aphorisms which outline the ancient spiritual texts
Sutra neti – nasal cleansing using a catheter
Sva/Swa – one's own
Swadharma – acceptance of one's own duty in life
Swadhisthana chakra – 'one's own abode'; second chakra associated with the sacral plexus and related to the subconscious mind

488

Swadhyaya – self-study

Swami – master of the Self

Swapna – dream state or subconscious

Swara yoga – science of the breathing cycle

Swastikasana – auspicious pose

Tabla – Indian drum

Tadroop pratishtha – knowledge of true identity; linking of name with form

Tamas – one of the three gunas; state of inertia or ignorance

Tanmatra – nature, quality or essence of the five elements, viz., smell, taste, sight, touch and hearing

Tantra – ancient, universal science and culture which deals with the transcendence of human nature from its limited level of evolution and understanding to the transcendental level of knowledge, experience and awareness

Tapas – austerity; heat; process of burning impurities

Tarka – process of understanding through discussion and analysis

Tat – 'that'

Tattwa – element

Tattwamasi – 'Thou Art That'; vedic mantra

Tattwa akasha – one of the five mental spaces of vyoma panchaka; elemental space of perfect stillness

Teerthasthana – holy places of India

Tejas – luminosity; golden light or flame; the seer who observes the state of swapna

Tham/ksham – syllable or sound representing the mental force; sound of ida nadi

Trataka – dharana practice of gazing steadily at one point to focus the mind

Trayate – freed, liberated

Trimurti dhyana – meditation on the three aspects of tamas

Turiya – fourth dimension of consciousness; superconsciousness; three states of consciousness experienced together

Tyaga – renunciation or gradual dissociation of the mind from the seed of desire

Udana – one of the five sub-pranas; energy located in the extremities of the body – arms, legs and head

Uddiyana – 'to raise up', 'to fly up'

Uddiyana bandha – lock applied to the abdomen which causes the diaphragm to rise into the chest, thereby directing prana into sushumna

Ujjayi pranayama – psychic breathing performed by contracting the epiglottis, producing a light sonorous sound

Upanishads – Vedantic texts conveyed by ancient sages and seers containing their experiences and teachings on the ultimate reality

Upanshu – whispered sound

Upa-pranas – five minor pranas responsible for such actions as sneezing, yawning, itching, belching and blinking

Upasana kanda – ritual of worship

Usha pan – literally, down water; traditional form of cold water neti performed in the early morning

Uttara Mimamsa – one of the six darshanas or systems of Indian philosophy which deals with the knowledge of ritual in the form of questions

Utthanpadasana – stretched leg pose

Utthita lolasana – 'swinging while standing pose'; a pre-pranayama exercise

Vacha – speech

Vairagya – non-attachment

Vaisheshika – a treatise on the subtle, causal and atomic principles in relation to the five elements

Vaishnava – one who worships Vishnu in the form of Rama, Krishna, Narayana, etc.

Vaishnavism – sect of Vishnu

Vaishwa – manifest universe

Vaishwanara – seer of the manifest universe or the external, waking consciousness

Vajrasana – thunderbolt pose

Vajroli mudra – contraction and release of the urinary passage in the male body to stimulate swadhisthana chakra and promote brahmacharya

Vama dhauti – hatha yoga method of cleaning the stomach by voluntary vomiting; includes kunjal kriya and vyaghra kriya

Vanaprastha ashrama – third stage of life from the age of fifty to seventy-five; retirement from worldly life in order to practise sadhana in quiet seclusion

Vashishtasana – balancing asana invented by Sage Vashishtha

Vastra dhauti – cleansing of the stomach and oesophagus using a cloth

Vata – wind, one of the three doshas described in ayurveda

Vata nadi – nadi running along the back of the neck and head into the brain; controls gas formation and elimination

Vatsara dhauti – hatha yoga method of stomach cleansing performed by drinking air through the mouth and belching

Vayu – wind, prana

Vedanta – one of the six darshanas or systems of Indian philosophy; 'the end of perceivable knowledge'; the mind experiencing its own limits and going beyond them; gaining realization and understanding of that exploration

Vedas – ancient spiritual texts of Sanatan Dharma

Veerabhava – warrior personality

Veerasana – warrior's pose, hero's pose (also known as the philosopher's or thinker's pose)

Vichara – reflection

Vidya – knowledge

Vidyut mandala – visualization of lightning within the white light of prakash mandala

Vijnana – intuitive ability of mind; higher understanding

Vijnanamaya kosha – higher mental sheath or body

Vikalpa – fancy; unfounded belief; imagination

Vikshepa – dissipation

Vipareeta – inverted

Vipareeta karani mudra – inverted psychic attitude

Viparyaya – wrong knowledge, false understanding

Vishaya – object

Vishnu granthi – psychic knot or block between manipura, anahata and vishuddhi chakras, symbolizing the bondage of personal and emotional attachment

491

Vishuddhi chakra – psychic centre located at the level of the throat; centre of purification

Vishwa – universe, world

Vitarka – reasoning

Viveka – right knowledge or understanding; discernment; power of discrimination

Vrischikasana – scorpion pose

Vritti – circular movement of consciousness; mental modifications described in raja yoga

Vyaghra kriya – cleansing the stomach by voluntary vomiting using warm saline water (performed on a full stomach)

Vyakta – manifest; seen

Vyakta prana – manifest life force

Vyana – one of the sub-pranas; reserve of pranic energy pervading the whole body

Vyoma – space

Vyoma panchaka – the five subtle spaces

Yam – bija mantra of anahata chakra

Yama – self-restraint, first step of ashtanga or raja yoga

Yantra – visual form of mantra used for concentration and meditation

Yoga angas – parts or aspects of yoga

Yoga mudra – attitude of psychic union

Yoga mudras – gestures which help to channel the flow of prana in the body

Yoga nidra – technique of yogic or psychic sleep which induces deep physical, mental and emotional relaxation, which eventually leads to higher states of meditation

Yoga Sutras – ancient authoritative text on raja yoga by Sage Patanjali

Yoni – womb, source

Yoni mudra – attitude by which the primal energy inherent in the womb, or source of creation, is invoked

Index of Practices

A Akashi Mudra (awareness of inner space) 426
Antar Kumbhaka (internal retention) 336

B Bandha Hasta Utthanasana 330
Bhastrika Pranayama (bellows breath) 363
Bhoochari Mudra (gazing into nothingness) 425

C Chakrasana (wheel pose) 315
Chandra Bheda Pranayama 381
Chin Mudra (psychic gesture of consciousness) 415

G Gomukhasana (cow's face pose) 297

H Hand mudras 413
Head mudras 418

J Jalandhara Bandha (throat lock) 386
Jnana Mudra (psychic gesture of knowledge) 413

K Kapalbhati Pranayama (frontal brain cleansing breath) 357
Kapalshodhana Pranayama 359
Khechari Mudra (tongue lock) 429
Koormasana (tortoise pose) 318
Kukkutasana (cockerel pose) 311
Kumbhaka (breath retention) 335
   Abdominal kumbhaka 338

Antar kumbhaka (internal retention) 336
Thoracic kumbhaka 337

L Locked mudras 432

M Maha Bandha (the great lock) 399
Maha Bheda Mudra (great piercing attitude) 436
Maha Mudra (great attitude) 434
Manduki Mudra (gesture of the frog) 423
Mayurasana (peacock pose) 313
Moola Bandha (perineal contraction) 389
Mooladhara Anusandhana 393
Mooladhara Dhyana 393
Mudra breathing 332

N Nadi Shodhana Pranayama
(psychic network purification) 344
Nasagra Mudra 343
Nasikagra Drishti (nose tip gazing) 421

P Padmasana (lotus pose) 309
Poorna Dhanurasana (full bow pose) 320
Pre-pranayama practices 326
Abdominal breathing 327
Hasta utthanasana 330
Prana Mudra (invocation of energy) 334
Sitting pre-pranayama practices 332
Standing pre-pranayama practices 329
Thoracic breathing 327
Utthita lolasana 330
Yogic breathing 327

S Shambhavi Mudra (eyebrow centre gazing) 418
Shanmukhi Mudra (closing the seven gates) 432
Sheetali Pranayama (cooling breath) 374
Sheetkari Pranayama (hissing breath) 371
Siddhasana (accomplished pose for men) 306
Simhasana (lion pose) 300
Standing Uddiyana 395

Sukhasana (easy pose) 303
Surya Bheda Pranayama (vitality stimulating breath) 375
Swastikasana (auspicious pose) 304

U Uddiyana Bandha (abdominal contraction) 395
Ujjayi Pranayama (the psychic breath) 353
Utthita lolasana 330

V Vajrasana (thunderbolt pose) 295
Veerasana (warrior's or hero's pose) 299
Vipareeta Karani Mudra (inverted psychic attitude) 406

Y Yoga Mudra (attitude of psychic union) 410
Yogic breathing 327
Yoni Mudra (attitude of the womb or source) 415

General Index

Abhinivesha 283–284
Advaita 57
Affliction see Kleshas
Agni mandala 420
Agni tattwa 36, 38–39, 370–371
Agnisar kriya 93, 94
Ahamkara see Ego
Ahimsa 102, 103–104, 132
Ajapa japa 170, 237
Ajna chakra 90, 96, 236, 275
Akasha tattwa 36, 37, 40,
Akashi mudra 176, 426–429
Amaroli 102, 105
Anahata chakra 249, 251, 275
Ananda samadhi 220–222
Anandamaya kosha 43
Anger 109–111
Annamaya kosha 40–41, 147
Antah karana 20, 37–38
Antar lakshya dharana 181–184
Antar mouna 172–173
Antaranga yoga 162–225
Anuman see Inference
Apas tattwa 39–40
Apana vayu 144, 145, 151–152,
    157–158

Aparigraha 133
Artha 13–14
Asamprajnata samadhi 208–212
Asana 25–26, 98–99, 104, 137–
    142, 294–321
Ashramas 17–19
Asmita 281–282
Asmita samadhi 222–223
Aspiration 288–289
Asteya 132–133
Atma 124–125, 255, 260–261,
    264
Attachment see Vairagya,
    Aparigraha
Aum 196–197, 258–260, 261
Austerity see Tapas
Avidya 281
Awareness 22–31, 205–207, 464

Bahir lakshya dharana 175–177
Bahiranga yoga 131–161
Baikhari 199, 238
Bandha hasta utthanasana 330–
    332
Bandhas 53–54, 105, 382–401

Basti 92–93
Bhakti 19–20, 193
Bhastrika 363–371
Bhoochari mudra 175–176, 425–426
Bhootas 36
Bhu loka 267
Bhrumadhya drishti see Shambhavi mudra
Boredom 64–65
Brahma granthi 383
Brahma nadi 182–183, 370
Brahmacharya 133
Brahmacharya ashrama 17
Brahman 34, 194–196, 200
Brahman dhyana 194–196
Brain 324–325
Buddhi 22–24, 26–29, 37, 227–228, 229

Celibacy see Brahmacharya
Chakras 105, 228–230, 235–237, 246–247, 274–276, 382–384, 457–459
Chakrasana 315–318
Chandra bheda pranayama 381
Chandra mandala 420–421
Charvak 5
Chetana see Consciousness
Chidakasha dharana 177–178
Chin mudra 415
Chit shakti see Ida Nadi
Chitta 20, 37, 227–228, 233
Cleanliness see Shaucha
Conflict 63–64, 111, 449, 461–462, 464

Consciousness 22–31, 135–137, 201–225, 245–253, 254–276, 468
Contentment see Santosha

Daharakasha dharana 178
Darshan 4, 182–183
Dehasamya 54–55
Desha 49–50
Desire 9–11, 264, 278–280
Dharana 168, 173–184, 286–287
Dharana dhyana 184, 191–193
Dharma 14, 74, 108–109, 111
Dhauti 91
Dhyana 184–201, 286–288
Diet 100–101
Discrimination see Viveka
Diseases 447–459
Divyaloka 257
Doshas 369–370
Dream 268–269
Drishtisamya 55–56
Duty see Dharma
Dwesha 283

Efficiency 71
Ego 35, 37–38, 62–63, 68–71, 72–73, 133, 228, 233, 272–273, 278–280, 461–462
Equanimity 71–72
Expectation 72

Fancy see Vikalpa

Gayatri mantra 150–151, 231
Gomukhasana 297–299

Granthis 382–401
Grihastha ashrama 18
Guilt 109–111
Guna rahita akasha 179–180
Gunas 76–77, 198–199, 258–259

Hand mudras 413–417
Hatha yoga 87–108, 325–326
Head mudras 418–434
Hridayakasha dharana 178

Ida nadi 144, 146–147, 154–156, 326
Indriyas 39, 60, 267–268
Inference 116
Intellect 26–27
Intuition 84–85, 117–118
Ishwara 135–137
Ishwara pranidhana 135–137

Jagriti 23–28, 258–259
Jalandhara bandha 386–389
Japa yoga 237–242
Jnana kanda 13
Jnana mudra 413–414
Jnana yoga 79–86
Jnanendriyas 39–40, 267–268

Kaala 53
Kala loka 257
Kama 14
Kapalbhati 95–96, 357–363
Karma 59–60, 75–77, 185–189, 286–287
Karma kanda 13
Karma yoga 59–78

Karmendriyas 40, 267–268
Khechari mudra 429–431
Kleshas 280–288
Koormasana 318–320
Koshas 38, 40–43, 141–142, 146–147, 403
Kriya yoga 245–246
Kukkutasana 311–313
Kumbhaka 152–153, 335–343
Kundalini 148, 182–183, 228–229, 245–246, 248–249, 325–326, 382–384, 455–459

Laghoo shankhaprakshalana 92–93
Laya yoga 245–253
Literary knowledge 106
Locked mudras 434–440
Lokas 246–247, 257, 266–267

Madhya lakshya dharana 177–181
Madhyama see Upanshu
Mahamrityunjaya mantra 231
Mahat 34–35, 227–228
Maha akasha 180
Maha bandha 399–401
Maha bheda mudra 436–440
Maha mudra 434–435, 437–440
Maha prana 88, 143–144
Manas 37, 227–228, 232
Manasi 199, 239
Manduki mudra 423–425
Mandukya Upanishad 123, 257–276
Manipura chakra 94, 251, 275
Manomaya kosha 41, 141–142

498

Mantra yoga 226–244
Maya 10, 32–33, 113, 200
Mayurasana 98, 313–315
Medhra 312
Memory see Smriti
Mind 9–11, 33, 463
Mitahara 102–103
Moksha 14–15
Moola bandha 389–395
Mooladhara anusandhana 393
Mooladhara chakra 248–252, 275, 276
Mooladhara dhyana 393–394
Mouna 49
Mudra breathing 332–334
Mudras 105, 402–440
Mumukshutva 17

Nada 183–184, 227–230
Nadi shodhana 343–352
Nadis 87–89, 144, 146–148, 153–156, 176–177, 326, 451–455
Nasagra mudra 344
Nashwara 135–136
Nasikagra drishti 421–423
Nasikagra mudra see Nasagra Mudra
Nauli 93–94
Neti 90
Nidra 24–28, 122–125, 203–204, 262–263
Nirbija samadhi 224–225
Nirguna dhyana 199–200
Nirvichara samadhi 220
Nirvishesha dhyana 200–201
Nirvitarka samadhi 216–218

Niyama 134–137
Non-attachment see Vairagya
Nyaya 5

Padmasana 309–311
Para 199, 239–240
Param akasha 180
Pashyanti see Manasi
Personality 107–108, 127, 461–462, 463–464
Physiology 441–446
Pingala nadi 144, 146–148, 154–156, 326
Poorna dhanurasana 320–321
Poorva mimamsa 5
Possessiveness see Aparigraha
Postural mudras 406–413
Prajna 258, 261–263
Prakasha mandala 421
Pramana 114–118
Prana 38, 41–42, 87–89, 142–161, 322–325, 380–381, 402–404, 417, 437–440, 451–459
Prana mudra 334–335
Prana nigraha 143, 148–151, 322–323, 325
Prana shakti 144, 324
Prana vayus 88, 144–146, 151–153, 159, 324
Prana vidya 453–454
Pranamaya kosha 38, 41–42, 142
Pranava dhyana 196–197
Pranayama 104–105, 142–161, 322–381
Pratyahara 29, 164–173
Pratyahara dhyana 184, 189–191

Pratyaya 97–98, 125, 185–189
Pre-pranayama exercises 326–
335
Prithvi tattwa 40
Psychic blocks 382–401, 451–
455
Psychic body 228–229, 235–237
Psychic breath 242–244
Psychic symbol 242–244
Purusharthas 13–15

Raga 282–283
Raja yoga 107–225, 287
Rajas 76
Relaxation 170–171, 465–466
Renunciation 47–49, 73–74
Ritam 247–248
Rudra granthi 382–384

Sabija samadhi 223–224
Saguna dhyana 198–199
Sahaja samadhi 204–205
Sahasrara chakra 275
Samadhi 31, 201–225
Samana vayu 144, 145, 146,
151–153, 158
Samapatti 202–203
Samkhya philosophy 5, 135
Samprajnata samadhi 205–208
Samskara 65–66, 126–130, 185–
189, 210–211
Samyama 201
Sanatan culture 3–4, 12–17
Sannyasa ashrama 18–19
Santosha 34
Sattwa 76
Satya 132

Satya loka 267
Satyam 247–248
Savadhan 30
Savichara samadhi 218–220
Savishesha dhyana 200
Savitarka samadhi 212–216
Seetkari pranayama 371–374
Self-acceptance 108–110, 271–
272, 464
Self-enquiry 79–86, 135, 188–
189
Self-preservation 278–280, 283–
284
Shambhavi mudra 418–421
Shankhaprakshalana 92–93
Shanmukhi mudra 432–434
Shatkarmas 89–98, 448
Shaucha 99–100, 134
Sheetali pranayama 374–375
Shoonya 83–84, 211–212
Shuddhata 16–17
Siddhasana 306–308
Siddha yoni asana 306–308
Siddhis 456–457
Simhasana 300–302
Sleep see Nidra
Smriti 125–130, 216–218
Spiritual psychotherapy 8–9
Sub-pranas see Prana Vayus
Sukhasana 303–304
Surrender 20, 77–78, 284
Surya akasha 181
Surya bheda pranayama 375–
381
Surya mandala 420
Surya shakti 256–257
Surya tantra 254–257

Surya vijnana see Surya tantra
Sushumna nadi 182–183
Swadhisthana chakra 249, 251, 275
Swadhyaya 135
Swapna 23–28, 263
Swara 95–96, 326
Swastikasana 304–305

Tamas 76
Tanmatras 35, 267
Tantra 5
Tapas 134
Tarka 46–47
Tattwa akasha 180–181
Tattwas 36–40, 180–181, 200, 263, 264
Tejas 258, 263–269
Tension 444–446
Testimony 116–117
Trataka 96–98, 171–172
Trimurti dhyana 197–198
Turiya 25, 31, 260
Tyaga see Renunciation

Udana vayu 144, 145–146
Uddiyana bandha 395–399
Ujjayi pranayama 353–357
Upanishads 6
Upanshu 199–200, 238–239
Upasana kanda 13
Uttara mimamsa 5

Vairagya 15, 114, 133, 464–465
Vaisheshika 5, 258
Vaishwanara 258, 269–276
Vajra nadi 296–297

Vajrasana 295–297
Vanaprastha ashrama 18
Vayu tattwa 36, 38
Vedanta 3–4
Veerasana 299–300
Vidyut mandala 421
Vijnanamaya kosha 42–43
Vikalpa 120–122
Vikshepa 226
Vipareeta karani mudra 406–409
Viparyaya 118–120
Vishnu granthi 382–384
Vishuddhi chakra 36, 250–251, 275
Viveka 16, 285–286
Vritti 111–130
Vyana vayu 144, 146
Vyoma panchaka 178–181

Yama 131–133
Yoga mudra 410–413
Yoga mudras 402–440
Yoga nidra 170–171
Yogic breathing 327–329
Yoni mudra 415–417

——————— Notes ———————